Müller
Colloidal Carriers
for Controlled Drug Delivery
and Targeting

Colloidal Carriers for Controlled Drug Delivery and Targeting

Modification, Characterization and In Vivo Distribution

By Priv.-Doz. Dr. Rainer H. Müller,
Department of Pharmaceutics and Biopharmaceutics,
University of Kiel, Germany

With 227 figures and 84 tables

Wissenschaftliche
Verlagsgesellschaft mbH
Stuttgart 1991

CRC Press
Boca Raton Ann Arbor Boston

Dedicated to my parents and Silke

Priv.-Doz. Dr. Rainer H. Müller
Department of Pharmaceutics
and Biopharmaceutics
University of Kiel
Gutenbergstr. 76–78
D-2300 Kiel (FRG)

The use of general descriptive names, trade names, trademarks, etc in a publication, even if not specifically identified, does not imply that these names are not protected by the relevant laws and regulations.

CIP-Titelaufnahme der Deutschen Bibliothek
Müller, Rainer:
Colloidal carriers for controlled drug delivery and targeting: modification, characterization and in vivo distribution / by Rainer H. Müller. — Stuttgart: Wiss. Verl.-Ges., 1990
    ISBN 3–8047–1096–4

Catalog record is available from the Library of Congress

Sole distribution rights for North America, South America, Australia, India, Singapore, Japan and China granted to CRC Press, Inc., Boca Raton, Florida

ISBN 3–8047–1096–4 Wissenschaftliche Verlagsgesellschaft mbH, Stuttgart
ISBN 0–8493–7714–5 CRC Press, Inc., Boca Raton, Florida

Printed in F. R. Germany

PREFACE

Controlled drug delivery including drug targeting are topics attracting increasing attention. They are of high interest for the delivery of drugs with major side effects (e. g. cytotoxics, peptides) and drugs possessing short biological half-lifes (peptides). The progress in gene technology provides us with many potent drugs requiring new delivery systems for their introduction to therapy.

Colloidal carriers (particles, emulsions) for intravenous administration are a promising approach to achieve controlled release and site-specific delivery of drugs. The success of these systems will depend on their ability to maintain in blood circulation (controlled release system) or to reach the target cells (e. g. bone marrow, blood cells). It is well known that the surface properties of i. v. injected particles are important factors determinig the organ distribution and fate in vivo. Controlled surface modification could therefore be used to direct the carriers to the desired tissues.

This book deals with the physico-chemical characterization of colloidal drug delivery systems and the influence of these parameters upon the in vitro cell uptake and the in vivo tissue distribution. The results demonstrate the importance of an extensive characterization. A range of different analytical methods was employed whereby the surface characterization has been markedly improved by the introduction of methods mainly used in other disciplines (e. g. hydrophobic interaction chromatography). Furthermore, the in vivo tissue distribution of nanoparticles different in size and surface properties (coatings with Poloxamer / Poloxamine / ethoxylated nonylphenols) could be very well explained in terms of the carrier properties. The obtained results contribute to a better understanding of the factors influencing the organ distribution of i. v. drug carriers. The presented research work does not deal with single aspects but offers a comprehensive treatment of the subject. From these points of view the book provides helpful information for the rational design of new carriers. It indicates new ways for future developments and optimization of carriers for controlled drug delivery.

Paris, August 1990

Prof. Patrick Couvreur
Université de Paris-Sud
Laboratoire de Pharmacie Galénique et Biopharmacie

CONTENTS

Contents

Contents

The controlled delivery of drugs to their desired site of action (drug targeting) and their release in a controlled profile will play a major role in the development of future drug formulations. It is the key for the introduction of new generations of drugs (synthetic peptides, immuno-modulators) into practise. The challenge of the future is less the search for new active compounds than the development of formulations which are capable to maintain the activity of the drug and to provide access for the drug to the desired tissues, cell population or even cell compartment.

Peptide synthesis and gene technology have opened the door to a new broad area of drugs with prospects for therapy which we can only suspect at present. Peptides such as tumour necrosis factor (TNF) which leads to the disappearance of tumours after direct injection into the tumour itself are already available.

However, associated with these potential new drugs are major problems, which are a challenge to pharmaceutical technology. The main problems are:

1. The short biological half-life of peptides such as LH-RH.

2. The highly active and effective new drugs are often correlated with strong systemic side effects. TNF cannot be systemically administered due to its side effect of cachexia.

New formulations are therefore required which protect the drug against _in vivo_ degradation and prolonging its biological half-life. Simultaneously protection of the host against systemic side effects by targeting of the drug to the desired tissue (e.g. targeting of TNF to the liver against tumour metastasis) is needed. In the desired tissue the formulation should release the drug in a controlled way to maintain a sustained, effective drug level.

One approach to this challenge is the use of colloidal drug carriers for intravenous drug administration. The drug can be incorporated into biodegradable carriers such as polymeric particles, liposomes and fat emulsion droplets. The major obstacle in the way of a breakthrough in the use of colloidal carrier systems is the rapid clearance of such particles from the blood stream by the macrophages of the reticuloendothelial system (RES), mainly in the liver and spleen. Modification of properties of the carriers, such as particle size, surface charge and surface hydrophobicity can however reduce the RES clearance. Optimization of these carrier properties should lead to the development of suitable carrier systems.

The presented work attempts to base the development of such carriers on systematic investigations rather than on empirical trials. For basic investigations, non-biodegradable model carriers were employed. Non-biodegradable carriers are more suitable than biodegradable particles

1

because in in vivo studies particle degradation can interfere with effects of particle properties on the organ distribution. The aims were:
- to modify the carrier properties in a controlled, reproducible manner
- to develop methods of characterization of the particle surface properties
- to obtain a complete characterization of the carriers
- to investigate the relationship between measured characteristics and in vivo organ distribution and
- to optimize the carrier properties in order to avoid RES uptake.

For practical utilization of the carrier systems, it is necessary to replace the non-biodegradable model particles by biodegradable carriers. Therefore investigations were undertaken, in order to:
- produce biodegradable carriers
- transfer the modifications performed on model carriers to the biodegradable systems
- characterize the biodegradable particles and determine their in vivo distribution

The aim of the investigations was to obtain more information about the relevant factors determining the in vivo distribution, which would ultimately lead to production and modification techniques and characterization methods suitable for the systematic development of particulate carriers for the controlled delivery of drugs.

1.1 The concept of controlled drug delivery and drug targeting

The controlled delivery of drugs is important for a broad range of pharmaceutical formulations which aim to optimize drug therapy. Such optimization by controlled drug delivery (Müller, B.W., 1987) includes:
- the increase of the therapeutic index of the drug and reduction of toxic side effects,
- the optimization of drug action by adjustment of the drug release rate or change in the rate of drug deposition,
- the design of prodrugs and
- the accumulation of the drug at its desired site of action, drug targeting.

The availability of new drugs with short biological half-lifes (e.g. peptide-drugs) and very potent drugs with strong side effects (e.g. tumour necrosis factor (Davis, J.M., 1987)) has led to increasing interest in the possibility of delivering drugs to their desired site of action (drug targeting). Such drugs demand new formulations which protect both the drug and the host and are able to direct the drug to the desired tissue.

Controlled drug delivery by controlled release formulations has been used for various routes of administration including oral dosage forms (Davis, S.S., 1987), rectal, buccal and nasal delivery, ocular delivery systems (Harmia et al., 1986; Li et al., 1986; Fitzgerald, P. et al, 1987) and a large number of systems for parenteral applications (Bundgaard et al., 1982). In addition to a controlled release, the drug formulation can be designed for site-directed (targeted) delivery. Systems used for site-specific drug delivery include prodrugs (Sinkula and Yalkowski, 1975; Higuchi et al, 1982), macromolecular prodrugs (Hoes et al, 1985), antibody-drug conjugates (Burstein, 1976; Hurwitz, 1982), drugs bound to macromolecular carriers containing targeting moieties such as saccharides or antibodies (Kopecek, 1987; Duncan, 1987) and particulate systems. The particulate systems include liposomes which have attracted very much attention (Gregoriadis et al., 1982 and 1982a) and a range of solid microspheres and nanoparticles (Marty and Oppenheim, 1977; Couvreur et al., 1977 and 1980; Kreuter, 1978, 1983 and 1983a; Marty et al, 1978; Oppenheim, 1981; Illum and Davis, 1982; Speiser, 1982; Widder and Green, 1985).

Liposomal and solid particulate carriers have been used to deliver cytotoxics in cancer chemotherapy (Brasseur, et al., 1980), for lymphatic drug delivery via subcutaneous injection of the carriers (Patel et al., 1984), for the delivery of drugs to the liver, spleen and lung by intravenous injection of carriers of different size (Yoshioka et al., 1981) or for targeting to the bone marrow (Illum and Davis, 1987b), for controlled release of drugs from an intramuscular injection site (Davis, S.S. et al., 1987a), for intra-arterial tumor targeting (Burger et al., 1985) and to change the pharmacokinetics of drugs by encapsulation leading to a slower plasma clearance (Juliano and Stamp, 1978; Juliano et al., 1978). Particulate carriers provide numerous opportunities for the formulation of controlled release and site-specific (targeted) drug delivery systems. In the following text, the design and optimization of intravenously administered carriers for controlled drug delivery and/or drug targeting will be discussed.

1.2. Interaction of i.v. administered carriers with blood components and the reticuloendothelial system

After i.v. injection particulate drug carriers will be recognized as foreign by the body and removed from the blood circulation by the macrophages of the reticuloendothelial system (RES). About 60 to 90% of the particles will be phagocytosed by the macrophages of the liver and spleen within 5 minutes of injection. This so called "RES clearance" is the major obstacle for the utilisation of particulate systems in controlled drug delivery. Because of this clearance, site-specific targeting of the particles to tissues other than the liver and spleen is not possible. The accumulation in the liver and spleen can however be used to "target" drugs to these organs or their RES cells (Schroit et al, 1983). The liver/spleen accumulation happens through the natural reaction of the body towards foreign particles, without an active influence of the particles on their fate; it is therefore known as "natural" or "passive" targeting. "Active" targeting involves a manipulation of the carrier system which directs it towards the target site, e.g. the coupling of a monoclonal antibody as a homing device to specific cells with the equivalent surface epitopes.

The recognition of particles by the RES is mediated by activation of the immune system due to the interaction of blood components with artificial surfaces. The complement system is activated at the interface between blood and 'activating' artificial surfaces (Kazatchkine and Carreno, 1988). The complement system consists of 19 components and regulatory plasma proteins, and at least nine cellular receptors for regulatory proteins and cleavage products (Brown, 1985; Kazatchkine and Nydegger, 1986). Activation can take place via the 'classical' or 'alternative' pathways. The classical pathway is in general initiated by an antigen-antibody reaction but can also be triggered in the absence of antibody by crystals, bacterial surfaces and complexes between positively and negatively charged molecules (Law and Levine, 1977). This might provide an explanation for the increased RES uptake observed with charged particles compared to low or non-charged particles _in vivo_ (Wilkins and Myers, 1966) and _in vitro_ in macrophage cultures (Schwendener et al., 1984). The alternative pathway is activated by surfaces with a certain chemical structure allowing binding of C3b and stimulation of enzymes leading to enhanced formation of C3b. The alternative pathway needs no antigen-antibody reaction for activation and is activated by the adsorption of the C3b complement protein onto the particle surface after particle injection.

Both pathways activate the enzyme C3 convertase which cleaves C3 to C3a and C3b. C3b binds covalently to the artificial surface through a transesterification mechanism. A glutamyl group of the C3b binds to active OH^- or NH_2 on the surface, leading to an ester or amide bond (Tack, 1983, Law and Levine, 1977). The binding of the C3b leads to further activation of complement proteins and to an amplification of the cleavage of C3 and binding of C3b to the artificial surface (Fig. 1.2./1).

Amplification of the complement system response takes place by the following reactions (Kazatchkine and Nydegger, 1982): Factor B binds to surface bound C3b forming the complex C3b,B. Cleavage of B from this complex C3b,B by factor D leads to the formation of the amplification convertase C3b,Bb which starts the pathway amplification.

The amplification is inhibited by factor H which binds to surface-fixed C3b. Factor H has two actions; firstly, it inhibits the C3b,Bb convertase by accelerating its dissociation and secondly, it acts as a co-factor in the conversion of C3b into the inactive C3bi.

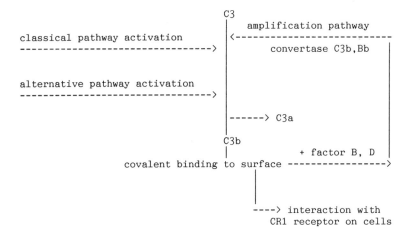

Fig.: 1.2./1: Complement activation (after Kazatchkine and Carreno, 1988)

The difference between a complement 'activating' and a 'non-activating' surface depends on the competitive affinity of the activating factor B and the inactivating factor H to surface fixed C3b. On a non-activating surface, the affinity of adsorption of factor H is 100 fold greater than that of factor B. (Kazatchkine and Carreno, 1988). The affinity of factor H depends on the biochemical characteristics of the surface. For example an increase in the content of sialic acid (Kazatchkine et al, 1979), and carboxymethyl groups on Sephadex surfaces has been shown to lead to a proportional suppression of complement activation (Kazatchkine and Carreno, 1988).

Circulating cells are protected against autologous complement by regulatory proteins such as the decay accelerating factor DAF in their outer membranes. Reduction in the amount of DAF in the membrane leads to clearance of the cells by the RES. A high density of hydroxyl groups leads to activation of the complement system as observed for Cuprophane dialysis membranes (Wegmuller et al., 1986). On polysaccharide membranes, the C3b binding sites are protected against inactivating factor H (Maillet et al, 1987) leading to uninhibited formation of the amplification convertase C3b,Bb. Such properties of polysaccharides would limit there use for modifying the surface of drug carriers. Polysaccharides such as Zymosan are used to activate the alternative pathway and to enhance phagocytosis by macrophages. Some materials can however avoid activation of the complement system because they do not possess surface binding sites for C3b. In order to avoid complement activation, artificial surfaces should:
- possess no binding sites for C3b,
- have surface properties which lead to the preferential binding of factor H,
- express no antigenic sites leading to recognition by antibodies (Kazatchkine and Carreno, 1988).

In vitro studies of the phagocytosis of polyacryl starch microparticles confirmed that they activate the alternative complement pathway. Phagocytic uptake was dependent on opsonization and could be partially inhibited by the use of a monoclonal antibody directed against the macrophage surface receptor for complement (Artursson and Sjöholm, 1986). However, the uptake of polyacrylamide microparticles was found not to be dependent on opsonization.

Injected particulates also interact with other blood components. Intravenous injection of liposomes has been shown to lead to a decrease in plasma fibronectin levels which correlated with the level of accumulation of the liposomes in the liver (Schreier et al, 1987). The surface-bound fibronectin may act as an opsonin leading to RES clearance or alternatively the fibronectin depletion might be a direct result of the phagocytosis process. The adsorption of fibronectin onto latex particles from both fibrinogen solutions and fresh human plasma has been reported (O'Mullane et al., 1988). Surface modification of the latex particles by coating with the hydrophilic, non-ionic polymer Poloxamer 338 led to a decrease in the fibronectin adsorption which is seen as evidence that the lower protein adsorption by coated particles reduces their interaction with the RES. Poloxamer 338 coated latex showed a reduction in RES clearance (Illum and Davis, 1984). There is however no conclusive evidence that the observed reduction in fibronectin adsorption is correlated to the reduced RES uptake. In general, a more hydrophilic surface (Poloxamer coated latex) shows a lower adsorption of any compound (e.g. fibronectin or Rose Bengal) than more hydrophobic surfaces (uncoated latex).

The hydrophobicity of surfaces is a major factor governing the adsorption of blood components such as human serum albumin (HSA) and human fibrinogen (HFb). The HFb molecule has a molecular weight of 340,000 and a cylindrical form with a length of 45 nm and a diameter of 9 nm (Bachman et al., 1975). Assuming a closely-packed monolayer, the HFb adsorbs end-on to the hydrophobic surfaces (ca. 0.8 $\mu g/cm^2$) and possibly to some extent side-on to the hydrophilic surfaces of poly(HEMA) and cellophane (Brynda et al., 1984). There is no difference in the adsorption on many hydrophobic materials (Table 1.2./1) indicating that above a certain degree of hydrophobicity, surfaces bind plasma proteins to the same level. HSA, a molecule with a weight of 69,000, a length of 14 nm and a diameter of 4 nm (McClure and Graven, 1974), seems to adsorb in several molecular layers onto hydrophobic polyethylene (Brynda et al., 1984).

Table 1.2./1: Air-water-solid contact angle and equilibrium adsorption data of HFb on hydrophobic and hydrophilic surfaces (after Brynda et al., 1984).

material	contact angle	HFb ($\mu g/cm^2$)	surface
polyethylene	95°	0.73	hydrophobic
carbon	60°	0.77	
poly(HEMA)	22°	0.23	hydrophilic
cellophane	15°	0.4	

The adsorption of bovine serum albumin (BSA) (Shirahama and Suzawa, 1985), fibrinogen and gamma globulin (IgG) (Wikström et al., 1982) onto hydrophobic latex particles and polymer surfaces is dependent on pH and ionic strength. A detailed thermodynamic analysis of protein adsorption onto polystyrene latex particles has been published by Norde and Lyklema (1979). Blood contains a mixture of components which will adsorb competitively onto foreign particles. In studies of competitive adsorption onto polystyrene latex using mixtures of HSA, human immunoglobulin G (HIgG) and HFb, a preferential adsorption of HFb was observed (Lensen et al., 1984). Preferential adsorption of fibrinogen has also been reported by Lee et al. (1974).

The reversible adsorption of apolipoproteins A-I and A-II onto surfaces of varying hydrophobicity is described by Shen (1985). This leads to the consideration that the composition of the adsorbed layer of serum components formed after i.v. injection might change with time. The initial composition of the adsorbed layer will be determined not only by the affinity of the compounds to the particle surface but also by their absolute concentration. Adsorbed blood components with low affinities but high blood concentrations will be gradually displaced by serum components present in low concentrations but having higher affinities.

The process of opsonization of latex particles was studied by relating the degree of in vitro phagocytosis of opsonized particles to a measured parameter of the particle surface in contact with serum, the particle electrophoretic mobility (Davies, W. et al, 1975). In whole serum, gamma globulin was adsorbed preferentially to form a monolayer. Uptake minima were found to be coincident with gamma globulin monolayers and it was concluded that the formation of an adsorbed monolayer is a prerequisite for the initiation of latex opsonization. The fixation of complement by gamma globulin coated latex has been shown by Bernhard et al. (1962).

Considering the dimensions of a human gamma globulin molecule (HgG) as 235 Å in length and 44 Å in diameter, the adsorbed layer can be formed by the molecules lying flat on the latex surface forming a random immobile film, or adsorbing as a double layer (Oreskes and Singer, 1961). Soderquist and Walton (1980) suggest an end-on configuration for gamma globulin on polymer surfaces.

The enhancing effect of gamma globulin and human fibronectin on in vitro phagocytosis is described for microspheres in cultures of mouse peritoneal macrophages. The adsorption of bovine serum albumin led to a reduction in particle uptake (Ikada and Tabata, 1986).

According to Kanke et al. (1983), the interaction of microspheres with blood components does not lead to antigenic stimulation of the immune system. The determination of serum protein levels (alpha 1 and 2, beta and gamma protein) after injection of microspheres into beagle dogs was found to be unchanged compared to the control. The cell-mediated immune response assessed by the responsiveness of blood lymphoctes to mitogenic stimulation did not change after i.v. particle injection.

The reaction of blood components with artifical surfaces (Vroman and Leonard, 1977) is a complex phenomenon. It is, however, likely that it holds the key to avoiding recognition and clearance of intravenous drug carriers by the RES. The ability to directly determine the level of blood components adsorbed onto carriers in vivo should contribute to the design of optimized carrier systems.

1.3. In vivo fate of i.v. administered drug carriers

Intravenous injection of non-modified polystyrene latex particles leads to a rapid uptake by the liver and spleen of 50 to 90% of the particles within the first 5 minutes after injection (Illum et al., 1986; Illum and Davis, 1983 and 1984). The same fate befalls particulates made from other materials, e.g. cyanoacrylate (Kreuter et al., 1979; Grislain et al., 1983; Gipps et al., 1988), polyhydroxybutyrate (Koosha, 1989) polyacryl starch (Laakso et al., 1986) and albumin (Sugibayashi et al., 1977). The organ affinity can be used to direct drugs to the liver and spleen, or to change the pharmacokinetics of drugs (Grislain et al., 1983). This affinity is however a major obstacle against targeting to tissues other than the liver and spleen or the production of circulating controlled release formulations. The clearance can be reduced by blockade of the RES with dextran sulphate or carbon before administration of the particulate carrier (Souhami et al., 1981). Administration of rare earth metal chlorides of lanthanum, cerium, neodynium, gadolinium, holmium and ytterbium has been shown to depress the RES activity in rats (Lazar, 1973). However, depressing the RES weakens the body's immune system and can therefore not be applied in therapy.

An alternative to RES blockade is modification of the surface properties of drug carriers. As discussed above, the biochemical composition and hydro-phobicity of the surface determine its interaction with blood components. Creation of a hydrophilic carrier surface by coating particles with the non-ionic polyoxypropylene-polyoxyethylene polymers Poloxamer 188 and 338 has been shown to lead to a reduction in their liver uptake (Illum and Davis 1983 and 1984; Illum et al., 1986). Coating with Poloxamine 908 was shown to totally eliminate the liver uptake. The coated particles (60 nm polystyrene latex) remained in circulation in the blood stream (Illum et al, 1987a). The reduction in liver uptake after coating with such polymers (Poloxamer 338) was previously described for emulsion carriers (Jeppsson and Rössner, 1975).

Coating of 60 nm model latex with Poloxamer 407 led to a targeting to the bone marrow (Illum and Davis, 1987b). The particles were protected against phagocytosis by liver and spleen macrophages but not against uptake by phagocytosing cells in the bone marrow.

These examples show the potential of surface modification for protection against RES clearance, and for altering the organ distribution of

administered carriers. However, surface modification has only been successfully applied to 60 nm non-biodegradable model carriers. To introduce such
a system into general practise, it would be desirable for it to be
applicable to larger particles in order to increase the absolute drug
payload per carrier. In addition, the carriers need to be made from a non-
toxic biodegradable polymer (c.f. 1.5.). To date it has not been possible
to coat biodegradable systems and to avoid RES uptake.

Polystyrene particles possess a relatively hydrophobic surface as indicated
by an air-water-solid contact angle of 90°. Coating polymers have a high
affinity for this surface and adsorb in a layer which is not displaced on
contact with blood. Biodegradable materials such as poly (lactic acid)
(PLA) also possess relatively hydrophobic surfaces (with regard to the
adsorption of blood components), but with contact angles of around 75° they
are less hydrophobic than polystyrene. This lower surface hydrophobicity
leads to a reduced affinity of Poloxamer and Poloxamine-type coating
polymers. Little coating or no coating is achieved (Müller and Wallis,
unpublished data) and the biodegradable carriers are rapidly cleared by the
RES.

The effect of the Poloxamer coatings is attributed to dysopsonic and anti-
adhesive properties of the polymers and from application of colloid theory
to a biological milieu to a steric stabilization effect (Illum et al.,
1986; Davis and Illum, 1988). The polymer layer is claimed to provide a
steric barrier to particle-cell interaction. Considering that phagocytosis
is an active process, steric stabilization as described for particle
suspensions, seems an unlikely phenomenon in a biological environment. In
addition, there is one contradiction which cannot be related to the theory
of steric stabilization. Poloxamer 407 coated particles larger than 100 nm
are not taken up by the macrophages in liver and spleen and consequently
circulate in the blood. These particles do not have access to the bone
marrow. However, Poloxamer 407 coated particles smaller than 100 nm
possessing an even thicker Poloxamer coating layer but are small enough to
pass the sinusoidal fenestrations in the bone marrow, are taken up by
phagocytosing cells in the bone marrow (Illum and Davis 1987b) - despite
the enhanced steric stabilization properties of the thicker Poloxamer layer
(c.f. 2.1. and 9.5.). The protection against phagocytosis seems to be
related rather to the surface properties of the coated carriers than to
steric stabilization. The work presented here makes a contribution to
attempts to establish the mode of action of coating films.

A better understanding of the factors influencing the body distribution of
i.v. administered particles should enable us to optimize the design of drug
carriers. To achieve this, techniques need to be available for thorough
characterization of the drug carriers in the factors relevant to the body
distribution. Therefore, as well as investigating the mechanisms of

protection of particles against RES clearance, and the reasons for the affinity to macrophage subpopulations, emphasis has also been directed towards the development of characterization methods. The methods should provide characterization parameters which can be related to the body distribution and thereby allow prediction of in vivo behaviour.

The importance of surface properties in determining the body distribution can be seen in studies of triglyceride chylomicrons. Unlike foreign particles they are not taken up by liver and spleen macrophages. The chylomicrons are not sterically stabilized but possess the 'correct' surface properties for avoiding uptake. The organ distribution of TPN fat emulsions also depends on the surface properties which are determined by the nature of the emulsifier (Kreuter 1983b). Addition of lysolecithins to lecithin emulsions led to increased RES uptake, whereas the use of Poloxamers as emulsifiers led to a reduction (Jeppsson and Rössner, 1975). The importance of the surface properties of the emulsion droplets on their phagocytosis was also shown by Davis and Hansrani (1985) using macrophage cultures. Changing the surface properties of the emulsion droplets by preparing 'gelatinized' emulsions leads to an increased uptake. Such emulsions can be used as test colloids to assess the functional state of the RES (Tonaki et al., 1976). Increased phagocytosis was obtained after surface modification of lipid emulsions by coating with E. coli lipopoly-saccharide (Schmeling and Zettervall, 1977). Such emulsions can be used as test systems for determining phagocytosis rates and opsonic activities of serum.

The use of liposomes has little advantage with regard to their organ distribution. Their main sites of uptake are also the liver and spleen (Kreuter, 1983b). Surface properties also play an important role in their organ distribution, e.g. the presence of surface charged groups leads to increased phagocytosis (Wilkins and Myers, 1966; Schwendener et al., 1984). Surface properties play a dominant role in the organ distribution and ultimate fate of i.v. injected colloidal drug carriers systems.

1.4 Biodegradable carriers for drug delivery

The production of carriers for controlled release and targeting of drugs requires materials which are non-toxic and can be degraded in the body with a sufficiently high velocity and without forming toxic degradation products. The term 'biodegradation' is used generally for the degradation in the body. However, degradation in vivo should only strictly be called biodegradation if the degradation velocity in vivo is faster than in vitro (e.g. by the activity of body enzymes in addition to a hydrolytic degradation process).

Introduction

Serum albumin is a natural material regarded as suitable for the production
of controlled release systems for intramuscular or subcutaneous injection
(Lee, T.K. et al., 1981; Royer et al, 1983). No adverse immunological
reactions were observed against these bovine serum albumin particles.
Smaller sized albumin spheres are suitable for i.v. injection (Ovadia et
al, 1982) but there are problems in the production of particles in the
size range << 5 μm. A detailed study of the influence of production
parameters on particle size is published by Gallo et al. (1984). As well
as spheres , albumin can also be used to produce microcapsules (Ishizaka
et al, 1981). Albumin particles can be used as carriers for potent drugs
such as cytotoxics (Widder et al., 1980; Willmott and Harrison, 1988), and
as diagnostics for the assessment of RES function (Scheffel et al., 1972)
replacing Tc-sulfur colloid and are meanwhile on the market (e.g. TCK-9,
Compagnie ORIS Industrie, France). A major disadvantage of using albumin
is the possibility of anaphylactic reactions which have been reported even
using human serum albumin (Littenberg, 1974). In addition, the cost of
human serum albumin is relatively high and it is only limitedly available.
Various other natural and chemically modified materials have been used
(gelatin (Sezaki et al., 1982; Krause and Rohdewald, 1985), ethylcellulose
(Gurny et al, 1979) dextran derivatives (Edman et al., 1980)).
Compared to natural products, synthetic polymers have the advantages of
being well characterized, less-immunogenic, relatively cheap and available
in larger quantities. A large number of carrier systems have been produced
using the alkyl-cyanoacrylates which were first introduced by Couvreur et
al.(1977, 1979, 1980 and 1982). However the toxicity of these polymers is
still a matter of discussion because of the formation of toxic degradation
products such as isobutanol and formaldehyde (Kante et al., 1982; Couvreur
et al., 1982; Müller, R.H. et al, 1988b). The toxicity of the degradation
products may not rule out the application of these particles as carriers,
at least for cytotoxic drugs.
Materials which are likely to be passed for use by the regulatory
authorities are polyesters of lactic acid (PLA) and its co-polymer with
glycolic acid (PLA/GA). In contrast to the cyanoacrylate particles which
are polymerised from monomers, the PLA and PLA/GA particle are produced
from the polymer, using the so-called 'solvent evaporation' method. The
polymer is dissolved in an organic solvent and the solution dispersed in
aqueous surfactant solution to form an o/w emulsion. Evaporation of the
solvent leads to the formation of solid particles (Beck et al., 1980, 1983
and 1983a; Tice and Lewis, 1983; Bodmeier and McGinity, 1987 and 1988;
Spenlehauer et al., 1988). The degradation products of PLA and PLA/GA are
lactic and glycolic acids which are normal human metabolic compounds. PLA
and PLA/GA have been extensively studied as potentially useful materials
for controlled drug delivery (Wise et al., 1976 and 1979; Heller, 1985;

12

Pierre and Chiellini, 1987). They are not limited to applications as microspheres, but can also be used for other controlled delivery devices such as tablets, coated tablets and drug loaded films (Entenmann et al., 1987).

A range of other polyesters such as poly(hydroxybutyric acid) (PHB) (Korsatko et al., 1983, 1983a and 1983b) and its co-polymer with hydroxy-valerianic acid (PHB/HV) (Holland et al., 1986 and 1987), polyorthoesters (Nguyen et al., 1984, 1985 and 1987; Heller and Himmelstein, 1985), polyanhydrides (Mathiowitz and Langer, 1987; Laurencin et al., 1987; Domb et al., 1987; Bindschaedler et al., 1988) and polyamides (Pierre and Chiellini, 1987) are under study. Reviews covering a range of synthetic and natural materials can be found in Polymers in Controlled Drug Delivery (Illum and Davis (eds.), 1987c). Although a variety of potential materials for the production of colloidal carriers are available an ideal material with regard to degradation velocity, toxicology and compatibility does as yet not exist.

1.5. Localisation of carriers in the target tissue

Preparation of carriers from a biodegradable and toxicologically acceptable material is possible and they may be employed to produce controlled release carriers for oral or parenteral (subcutaneous, intramuscular) drug delivery. The avoidance of RES clearance after i.v. injection of colloidal carriers by surface modification of the carrier to reduce opsonization and avoid recognition by the body seems feasable. The ultimate goal of these studies is the development of intravenous controlled release formulations.

To direct the carriers to a specific site of action (drug targeting), an avoidance of the RES is not sufficient. The carriers need a 'guidance system' which directs them to their target tissue. A very simple guidance system is the physical approach of localizing particles by using a magnetic field. Particles with magnetic properties can be guided by an externally placed electromagnet (Widder et al., 1978, 1979 and 1980). Such carriers have been made from albumin microspheres containing Fe_3O_4 particles (10-20 nm in diameter). Despite the facts that most of the particles also accumulate in the liver and that long term therapy with such particles will lead to accumulation of Fe_3O_4 particles in the body causing toxicological problems, the concept of magnetic targeting has been examined by a number of research groups (Ovadia et al., 1982; Papisov et al., 1987; Papisov and Torchilin, 1987).

Alternatively antibodies can be used to direct carriers. For example, the fact that antibodies are preferentially taken up by tumor xenografts demonstrates their potential for diagnostic purposes and as a carrier for therapeutic agents (Pimm et al, 1982). Intravenously injected drug-antibody conjugates might conceivably leave the blood vessels by penetration of the endothelial barrier and the basement membrane of the capillary walls. In contrast, colloidal carriers cannot penetrate the walls and are therefore localized within the blood system. Their only means of escape from the blood system is across the sinusoidal fenestrations in liver and bone marrow, thereby allowing the possibility of targeting to these tissues. The use of antibodies bound to colloidal particles is therefore limited to targeting to cells in the blood (e.g. lymphocytes, monocytes, leukemia cells) or to cells in tissues accessible to particles. Targeting to extravascular tumor cells seems not to be feasable.

Antibodies attached to latex particles (immunolatex spheres) have been successfully employed as visual markers of antigens on lymphocytes (Molday et al., 1975; Mirro et al., 1981). The antibodies can either be simply adsorbed or covalently attached. In vitro the attachment of antibodies leads to an increased affinity of the particles to tumor cells in culture (Illum et al., 1983), whereas in vivo the particles accumulated mainly in the liver and spleen and no significant uptake in the tumor was found. This illustrates the problem of particles with attached antibodies - they will be cleared by the RES. An alternative possibility is linkage of the antibodies to particles which are protected against RES clearance by the presence of a coating layer of a surface modifying polymer (e.g. Poloxamine 908 coated 60 nm latex particles). One needs to determine however whether the attachment of antibodies to the dysopsonising surface coat will destroy its properties and lead again to opsonization and clearance of the particle-polymer-antibody conjugate by the RES. It is possible that the coupling of the antibody to the coating polymers would increase the interaction with blood components.

A number of other problems can be foreseen:

1. In order to avoid an immunological response to the conjugates, human, and not mouse monoclonal antibodies need to be used.

2. The epitopes on target cells, e.g. tumor cells, are heterogeneous and alter with time.

3. A monoclonal antibody would need to be produced specifically for each patient according to the epitopes expressed on their tumor cells.

4. On binding to the carrier, the activity of the antibody may be affected; attaching via its antigen-binding sites would essentially render it functionless.

As an answer to this problem, the antibodies can be bound to the carrier surface via proteins A or G. Protein A is derived from Staphylococcus aureus and binds to most classes of immunoglobulins via their Fc portion. If the protein A is conjugated to the particle surface, and the coated particle exposed to the antibodies, they will automatically be attached via their Fc portion in the correct position for display of their antigen-binding sites (Kandzia et al., 1984).

Alternative 'homing devices' to antibodies for targeting are sugar residues which interact with specific cell surface bound lectins. Lectins are sugar-specific receptors located not only on plant but also on vertebrate cells (Gabius, 1987). On the molecular level neoglycoprotein-drug conjugates can be used to target to lectins. These conjugates contain carbohydrate and drug moieties linked to a carrier molecule (e.g. human serum albumin). The presence of surface lectins was shown on human embryonal carcinoma cell lines (α-glucosyl- and α-fucosyl specific receptors) and a specific uptake of neoglycoprotein conjugates mediated by lectins was observed in cell cultures (Gabius et al., 1987). Lectins were also found on human colon carcinoma cells (Gabius et al, 1987a). L-fucose-terminated glycoconjugates are recognized and internalised by pinocytosis receptors on macrophages (Shepherd et al., 1981), and mannose receptor-mediated phagocytosis is described for mouse peritoneal macrophages (Bar-Shavit et al., 1977) and rat alveolar macrophages (Ponpipom et al., 1981). Galactose-specific lectins have been described for rat hepatocytes and Kupffer cells (Kolb et al., 1979, 1980), an asialoglycoprotein receptor for hepatocytes (Kolb-Bachofen, 1981).

It is important that the receptors are specific and that other saccharide residues do not interact. In addition, simply binding to the receptor is not sufficient. The drug conjugate needs to be internalised by endocytosis. These receptors are capable of endocytotic transport (Gabius et al., 1987). Galactose receptors mediate particle uptake by liver cells leading to a different affinity of particles of various size to hepatocytes, endothelial and Kupffer cells (Kolb-Bachofen, 1983 and 1984). Glycoprotein-drug conjugates show increased affinity for the target cell in vitro but in vivo these large molecules will have the same fate as particulates; they will be taken up by the macrophages of liver and spleen. This therefore limits their application as targeting vehicles.

Carbohydrate moieties bound to liposomes have been employed for targeting to liver cells in vivo. The binding of β-galactoside to the liposomal surface led to a shift in the distribution from Kupffer cells to hepatocytes in rats (Ghosh et al., 1982). Also, the coupling of 6-aminomannose to cholesterol in liposomes was found to lead to an increased affinity for leukocytes after subcutaneous injection in mice (Mauk et al., 1980). However, although the use of glycoconjugates to target to lectins seems a promising idea, e.g. to target to endogeneous lectins of tumor cells in cancer therapy (Gabius et al., 1987b), to date, no colloidal carriers bearing lectin-binding sugar moieties which avoid the RES clearance have been produced.

As an alternative to using bound sugar residues directed towards a cell surface lectin, lectin-conjugates could be used to target towards cell surface sugar residues. The specifity of plant and animal lectins for glycoconjugates can be used for characterization and separation of cells (e.g. leukemia cells) (Gabius et al., 1988). Apart from lectins and sugar residues other receptors on cell surfaces can be used for targeting, e.g. lipoprotein receptors such as the°low density lipoprotein (LDL) receptor . A large number of possibilities are available for the direction of carriers to their target. The success of targeting using these 'tools' for intravenous carrier systems will be mainly determined by the extent to which the drug carrier-homing device conjugates will be cleared by the RES. This principle is equally applicable to particulate and macromolecular carriers.

1.6. Targeting with i.v. administered carriers - potentials and limitations

The potentials and limitations of drug targeting are an important topic, but one that needs to be discussed realistically. A lot of expectations and research efforts have been directed towards liposomal delivery systems. The resulting achievements are however limited compared with the huge investment of research funds. A major fault has been the unrealistic expectations which implied that liposomal colloidal carriers were the ultimate solution for all drug delivery problems.
Polymeric carriers systems have a number of advantages.
1. They can protect the drug against the host (e.g. enzymatic degradation) or the host against the drug (reduction of toxic side effects).
2. The release profile of the drug can be optimized according to the pharmacological and pharmacokinetic requirements by creating controlled release delivery systems.
3. A site-directed delivery is possible by simple compartmental delivery (e.g. intramuscular injection).
Gardner described the limitations of the carrier-vehicle approach (Gardner, 1983):
- preparative methods,
- limited ability to cross capillary endothelium,
- susceptibility to removal by the RES,
- limited access to non-phagocytic cells,
- immunogenicity,
- degradability.
He described the uptake by the RES as 'the major' obstacle against the successful utilisation of carriers as targeting agents. Subsequently, it has been possible to successfully avoid RES uptake by using Poloxamine 908 coated latex particles (Illum et al., 1987a) and the major obstacle has

16

therefore been overcome, but only for small (60 nm) non-biodegradable model particles. By applying the same principles it should be possible, to produce biodegradable particles with the same properties. The work presented here outlines the principles for the rational design of such carriers. Currently available preparative methods still need improvement. The main problems are in the production of polymeric particles without solvent residues, the wettability and dispersability of freeze dried surfactant-free particles and in the scaling up of production techniques. The production of virtually solvent free biodegradable polymeric particles has been achieved by Müller and Fischer (1989).

With current techniques, the access to non-phagocytic cells is limited, but improvements seem achievable by the use of human monoclonal antibodies, glycoconjugates and lectins. There are 3 different levels of targeting:
1. a tissue (e.g. liver)
2. a specific cell population in the tissue (e.g. hepatocytes)
3. an intracellular compartment (e.g. the lysosomes)
whereby the difficulties of getting access increase from the targeting level 1 to 3.

The immunogenicity of particles will remain a problem, especially considering the potential immunogenic effects of the carbohydrate moieties in glycoconjugates. The immunogenicity of the carrier material can however be minimized by careful selection of the polymer material.

Degradability of carriers is less of a problem for single-dose treatments than it is for chronic administration of carriers. Although polymers such as PLA/GA (50:50) degrade within one or two weeks after injection, long-term treatment might still lead to a build-up of non-degraded polymer. Alkylcyanoacrylates degrade between a few hours and 2 days depending on the composition but possess a higher toxicity.

No success has yet been reported in improving capability of the carrier at leaving the blood stream by penetration of the capillary wall. The only current exit route available to colloidal carriers is via the fenestrations in the sinusoids of the liver and the bone marrow. Diversion of particles away from the liver and accumulation in the bone marrow has been reported by Illum and Davis (1987b). Attempts to penetrate the endothelial lining with colloidal carriers in order to reach extravascular sites (e.g. by using wall permeability enhancing compounds) are regarded as not realistic and potentially dangerous.

The limited ability of intravenously injected colloidal carriers to leave the blood system has to be accepted and considered when designing drug targeting systems. At present therefore, a targeting to tumors using colloidal carriers seems to be improbable. The anatomical location, poor blood supply of solid tumors and structure and permeability of the tumor microcirculation provide little access for carriers, even though the

Introduction

permeability of the capillary wall may be enhanced in the presence of necrosis or inflammation (Poste, 1984).

The options for intravenous colloidal carriers can be summarized:
- targeting to <u>extravascular</u> sites: difficult, if not impossible
- targeting via <u>fenestrations</u>:   feasable
    - to hepatocytes
    - to bone marrow
- targeting to <u>intravascular</u> targets:
    - Kupffer cells   feasable
    - blood monocytes
    - lymphocytes
    - leukemia cells
- targeting to <u>specific intracellular</u> sites: difficult

- <u>controlled release</u> formulations in blood: feasable

- <u>reduction of toxic side effects</u>:   feasable

- treatment of <u>infectious diseases</u>:   feasable

One of the main areas of future application of colloidal carriers will be in the controlled release of proteins and peptides which at present pose many problems and are a challenge for drug delivery (Crommelin, 1987).

18

2. MODIFICATION OF DRUG CARRIERS

2.0 Surface modification by polymer adsorption

To avoid RES recognition, the surface of polymeric carriers should be hydrophilic. However, the polymers used for the production of non-biodegradable model carriers are hydrophobic, e.g. polystyrene with a contact angle of $90°$. Even polymers used for the production of biodegradable carriers produce relatively hydrophobic surfaces and contact angles of around $75°$. These surfaces are opsonized in vivo and the i.v. injected particles made from these materials will be cleared by the RES. The hydrophobicity of the surface can be reduced by chemical modification, e.g. the introduction of functional groups (OH, COOH) or the attachment of polyethylene glycol (PEG) (Abuchowski et al, 1977). Modification with PEG reduced the immunogenity of albumin particles and the blood clearance rate of intravenously injected modified particles. The surface chemical modification of particles leads to the formation of new substances with unknown toxicity. Toxicity studies are required for the registration of such drug carriers by the regulatory authorities. A much simpler approach is surface modification by the adsorption of polymers. Such modification requires, that the polymer layer is not desorbed or displaced after intravenous injection. Successful coating has been performed with Poloxamine 908 on 60 nm polystyrene model carriers (Illum et al., 1987a). The coated particles circulated in the blood over a few days. This indicates no desorption or displacement of the polymer layer, in which case the particles would have accumulated in the liver and spleen.

The adsorption behaviour of non-ionic ethoxylated nonylphenol surfactants on polystyrene latex particles has been described by Kronberg et al. (1981). The adsorption isotherms reach a plateau (maximum adsorption) somewhat higher than the critical micelle concentration (cmc). The affinity for the particle surface decreases with increasing ethylene oxide (EO) chain length. In commercial products of ethoxylated surfactants there is a range in the EO chain length; under these conditions the species with the highest affinity will replace species with lower affinities (molecules with longer EO chain).

The adsorption isotherms were Langmurian, i.e. the affinity of the adsorbate (nonylphenol) for the surface is strong. Only in such cases the Langmuir isotherm is valid for the adsorption of non-electrolytes from solution. Some of the affinity of the EO chain for the surface was attributed to the presence of carboxylic groups leading to hydrogen bonds with the EO chains. Displacement of non-ionics by ionic surfactants (e.g. sodium dodecyl sulphate - SDS) in surfactant mixture does not take place.

On the contrary, the non-ionic surfactants adsorb more strongly and will displace the ionic surfactants from the surface. This is of importance for the coating of drug carriers produced in the presence of SDS (c.f. 5.). The SDS will be replaced and not interfere with the coating by the non-ionic polymer. Cleaning of coated particles in an ultrafiltration cell revealed that SDS is easily washed off but the non-ionic surfactant remains strongly bound to the surface. Removal of strongly adsorbing species from latex using ultrafiltration is therefore impossible and it is unlikely that these non-ionic surfactants will be desorbed or displaced in serum. They are therefore suitable materials for surface modification by adsorption.

The adsorption characteristics of polyoxyethylene-polyoxypropylene co-polymers (Poloxamer™) on polystyrene latex particles were studied by Kayes and Rawlins (1979) who found a Langmuir type adsorption with a maximum for all surfactants above the critical micelle concentration (around 0.005 to 0.01% w/v surfactant). The Poloxamers possess a high affinity for the surface as indicated by measurable adsorption below the cmc. The polyoxy-propylene part of the molecule (POP) adsorbs onto the surface either tightly coiled or by forming small loops; the structure of the polyoxy-ethylene chains (POE) varies within the Poloxamer series. For Poloxamer 181 and 182 the POE chains adsorb flat onto the surface, whereas for Poloxamer 108, 283 and 338 the EO chains must also be present as loops and tails. The conformation of the POP and POE chains will have an important influence on the resulting surface hydrophobicity of the adsorbed layers. Increased fractions of flatly adsorbed POE will lead to exposure of the more hydrophobic POP parts of the molecule resulting in a more hydrophobic surface, whereas the presence of POE loops and tails can cover the more hydrophobic POP parts of the molecule leading to a more hydrophilic surface. The loop conformation of polyoxyethylene on polystyrene latex was confirmed by small angle neutron scattering (SANS) experiments (Cosgrove et al., 1983), some POE tails were highly extended (given that the fully extended length for POE 4800 is 30.5 nm - Cosgrove et al., 1981). NMR studies of POE chains grafted onto particles showed that the chains were highly mobile and not in close contact with the surface (Cosgrove et al., 1981). Determination of the critical flocculation temperature (CFT) showed that the particles were sterically stabilized (CFT 60° C).

Differences in the amount of non-ionic polymers adsorbed onto the surface of particles is attributed to differences in their surface hydrophobicities (Rawlins and Kayes, 1983; Law and Kayes 1983). The steric stabilizing effect of polymers at the solid/water interface depends on the composition and thickness of the adsorbed layer (Law and Kayes, 1983).

The adsorption of Poloxamer polymers was found to increase with temperature and electrolyte concentration due to a reduction in the solvency of the polymer (Tadros and Vincent, 1980). This is of importance for the preparation of coated carriers. Coating of carriers in physiological salt solutions might lead to increased adsorption and a thicker coating layer. The CFT values were found to be below the θ temperature of the stabilizing moieties (POE) indicating that the polymers adsorb in loop/train configuration (Tadros and Vincent, 1980).

Driving forces for the adsorption of non-ionic surfactants according to Kronberg (1983) are:

1. the gain in interaction energy with the surface when water is replaced by a hydrocarbon on the surface,

2. the difference in surfactant-water interaction in the surface and bulk phases (lower number of hydrocarbon-water contacts in the surface phase).

The difference in surfactant-water interaction is regarded as the driving force for adsorption, whereby it is assumed that the non-ionic surfactant molecules adsorb only with their hydrophobic part in contact with the surface. For ethoxylated nonylphenols it is likely that at very low surface coverage the molecules lie flat on the surface, whereas they rise up when the surface is completely covered (Kronberg, 1983).

The adsorption of non-ionic surfactants decreases as the polarity of the particles increases (Kronberg and Stenius, 1984). Hence the polarity of the latex surface or the solubility parameter can be determined from adsorption measurements. The plateau of the adsorption isotherm decreases as the surface polarity increases, (i.e. the density of adsorbed surfactant molecules per surface unit is lower). These findings are of importance for the adsorption of the surfactants onto model latex particles. Surface-modified latex with a polarity, increased by the introduction of polar groups (OH, COOH) will adsorb less surfactant, resulting in a thinner coating layer. The configuration of the polymer in a thinner layer might be different to that in a thick layer (high density of molecules adsorbed per surface unit). As a consequence, different parts of the molecule might be exposed to the water bulk phase, resulting in a different surface hydrophobicity of the adsorbed polymer layer.

Comparitive adsorption studies of ethoxylated nonylphenols on poly(methyl methacrylate) (PMMA) and poly(styrene) (PS) latex particles revealed only a slightly lower amount adsorbed onto PMMA latex, - despite the fact that the PMMA particles possess a higher surface polarity than PS particles (Kronberg et al., 1984). It was concluded that the driving forces for adsorption are the solution properties of the surfactant and not the specific interaction between latex surface and surfactant. The probability of hydrocarbon-water contacts for the surfactant is lower in the adsorbed state compared to surfactants free in solution. About 80% of the adsorption-free-energy is attributed to the orientation of the surfactants on the surface. The hydrophobic moiety of the surfactant orientates towards the surface, and the hydrophilic moiety towards the water bulk phase, leading to a replacement of water-hydrophobic moiety contacts by surfactant-surfactant contacts. Only 20% of the adsorption free energy is influenced by the nature of the adsorbent surface (Kronberg et al., 1984). Consideration of the solution properties of the surfactant as the driving force is in accordance with the observed adsorption behaviour of human plasma albumin which was found to be similar at sorbent surfaces differing in electrical charge and hydrophobicity. The adsorption behaviour seemed to be determined rather by the properties of the albumin molecule than by the sorbent surface (Norde et al., 1986). The fact that no desorption of albumin adsorbed onto polystyrene particles was measured, was regarded to be due to the large loss in entropy which would result because of hydration of the hydrophobic sorbent surface.

Adsorption of polyoxyethylene-polyoxypropylene block co-polymers (Poloxamer) onto liposomes was reported. The thickness of the adsorbed layer showed a distinct increase with incubation time over 48 hours (Jamshaid et al., 1988). This is in contrast to observations with latex particles where the adsorption layer thickness shows only a slight increase with time. The fact that the adsorbed layer was thinner on liposomes than on polystyrene latex particles was attributed to a degree of bilayer penetration by the polymers (Jamshaid et al., 1988). The interaction of Poloxamer with the liposomes increased the efflux of solutes present in the aqueous liposome core, possibly due to a change in membrane permeability because of Poloxamer penetration.

The critical micelle concentrations of ethoxylated surfactants were found to be between 0.09 - 1.5 % w/v for Poloxamer (Saettone et al., 1988), 0.3 - 0.8 x 10^{-4} M for polyoxyethylated nonylphenols, 1.1 - 4.8 x 10^{-5} M for polyoxylated sorbitan fatty acid esters (Tween) and between 10^{-6} and 10^{-4} M for polyoxyethylated ethers (Brij) (Samaha and Naggar, 1988).

2.1. Coating with Poloxamer and Poloxamine polymers

The surface of polymeric particles can easily be modified by coating with non-ionic polymers using a simple adsorption process. To create a more hydrophilic surface, latex particles were coated with a series of Poloxamers and Poloxamine polymers. Poloxamers are A-B-A block co-polymers with the general structure $(EO)_n$-$(PO)_m$-$(EO)_n$. The centre section (B) consists of a polypropylene oxide (PO) chain, the terminal chains are polyethylene oxide (EO), where n and m are the number of units EO and PO. The Poloxamine series has the general structure:

$$(EO)_n\text{-}(PO)_m \diagdown \qquad \diagup (PO)_m\text{-}(EO)_n$$
$$\qquad\qquad N\text{-}CH_2\text{-}CH_2\text{-}N$$
$$(EO)_n\text{-}(PO)_m \diagup \qquad \diagdown (PO)_m\text{-}(EO)_n$$

Poloxamer and Poloxamine polymers adsorb onto the surface of latex particles mainly through the central PO section with the EO chains protruding into the latex dispersion medium (Cosgrove et al, 1983). An overview of the Poloxamine and Poloxamer polymers used in the studies is given in Tables 2.1./1 and 2. Coating was performed by overnight incubation of equal volumes of 60 nm latex dispersion (2.5 % w/v) with 2.0 % coating solutions of the relevant Poloxamer or Poloxamine. The thicknesses of the obtained coating layers are given in Tables 2.1./1, 3 and 4.
In general, the coating layer thickness of the Poloxamer polymers increases with molecular weight. The coating layer thickness of polymers with identical PO centre regions increases with increasing lengths of the EO chains (Table 2.1./3). This indicates that the EO chains make a major contribution to the thickness of the coating layer .

Table 2.1./1: Poloxamine™ (=Tetronic™) polymers used for the coating of latex particles (HLB - Hydrophilic Lipohilic Balance value of the surfactant).

Poloxamine /Tetronic	coating layer (Å)	molecular weight	percentage of EO	HLB
908	134	27,000	80%	30.5
1107	88	14,500	70%	24
1307	98	18,600	70%	23.5
1508	115	27,000	80%	27

Table 2.1./2: Poloxamers used for the coating of latex particles and their Pluronic nomenclature (the number of EO units is given per **single** A chain; HLB - Hydrophilic Lipohilic Balance value of the surfactant).

Poloxamer™	Pluronic™	Average Molecular weight	No. EO units, A chain	No. PO units, B chain	HLB
181	L61	2000	3	30	3
182	L62	2500	8	30	7
184	L64	2900	13	30	15
331	L101	3800	7	54	1
402	L122	5000	13	67	4
234	P84	4200	22	39	14
235	P85	4600	27	39	16
333	P103	4950	20	54	9
335	P105	6500	38	54	15
108	F38	5000	46	16	30.5
188	F68	8350	75	30	29
217	F77	6600	52	35	25
237	F87	7700	62	35	24
283	F88	10800	97	39	28
288	F98	13500	122	47	28
338	F108	14000	128	54	27
407	F127	11500	98	67	22

The coating layer thickness of polymers with **similar EO** chain lengths increases with increasing length of the PO block (Table 2.1./4). This might be attributed to the formation of larger PO loops on the surface leading to a greater extension of the EO chains protruding from the polymer surface into the dispersion medium.

Based on the results obtained with the Poloxamers, only selected promising Poloxamine polymers with high molecular weights and containing a large percentage (70-80%) of ethylene oxide were investigated (Table 2.1./1). As predicted, they led to coating layers in the range of 100 Å and above. From these results it appears likely that Poloxamine 1508 coated particles might be able to reduce RES clearance to a similar extent as Poloxamine 908 (Illum et al, 1987).

The coating layer thickness obtained with high molecular weight Poloxamer and Poloxamine polymers varied slightly between preparations. For Poloxamine 908 values between 130 Å and 155 Å were found. To investigate the reason for this variation, a number of samples were prepared and the coating layer thickness determined both immediately after mixing of the latex particle suspension (2.5 %) and the Poloxamer/Poloxamine solutions (2 %), and after 24 hours incubation (Table 2.1./5).

Table 2.1./3: Coating layer thickness of Poloxamers ordered in groups of constant length of PO chain but increasing length of EO chain.

number of units PO	EO	coating layer (Å)	Molecular weight	Poloxamer
16	46	58	5000	108
30	3	16	2000	181
	8	18	2500	182
	13	24	2900	184
	76	76	8350	188
35	52	58	6600	217
39	22	29	4200	234
	27	35	4600	235
	62	80	7700	237
	97	132	10800	238
47	122	130	13500	288
54	7	48	3800	331
	20	58	4950	333
	38	53	6500	335
	128	154	14000	338
67	13	57	5000	402
	98	119	11500	407

Table 2.1./4: Coating layer thickness of Poloxamers ordered in groups of similar length of EO chains but increasing length of the PO block.

number of units EO	PO	coating layer (Å)	Molecular weight	Poloxamer
3	30	16	2000	181
8	30	18	2500	182
7	54	48	3800	331
13	30	24	2900	184
13	67	57	5000	402
22	39	29	4200	234
27	39	35	4600	235
20	54	58	4950	333
46	16	58	5000	108
52	35	58	6600	217
38	54	53	6500	335
97	39	132	10800	238
98	67	119	11500	407
122	47	130	13500	288
128	54	154	14000	388

25

Table 2.1./5: Coating layer thickness obtained without incubation and after 24 hours incubation overnight (mixing of equal volumes of 2.5% 60.2 nm latex stock dispersion and 4% polymer coating solution).

coating material	coating layer thicknesses (Å) obtained	
	without incubation	24 hours incubation
Poloxamer 338	120	139
	115	139
	125	143
	-	150
Tetronic 908	107	146
	137	154
	113	138
	-	138

The coating layers obtained for Poloxamer 338 directly after mixing were thinner than after incubation. The thickness of the coating layer was in the size range obtained in the plateau region of the adsorption isotherm (appr. 120 Å, Fig. 2.1./1). Incubation led to an increase in the thickness of the adsorbed layers (up to 140 to 150 Å). This might be due to the replacement of low molecular weight polymer with a short PO central region

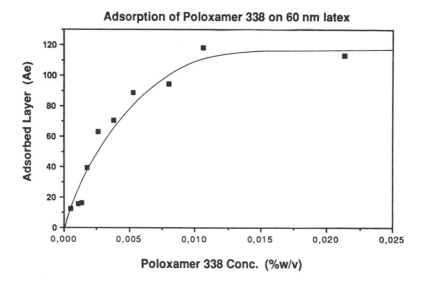

Fig. 2.1./1: Adsorption isotherm determined by PCS measurements of the coating layer thickness of Poloxamer 338 on 60 nm polystyrene particles.

by higher molecular weight Poloxamer with larger PO region and higher affinity for the particle surface.

Preparations of Poloxamer polymers are not homogenous and possess a wide molecular weight distribution. Preparations of some polymers show a bimodal molecular weight distribution and are a mixture of two Poloxamer polymer fractions. The quoted nominal molecular weight is the mean value of the two molecular weight distributions. It is very likely that in the coating procedure, both Poloxamer polymer fractions compete in the adsorption process and with increasing incubation time, molecules with lower affinity are displaced from the polymer surface and replaced by high affinity molecules. This replacement can be shown by coating latex particles with low molecular weight Poloxamer and incubating the coated particles with a high molecular weight Poloxamer solution. The replacement leads to an increase in the coating layer thickness which can be measured by PCS.

Adsorption isotherms of Poloxamer onto latex can be determined by measuring the adsorption layer thickness by Photon Correlation Spectroscopy (PCS). The data obtained for Poloxamer 338 was in good agreement with the adsorption isotherms obtained by Kayes and Rawlins (1979). The isotherms are easily obtained by PCS measurements but the technique is limited to the adsorption of high molecular weight polymers onto small particles (30 to 60 nm). The measured adsorption layer has to be relatively large compared to the particle size. The reproducibility of PCS (+/- 1.0%) limits the accuracy of the measurement of the adsorption layer thickness; e.g. for a large particle of 300 nm diameter the accuracy is +/- 3nm. Measurements can therefore only accurately be made of adsorbed layers of a thickness much greater than this variation (>> 30 Å).

2.2. Coating with polyoxylated alkyl phenols

To replace Poloxamer and Poloxamine polymers, various polyoxylated alkyl-phenols were investigated. The hydrophobic nonylphenol adsorbs onto the latex particle surface and is equivalent to the PO centre part of Poloxamer and Poloxamine surfactants. Due to the more hydrophobic character of a nonylphenol compared to a PO chain, the affinity of the alkyl-phenols for the particle surface was hoped to be increased. However, polymers containing PO chains provide a multipoint attachment of the polymer chain to the surface and are less likely to be desorbed. Investigations in the affinity of alkyl-phenols to particle surfaces and the stability of the resulting coating layer are currently undertaken (Müller, R.H. and Wallis, 1988).

The polyoxylated alkyl-phenols are available containing different alkyl groups and varying ethylene oxide (EO) chain lengths. The Antarox™ series consists of ethoxylated nonyl-phenols:

$$R \text{---} \bigcirc \text{---} O(CH_2CH_2O)_{n-1}CH_2CH_2OH$$

The Antarox™ CO series are p-nonyl-phenols (R = nonyl), the Antarox™ DM series are dinonyl-phenols (nonyl groups are predominantly ortho-para oriented).

Antarox surfactants containing large amounts of ethylene oxide are highly water soluble and excellent stabilizers even effective at high temperatures (steric stabilization). The acute oral toxicity of the Antarox surfactants is relatively low (e.g. > 31.5g/kg in rats, (GAF Corporation Technical Bulletin, 1969)). The primary dermal and ocular irritation decreases with increasing EO chain length and is mild for products with large ethylene oxide content. Most of these surfactants possess the FDA indirect food additive status (GAF Corporation, Antarox CO Technical Bulletin 2550-023). The Gafac™ surfactants possess the same structure as Antarox CO but carry a phosphate group at the end of the EO chain:

$$R \text{---} \bigcirc \text{---} O(CH_2CH_2O)_n \begin{array}{c} O \\ \diagdown \; \diagup\!\!\diagup \\ P \\ \diagup \; \diagdown \\ MO \quad\quad OM \end{array}$$

Despite the ionic character of the Gafac surfactants, they have a low toxicity, low skin and eye irritation. They are used as cosmetic emulsifiers and solubilizers.

The Antarox and Gafac surfactants are suitable to study the influence of:
- the EO chain length on the coating layer thickness (CO series)
- the hydrophobic region of the surfactant on the coating layer thickness (comparing nonyl-phenols with dinonyl-phenols)
- charged groups at the end of the EO chain (comparing Antarox CO970 and Gafac RE960) on the adsorption (e.g. layer thickness) and the in vivo organ distribution (c.f. chapter 8).

Mulgofen ON870 is a nonionic polyoxylated oleyl alcohol with 20 EO units. It is used as stabilizer for natural and synthetic latices and as emulsifier in cosmetics and pharmaceuticals. Due to the short EO chain the oral toxicity is 2.25g/kg (white rats and guinea pigs, (GAF Corporation, Mulgofen ON870 Technical Bulletin 9676-010)). Mulgofen ON870 was used to study the influence of replacing the hydrophobic nonylphenol part of the molecule (Antarox CO) by oleyl alcohol.

Table 2.2./1: Coating layer thickness of polyoxylated alkyl-phenols on 57.0 nm latex in distilled water pH 4.1 (* - layer thickness in 0.01 M phosphate buffer pH 7.4).

coating surfactant	EO units per chain	coating layer thickness (Å)
Antarox CO630	5	3.3
CO660	9	10.0
CO730	10	10.6
CO850	20	14.2
CO880	30	23.3
CO890	40	31.8
CO970	50	61.4 / 77.7*
CO990	100	72.9 / 89.1*
Antarox DM530	5	28.0
DM970	150	99.6 / 107.0*
Gafac RE960	50	51.6
Mulgofen ON870	20	21.0

For studies of coating layer thickness, 57 nm polystyrene latex particles (2.5% w/v) were mixed with 2.0% surfactant solution and incubated overnight. With increasing length of the EO chain an increase in the coating layer was obtained (Table 2.2./1). Assessing the thickness of thin coating layers, the reproducibility of PCS measurements has to be considered leading to less reliable values. The coating layer thickness of Antarox CO970 seems to be slightly lower than Poloxamer 188 whereas that of Antarox CO990 was similar or slightly higher. The dinonyl derivatives (Antarox DM 530) seem to have a different conformation in the adsorbed layer resulting in a thicker coating layer compared to Antarox CO surfactants with similar EO chain length. Antarox DM530 (5 EO units) leads to a much thicker layer (28 Å) than the equivalent nonyl derivative Antarox CO630 (< 10 Å). The comparison of Antarox CO990 and DM 970 (100/150 EO units) indicates a thicker layer for the latter which is most likely due to the longer EO chain. In 0.01 M phosphate buffer, the thickness of the coating layers increased (Table 2,2,/1, *). The change in pH should not directly affect the adsorption of the non-ionic surfactants, but, the increase in the salt concentration might have some effect by reducing the solvency of the stabilizing moiety.

The charged Gafac RE960 possessed a slightly thinner layer (51 Å) than the equivalent uncharged Antarox CO970 (61 Å). This might be an effect of the charged phosphate group. The adsorption layer could be increased by coating in the presence of 0.9% NaCl (Table 2.2./2). An increase in the size of the coated particles due to flocculation seems unlikely because the polydispersity index did not change. For the in vivo studies latex were coated with Gafac RE960 in the presence of physiological salt solution to create a larger coating layer.

The dependence of the coating layer thickness on the concentration of the coating surfactant was investigated by incubating the latex with increasing amount of surfactant (10 µl 2.5% w/v latex suspension in 1.0 ml surfactant solution, incubation overnight). No adsorption layer was detectable by PCS at 0.001% surfactant concentration, a distinct coating layer of about half the maximum coating layer thickness was found at 0.005% (Fig. 2.2./1).

Table 2.2./2: Table of coating layer thickness and polydispersity index of latex coated with Gafac RE960 in different salt concentrations.

coating layer (Å)	polydisp. index	coating medium
51.6	0.100	pH 4.1 distilled water
101.1	0.110	pH 4.1 0.9% NaCl

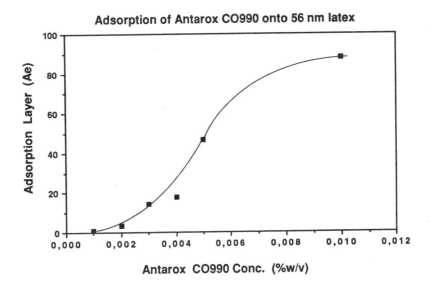

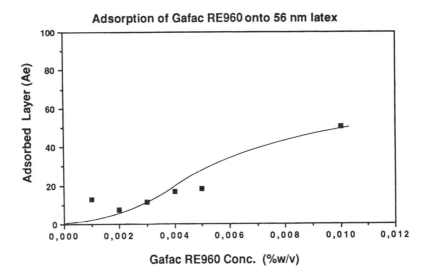

Fig. 2.2./1: Adsorption layer thickness of Gafac RE960 and Antarox C0990 in dependence on surfactant concentration.

The maximum coating layer thickness was obtained at concentrations of 0.01% and above. The concentration of surfactant at which plateauing of the coating layer thickness is achieved is similar to Poloxamer 407 (c.f. Fig. 2.1./1). The affinity of Antarox CO990 for the surface is however slightly lower than the block co-polymer. Poloxamer 407 reaches about 50% of the maximum thickness of the coating layer at about 0.003% and Antarox CO990 at 0.005%.

2.3. Coating with phospholipids

Parenteral fat emulsions based on natural egg lecithin are of particular interest because of their low clearance by the reticuloendothelial system following intravenous injection. Therefore, a study of the surface coating of latex particles with phospholipids was performed. The phospholipids employed were obtained from Nattermann:
Infusol™ (soya lecithin,60-80% phosphatidylcholine (PC),8-15% PE)
NC 95 (90-96% PC))
NC 95H type I (96% PC, hydrogenated)
NC 95H type II (92% PC, hydrogenated)
DPPC (97.7% dipalmitoyl-PC)
Egg-PG (96-98% egg phosphatidylglycerol)
Egg-PC-H (99.9% egg PC, hydrogenated)
Soya-PE-H (92.2% phosphatidylethanolamine, hydrogenated)
Aqueous coating solutions could not be prepared due to the low solubility of the phospholipids in water. They were therefore dissolved in 96% ethanol

Table 2.3./1: Coating layer thickness of different phospholipids on 57.0 nm polystyrene latex and the polydispersity index (PI) of the coated carrier population (PCS data, PI of standard latex = 0.07).

phospholipid	coating layer (Å)	polydispersity index
Infusol	33.7	0.122
NC 95	43.4	0.136
DPPC	36.2	0.141
Egg-PG	23.7	0.103
Egg-PC-H	---	0.225
Soya-PE-H	36.4	0.168

(to concentrations of 0.5-2.0% phospholipid) and 15 µl of the resulting coating solution was added to the latex suspension (15 µl 2.5% latex stock dispersion in 2.0 ml water). Ethanol was seen to cause flocculation of the 60nm latex, so to reduce this effect as much as possible the particles were measured immediately after mixing with the coating solution.

The hydrogenated NC 95 and Egg-PC-H coating solutions caused too much flocculation measured by increase in polydispersity index and a coating layer thickness could not therefore be obtained. The coagulation suggests that the coating method needs further optimization. From the data obtained (Table 2.3./1) the phospholipids appear to be coating the latex but the resulting increase in particle size is not solely due to the coating process. The flocculation (increase in polydispersity index) contributes to the size increase. The actual coating layer is therefore slightly thinner than the values given in Table 2.3./1. That a coating took place and that there are differences in the extent of coating could be shown by aqueous two-phase partitioning (c.f. chapter 3.4.3).

2.4. Coating with miscellaneous ethoxylated compounds

The coating efficiency of a range of ethoxylated monoglycerides (Tagat series), castor oils (Tagat R series) and ethoxylated sorbitan fatty acid esters (Tween) was investigated. The lipohilic regions of the molecule, consisting of fatty acids, should have a sufficiently high affinity for the polymer particle surface to provide a good coating layer.

Coating took place (coating procedure as described previously in 2.3) and layers of about 25 Å were obtained for most of these surfactants (Table 2.4./1). The lipohilic regions and the EO chains are of similar molecular weight for all the potential coating molecules, except Tagat R. For Tagat R60 (containing 60 mol EO) a coating layer thickness of 74 Å was obtained;

Table 2.4./1: Coating layer thickness of Tagat and Tween surfactants on 60 nm polystyrene latex.(For each surfactant the number of mols EO used per mol fatty acid/ sorbitan fatty acid ester in the ethoxylation process is given).

surfactant	fatty acid component	no. of C atoms	mol EO per molecule	coating layer thickness (Å)
Tagat L2	laurate	12	20	21
Tagat L			30	26
Tagat O2	oleate	18	20	28
Tagat O			30	26
Tagat TO	trioleate	3x18	25	24
Tagat I2	isostearate	18	20	24
Tagat I			30	24
Tagat R40	castor oil	-	40	30
Tagat R60		-	60	74
Tween 20	laurate	12	20	23
Tween 40	palmitate	16	20	25
Tween 60	stearate	18	20	26
Tween 80	oleate	18	20	22

this is similar to that obtained with Poloxamer 188 (75 EO units in terminal chains, 76 Å coating layer).

The successful coating with these coating materials and the relatively thick layer obtained with Tagat R60 suggest to synthesize similar optimized compounds. They should comprise a lipohilic part based on fatty acids or similar structures to provide a high affinity and strong binding to the surface of the carriers. Optimization of this lipophilic anchor part has to be performed by determining the affinity to the surface and - extremely important - the desorption behaviour. Poloxamer and Poloxamine show little desorption due to the multipoint attachment of the polymer chain. Such a multipoint attachment does not exist for the proposed compounds but the fatty acid chain provides increased hydrophobic interaction with the carrier surface compared to the polypropylene oxide blocks of Poloxamer/Poloxamine. Optimization of the hydrophilic EO chain can be performed by increasing the number of EO units. However, this cannot be done indefinitely. There will be an optimum number of EO chains to provide the most hydrophilic coating and simultaneously still high affinity of the molecule to the carrier surface. Increasing the length of the EO chain further might reduce the affinity of the molecule to the carrier surface due to the increased solvency in the dispersion medium. It might be energeticly more favourable to stay in solution, possible acquiring a coil structure which encloses the lipophilic part inside.

2.5. Gamma-irradiation and plasma etching

2.5.1. Effects of irradiation and plasma etching on polymers

Alternative methods of changing the surface properties of polymeric materials are gamma-irradiation or plasma treatment. Both methods lead to a reduction in the surface hydrophobicity, resulting in an increased wettability. The extent of the change in the surface properties can therefore be monitored by contact angle measurements. The reduction in surface hydrophobicity leads to an increased biocompatibility of polymers. New surface groups introduced by plasma treatment can be utilised as functional groups for chemically anchoring coating films (e.g. covalent binding of EO chains instead of physical adsorption of EO chain-containing polymers).

Irradiation of polymers mainly leads to chain scission (degradation) and to intermolecular crosslinking. The type of reaction which dominates depends on the nature of the polymer. Sterilization of polystyrene latex particle suspension by gamma-irradiation leads to a decrease in particle size indicating polymer degradation (c.f. chapter 5.3.1.). The effect of irradiation is of importance for the coating of carriers which have been sterilized. A change in the surface hydrophobicity of the irradiated carriers will certainly have an effect on the subsequent coating and the resulting properties of the adsorption layer. Polymer sensitivity towards irradiation depends tremendously on the polymer structure. Aromatic polymers such as polystyrene are relatively resistant. Aliphatic polymers such as Polyhydroxybutyrate (PHB) are damaged more easily. Irradiation of PHB particles with higher doses (e.g. 2.5×10^4 Gy) leads to particle coagulation (c.f. chapter 5.3.1.).

Treatment of polymer surfaces with a plasma leads to the introduction of new functional groups on the surface. The type of functional group depends on the polymer and on the plasma used (e.g. introduction of hydroxyl groups by oxygen plasma). In addition, under plasma treatment polymer radicals can undergo chain scission or recombination.

2.5.2. Materials and methods

Gamma-irradiation was performed using a Co-60 source at dose rates of 58 Gy/h and 169 Gy/h (Type H2 Multiple Source Irradiation Unit, Nuclear Engineering Ltd., UK). Plasma etching was performed using a Polaron E2000 plasma chemistry unit (Fig. 2.5./1). The etching process is influenced by the gas composition, the discharge power, the plasma pressure and the

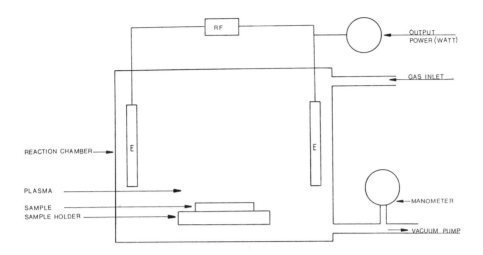

Fig. 2.5./1: Principal set up of plasma etching unit. Samples are cast on a microscope slide, placed in the reaction chamber and treated with a plasma at low pressure (E - electrode, Rf - Radio frequency).

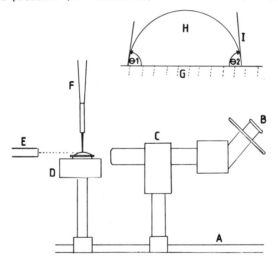

Fig. 2.5./2: Set up of goniometer (A - optical stage, B - goniometer eye piece, C - telemicroscope, D - sample holder, E light source, F - micrometer syringe, G - polymer film, H - liquid (water droplet of 20 µl), I - vapor, θ - contact angle 1 and 2, both were used and a mean value calculated).

exposure time. An oxygen plasma, a discharge power of up to 40 Watt, a pressure of 0.1 Torr and exposure times of up to 40 seconds were applied. For both irradiation and plasma treatment polymer films were cast on microscope slides by dissolving the polymers in chloroform (to a concentration of 1% w/v). Polyhydroxybutyrate with different molecular weight has been investigated:

- mw 3,000 and 70,000 (Chemie Linz)
- mw 17,000 and 21,000 (Marlbrough)

The changes in the surface properties were monitored by air-water contact angle measurements using a goniometer (Fig. 2.5./2). Measurements were taken immediately after treatment.

2.5.3 Treatment of Polyhydroxybutyrate (PHB)

The surface hydrophobicity of the four PHB polymers has been measured before and after various treatments (Galazka et al., 1987). Identical contact angles were found for all four molecular weights of the untreated polymers indicating similar surface free energies (Table 2.5./1).

Table 2.5./1: Contact angles of untreated PHB of different molecular weight (Galazka et al., 1987)

molecular weight of PHB	contact angle (°)	standard deviation (°)
3,000	67.0	0.8
17,000	67.0	1.2
21,500	67.1	1.3
70,000	67.3	1.0

The contact angles for PHB are similar to those obtained for Poly L-lactide (68.0°) but are much lower than those for polystyrene (89.7°) (Galazka, 1987). The distinctly lower contact angle (and surface hydrophobicity) of the biodegradable polymers compared to polystyrene is very important for coating with non-ionic polymers (Poloxamer and Poloxamine). Lower surface hydrophobicity leads to a reduced affinity of the Poloxamer and Poloxamine surfactants for the polymer surface, resulting in a thin or non-existing coat. Reduced coating was even found for polystyrene particles slightly less hydrophobic than 60nm polystyrene latex (c.f. chapter 8.2).
Irradiation treatment of PHB led to a distinct time-dependent reduction in

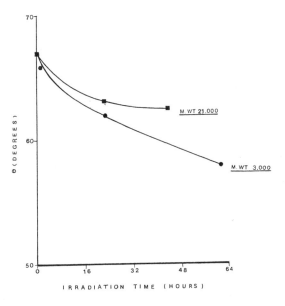

Fig 2.5./3: Decrease in contact angle of PHB mw 3,000 and 21,000 with increasing irradiation time at constant dose (169 Gy/h).

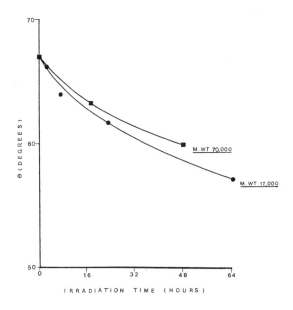

Fig 2.5./4: Decrease in contact angle of PHB mw 17,000 and 70,000 with increasing irradiation time at constant dose (169 Gy/h).

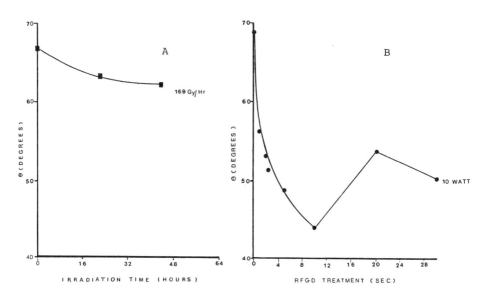

Fig. 2.5./5: Effect of irradiation treatment in comparison to plasma etching on the contact angle of a PHB 21,000 film (A - irradiation treatment, dose 169 Gy/h, B - plasma etching, discharge power 10 Watt).

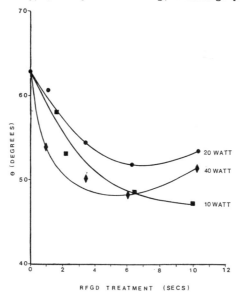

Fig. 2.5./6: Effect of irradiation treatment on the contact angle of D,L-PLA at a discharge power of 10, 20 and 40 Watt (after Galazka, 1987)

the contact angle (Fig. 2.5./3 and 4). Little difference was found between the different molecular weight polymers. The reduction in surface hydrophobicity will influence the adsorption process of coating polymers and the properties of the resulting coating layer.

Plasma etching led to a faster and stronger reduction in contact angle than irradiation treatment (Fig. 2.5./5). Plasma etching with oxygen introduced more hydrophilic hydroxyl groups than irradiation. For both methods, there seems to be a maximum level of introduction of functional groups. The contact angle tends towards a plateau level in both methods. This plateau effect for irradiation treatment occurred more distinctly for PLA than for PHB (Galazka, V., 1987). The slight increase in contact angle at 20 seconds plasma treatment of PHB (Fig. 2.5./5) might be due to surface damage and breaking away of oxidized material revealing the more hydrophobic original surface. This effect was observed more distinctly with PLA when the discharge power was increased from 10 to 20 and 40 Watt (Fig. 2.5./6).

2.5.4. Summary

Gamma-irradiation of drug carriers leads to a distinct reduction in the surface hydrophobicity of biodegradable polymers. This has important implications for the coating process for drug targeting. The reduced surface hydrophobicity effects the adsorption of the polymers and subsequently the properties of the coating film.

Oxygen plasma etching increases the surface hydrophilicity and therefore the biocompatibility of polymeric materials. This effect can be used to increase the biocompatibility of intramuscular administered drug carriers. Additionally, plasma etching also sterilizes the carrier surfaces.

The number of hydroxyl groups which can be introduced is limited and is lower for the aliphatic PHB than for aromatic polymers such as polystyrene. The functional groups which are introduced by such methods can be used as a means of modifying the surface by chemical linkage of hydrophilic chains (e.g. ethylene oxide).

3. CHARACTERIZATION OF CARRIERS

3.1. Model Carriers

For development of characterization methods for drug carriers a range of non-biodegradable standard Polybead™ particles were used (Polysciences, Inc.). These particles are widely employed as calibration standards in light scattering techniques and scanning and transmission electron microscopy. For use as standards, it is essential that they should be well defined in size and surface properties. During the development of characterization methods well characterized materials of known properties were included as internal standards. Comparing the known particle properties with the results obtained with methods enabled decisions to be made as to the suitability of each method. For cell culture and in vivo animal studies, non-biodegradable polystyrene particles were chosen in order to avoid any interference of biodegradation on the particle action.

For investigation of the effect of size in particles with identical surface properties (prepared from the same polymer), polystyrene latex particles in three different sizes from 60 to 900 nm were purchased (Table 3.1./1).

For investigation of the influence of surface charge, latex particles with additional surface COOH-groups were used. The nature of the additional chemical group was varied by the use of hydroxylated and amino particles.

For some studies fluorescently labelled particles are desirable (e.g. for particle analysis with a Fluorescence Activated Cell Sorter - FACS). Labelling might however cause a change in the particle surface properties. Therefore two standard particles labelled with the fluorescent dye Yellow-Green were included (Table 3.1./1) in the studies.

According to the manufacturer's specification the polystyrene particles should be monodisperse and free from surfactants or other additives. Among the functionalized latices used were carboxylated spheres with a surface charge of 0.12 meq per gram of co-polymer, hydroxylated spheres with a typical hydroxyl content of 0.2 meq per gram and amino spheres containing 0.2 meq amino groups per gram of polymer. The fluorescent particles were produced by the attachment of the Yellow-Green dye to non-carboxylated (PSF) or carboxylated monodisperse latex (PSF-COOH).

The number of polystyrene particles (density 1.05) per ml in a 2.5 % dispersion is given below (Polysciences data sheet no. 238):

50 nm	3.64×10^{14}
100 nm	4.55×10^{13}
200 nm	5.68×10^{12}
500 nm	3.64×10^{11}
1000 nm	4.55×10^{10}

Table 3.1./1: Non-biodegradable polystyrene latex particles used as model carriers with "defined surface properties". Some of the polystyrene particles (PS) are surface modified by the introduction of chemical groups or attachment of a fluorescent label (F). The particle size was determined by Photon Correlation Spectroscopy (PCS).

particle code	introduced surface groups	particle size
PS-0.06	none	60 nm
PS-0.14	none	142 nm
PS-0.9	none	900 nm
PSF	Yellow-Green	205 nm
PSF-COOH	Yellow-Green, carboxyl	275 nm
PS-COOH	carboxyl	269 nm
PS-OH	hydroxyl	238 nm
PS-AL-NH$_2$	aliphatic amino	123 nm
PS-AR-NH$_2$	aromatic amino	178 nm

The particle number can be determined by the equation:

$$\text{number of particles per ml} = \frac{6\ W \times 10^{12}}{p \times \pi \times d^3}$$

W - grams of polymer per ml in latex
d - diameter in micrometer of monodisperse latex
p - density of polymer in grams per ml

The latex particles have a shelf life of 1 to 2 years. The addition of sodium azide is recommended to avoid bacterial contamination. However, the preservative might adsorb onto the particle surfaces and change their properties. Therefore, no preservative was added. It was noted that bacterial contamination led to a change in the particle properties. The coating of bacterially contaminated particles with sterically stabilizing polymers led to a level of flocculation of the particles which was dependent on the coating polymer concentration.

3.2. Size Determinations

3.2.0. Importance of size for drug carriers

Size and shape are important parameters which influence the organ distribution of intravenously injected particles. As particles in excess of 7 µm are larger than the blood capillary diameter (about 6 µm) they will be mechanically filtered by the capillary bed of the lung (Kanke et al., 1980; Davis et al., 1986). Such a filtration effect can be used for targeting via compartmental delivery. Intraarterial injection of such large particles can be used to localize them in the next capillary bed following the point of injection. However, using this phenomenon care has to be taken to avoid tissue damage due to this artifical embolism. Indeed, high doses of large particles can lead to death. The LD_{50} for rats was found to drop from 154,000 to 705 particles per gram body weight as the microsphere diameter increased from 13.5 µm to 90.7 µm (Davis and Taube, 1978). However, in beagle dogs, no acute toxic effects were observed after administration of 200,000 particles per gram (four size ranges, 3, 8, 15 and 25 µm), and no tissue damage due to the particles was observed in histological examinations 4 weeks after administration (Schroeder et al., 1978). No hemodynamic effects were observed in beagle dogs after administration of large particles (7.4 and 11.6 µm, doses up to 3×10^9 particles) but intravenous injection of 3.4 µm latex led to a dose-dependent systemic hypotension and depression of myocardial performance at dosages of 10^{10} particles and above (Slack et al., 1981).

The shape of entrapped particles influences their toxicity. Cellulose fibres which were filtered by the lungs (30 µm diameter) and taken up into lung tissue proved to be toxic, whereas large microspheres (15.8 µm) were well tolerated (Illum et al., 1982). The embolism caused by the cellulose fibres led to the death of the injected rabbits within a few minutes. Filtering of particles by the lungs has been used to deliver drugs incorporated in degradable gelatin microspheres to the lungs (Yoshioka et al., 1981). Particles smaller than 5 µm can also be found in the lungs due to phagocytosis by lung macrophages, but the number of phagocytosed particles is relatively small. The majority of particles which pass the lung capillary bed are taken up by the macrophages of the liver (Kupffer cells) and the spleen (up to 90% of injected dose). The mean size of the particles which become localized in lung and liver is similar (Lee, K.C. et al., 1988) indicating that size is not a factor in determining the uptake by different macrophage populations.

The uptake of particles by the liver and spleen was found to increase with increasing particle size. Larger particles are cleared faster than small

45

particles (Davis, 1981) whether they are liposomes (Gregoriadis et al., 1977; Senior et al., 1985; Sato et al., 1986) or fat emulsion droplets (Karino et al., 1987). In the design of a colloidal carrier with a reduced RES clearance, it will be favourable to produce a small size. Consequently, 60 nm polystyrene model carriers were used in the in vivo studies on the development of RES-avoiding carriers.

The size-dependence of the rate of clearance of colloidal gold particles as small as 10 to 40 nm has already been described by Zilversmit et al. (1952). There was however little difference in the total uptake of the liver and spleen, indicating that the size influences mainly the kinetics of clearance and less the total uptake. Colloidal carriers are able to exit the blood capillary system via the sinusoidal fenestrations of the liver and bone marrow, provided they are smaller than the size of the fenestrations (150 nm) (Davis et al., 1986).

In order to consider the effect of size on the observed clearance of carriers and subsequent their organ distribution, a detailed knowledge of carrier size, width of the size distribution and the presence of larger particles (e.g. aggregates larger 5 μm which lead to lung accumulation) is essential.

3.2.1. Methods and Experimental

3.2.1.1 Photon Correlation Spectroscopy

Photon Correlation Spectroscopy (PCS) was employed to determine the mean particle size (PCS diameter), size distribution (polydispersity index), and particle coating layer thickness, and to follow aggregation or de-aggregation processes in particle suspensions. PCS is a laser light scattering technique suitable for application to particles ranging in size from 5 nm to approximately 3 µm. The light scattered from a dispersion is used to calculate the correlation function g(τ):

$$g(\tau) = 1 + e^{-2DK^2\tau}$$

D - diffusion coefficient of particles
K - scattering vector of light
τ - sample time

The scattering vector is given by:

$$K = \frac{4\pi n}{\lambda} \sin(\theta/2)$$

n = refractive index of the suspending medium
λ - wavelength of the light
θ - scattering angle

The diffusion coefficient D obtained from the fit of the measured correlation function can be used to calculate the mean particle diameter by application of the Einstein equation:

$$d = \frac{kT}{3\pi\eta D}$$

k - Boltzmann's constant
T - absolute temperature
η - viscosity of medium

The PCS apparatus (Fig. 3.2.1./1) consists of a laser, a temperature controlled sample cell and a photomultiplier (PM) for detection of the light scattered at a certain angle (e.g. 90°). The PM signal is transferred to a correlator for calculation of the correlation function. This correlation function is relayed to a microprocessor for calculation of the diffusion coefficient of the particles and the correlated mean particle size.

PCS does not exploit the absolute intensity of the scattered light, but rather fluctuations in intensity. Small particles diffuse faster than large ones causing a stronger fluctuation in the scattering signal and a more rapid decaying correlation function. For a monodisperse particle population the correlation function is a single exponential, in the presence of more

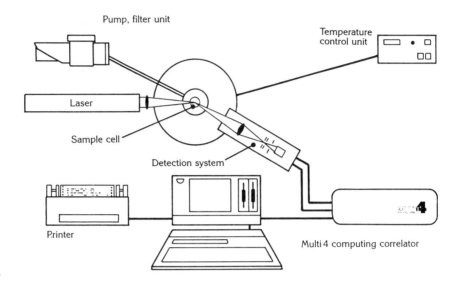

Fig. 3.2.1./1: Principal set up of Photon Correlation Spectroscopy (PCS) (after Malvern Instr. product information).

than one size the function is polyexponential. Deviation from a single exponential is used to calculate the polydispersity index (PI), as a measure of the width of the size distribution. For a monodisperse population the PI is theoretically zero. Latex particle suspensions with a PI between 0.03 and 0.06 were considered to be 'monodisperse'. Those with a relatively narrow size distribution had a PI between 0.10 and 0.20. A PI of 0.5 and larger indicated a very broad size distribution without a distinct distribution shape.

The measured PCS diameter is based on the intensity of scattered light and therefore is not identical to the number diameter except in case of monodisperse particle suspensions. For polydisperse samples, the PCS diameter is larger because it is based on the scattering intensity of the particles. The scattering intensity does not linearly depend on the particle size but is proportionally related to the 6th power of the radius (Rayleigh scattering, $I \sim r^6/\lambda^4$). Therefore, the broader is the particle size distribution, the greater is the disparity between the PCS and number diameters. This phenomenon makes the measurements of PCS very sensitive for following aggregation or de-aggregation processes in suspensions.

The PCS equipment used were a Malvern Photon Correlator Spectrometer (RR102), a Multibit Photon Correlator (K7025), a LogLin Correlator (K7027) in connection to Commodore 3000/8000 computers (Malvern Instruments, UK).

3.2.1.2 Laser diffractometry

Laser diffractometry was used for determination of the sizes of particles in the ranges 0.5 µm to 100 µm (Malvern Droplet Particle Sizer 2600, Malvern Instr.) and 0.1 µm to 87.5 µm (Sympatec Helos, Sympatec Clausthal, FRG).

Both instruments use Fraunhofer diffraction of laser light scattered from particles in suspension to calculate a size distribution. The particles cause diffraction of laser light through different angles and create a diffraction pattern of light rings with varying radii (Fig. 3.2.1./2). The diffraction pattern is unique for a given particle size. The diffraction ring patterns created by different sized particles are detected on a ring detector and used to calculate the size distribution.

The laser diffractometers consist of a laser, an optical unit to expand the beam, and a Fourier Transform lens for focussing of the scattered light onto a ring detector (Fig. 3.2.1./3). The use of a Fourier Transform lens allows size measurement of moving particles. The particle suspension is located in a measuring cell at a certain distance from the receiver lens. A great advantage of the laser diffractometers, is that any transparent dispersion medium can be used (aqueous or organic liquid, air). In contrast to other equipment e.g. the Coulter Counter which requires an electrolyte solution (0.9% NaCl or higher) for the size measurement, the particles can

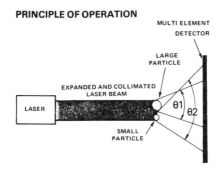

PRINCIPLE OF OPERATION

MULTI ELEMENT DETECTOR

LARGE PARTICLE

EXPANDED AND COLLIMATED LASER BEAM

LASER

θ1   θ2

SMALL PARTICLE

Diffraction angle θ' small for large particles.
Diffraction angle θ' large for small particles.

Fig. 3.2.1./2: Principle of operation of a laser diffractometer. The diffraction angles and the diffraction pattern created are a characteristic function of particle size (after Malvern Instruments product information leaflet). The diffraction angle θ is small for large particles, the angle is large for small particles.

49

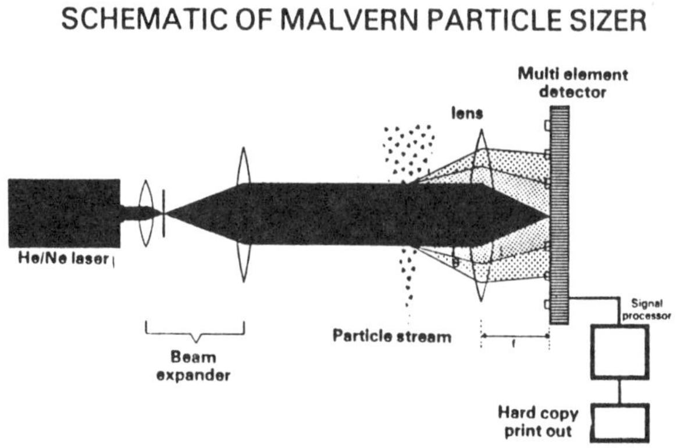

SCHEMATIC OF MALVERN PARTICLE SIZER

Fig. 3.2.1./3: Schematic set up of a laser diffractometer (after Malvern Instruments product information).

be measured in their original dispersion medium thereby minimizing changes in the sample due to changes in the measurement conditions. Added salts can cause aggregation of particles or coalescence of emulsion droplets due to a reduction in the particle zeta potential.

The laser diffractometers were mainly used for characterization of the biodegradable polymeric particles during optimization of the production process (c.f. chapter 5).

3.2.1.3 Transmission electron microscopy (TEM)

TEM investigations were performed to verify the nominal sizes of the latex standard particles given by the manufacturer. The latex particle suspensions were diluted with water. One drop of the diluted suspension was placed on a copper grid and left to dry. The particles were stained with a 2% phosphotungstic acid solution (pH 4.2) and visualised under a Philips EM 400. The photographic negatives obtained were analysed using a Magiscan 2A (Joyce-Loebl, Gateshead, England).

3.2.2. Results of size determinations

3.2.2.1 Range of latex model carriers

Each new batch of latex particles purchased was characterized by PCS and TEM. The size determinations proved to be necessary because in 6 out of 9 of the samples used, there was a large discrepancy between the nominal size given by the particle manufacturer (Polysciences - determined from TEM measurement) and the TEM size measured by the author (Table 3.2.2./1). Such differences in size will lead to errors in calculations of the surface area of the particles needed for determination of binding constants of molecules to the particle surface. The level of discrepancy is a matter of concern considering that these particles are sold as standards for the calibration of instruments, e.g. the Coulter Counter.

Table 3.2.2./1.: Non-biodegradable polystyrene latex particles used as model carriers with "defined" surface properties. The particle size was determined by Photon Correlation Spectroscopy (PCS) and Transmission Electron Microscopy (TEM) (*- after Johnson, 1986).

particle code	nominal size (nm)	TEM size (nm)	PCS size (nm)
PS-0.06	60	58	64
PS-0.12	170	119	159
PS-0.8	1000	780 / 820*	1078
PSF	190	100	123
PSF-COOH	280	184	213
PS-COOH	190	200	255
PS-OH	250	208	220
PS-AL-NH$_2$	190	142	212
PS-AR-NH$_2$	180	166	179

Some of the latex suspensions were (despite the inaccurate quoted nominal size) very monodisperse (Fig. 3.2.2./2 and 3). Both particle suspensions were in the range 180 to 200 nm and appeared to be uniform in size. The author found that it was possible to produce monodisperse polystyrene particles within this size range without difficulty (c.f. chapter 4). The mean size given is calculated as the arithmetic mean of the biggest breadth (BB), height (BH), length (BL) and width (BW). A typical size distribution obtained with the Magiscan 2A is given in Fig. 3.2.2./1.

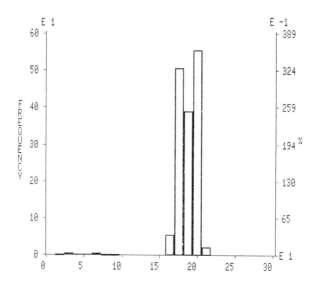

Fig. 3.2.2./1: Size distribution obtained from a sample of PS-COOH particles (TEM graph in Fig. 3.2.2./2). The frequency (y-axis) is plotted versus 30 size classes (x-axis) which are chosen according to the particle sizes present in the sample (total number of objects counted: 1543).

Other latex particles examined were less monodisperse, for example the 0.8 um (PS-0.8) and the PS-0.12 particles (Fig. 3.2.2./4 and 5). In the TEM graphs more particles of sizes greatly differing from the main population could be seen.

The PCS measurements yielded size values larger than the TEM diameters. This is due to the fact that PCS measures the hydrodynamic radius of the particles and also measures aggregates in the particle suspension. In TEM determinations, aggregates are not considered and the monolayers of separated particles are counted. In the presence of a large number of

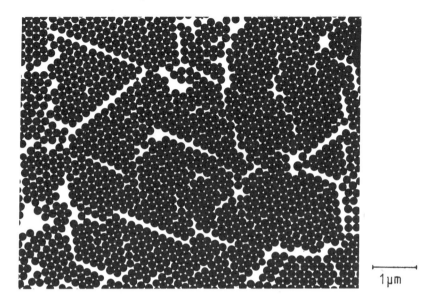

Fig. 3.2.2./2: TEM graph of PS-COOH particles with a mean size of 200 nm; standard deviation 4.0 nm (magnification 17,000).

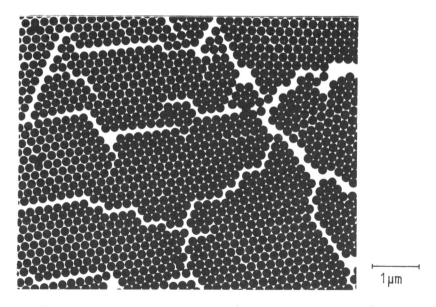

Fig. 3.2.2./3: TEM graph of PSF-COOH particles with a mean size of 184 nm; standard deviation 2.0 nm (magnification 18,000).

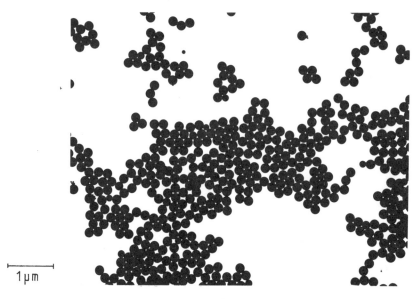

Fig. 3.2.2./4: TEM graph of PS-0.8 particles with a mean size of 780 nm; standard deviation 17.0 nm (magnification 3,650).

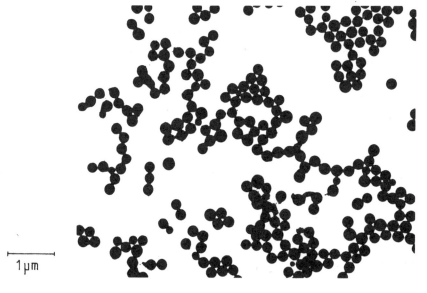

Fig. 3.2.2./5: TEM graph of PS-0.12 particles with a mean size of 119 nm; standard deviation 2.0 nm (magnification 35,000).

aggregates (indicated by the polydispersity index) the size difference between PCS and TEM might be very large. However, diameters measured by PCS and TEM are very close when the latex particle suspensions are relatively monodisperse <u>and</u> no aggregates are present. PCS measurements which are quick and easy to perform can therefore be used to check the quoted nominal TEM sizes.

3.2.2.2 Laser Diffractometer measurements

As the Malvern Particle Sizer 2600 can only measure particles >0.5 µm, it was not used for measurement of particles with nominal diameters <1.0 µm. There is only one size class for particles from 0.5 to 1.2 µm. It was however used to characterize biodegradable polymeric particles and emulsion carriers (c.f. 5 and 6).

Recently developed diffractometers, applicable for sizing particles as small as 0.1 µm in diameter were used to measure latex particles of a diameter less than 1 µm. For the latex particles used in the <u>in vivo</u> studies (c.f. 8.2.) (PCS size: 383 nm and 496 nm), volume mean diameters

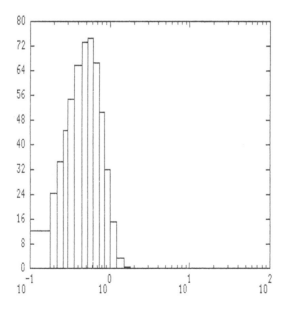

Fig. 3.2.2./6: Size distribution of 383 nm latex particles (PCS diameter) obtained with the laser diffractometer Sympatec Helos (y-axis: frequency, x-axis: size (µm)).

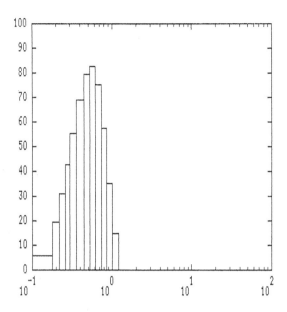

Fig. 3.2.2./7: Size distribution of 496 nm latex particles (PCS diameter) obtained with the laser diffractometer Sympatec Helos (y-axis: frequency, x-axis: size (μm)).

were found to be 460 nm and 490 nm respectively. However, the size distributions given by the laser diffractometer are far too broad ranging from 0.1 to 1.2/1.8 μm (Fig. 3.2.2./6 and 7). The broadening of the distribution is due to the technique and not avoidable. In this particle size range, PCS or TEM determinations appear to provide more information about the width of the distribution. The advantage of laser diffractometry is the fact that it also measures the size range above 1 μm which is valuable for the detection of particle aggregates (e.g. formed during the production of polymeric carriers, c.f. chapter 5). When compared to instruments such as the Coulter Counter which count single particles, the laser diffractometer is particularly sensitive detecting a few larger particles or aggregates in the presence of a large population of small particles (Müller, R.H. et al, 1986d).

3.3. Charge Determinations

3.3.0. Influence of carrier charge on in vivo fate

The binding of particles to macrophages is mediated by receptors to immunoglobulins (Berken and Benacerraf, 1966) or to complement (Mantovani et al., 1972) and results in internalisation of the particles. In contrast to this specific interaction, a non-immunologic (Rabinovitch and De Stefano, 1973) or non-specific recognition (Ogmundsdottir and Weir, 1980) is described, which can be explained as a surface phenomenon depending on the surface hydrophobicity of the particles (Van Oss et al., 1975).
The in vitro binding of human glutaraldehyde-treated red blood cells to rat peritoneal macrophages is mediated by hydrophobic interaction (Capo et al., 1981). A reduction in the surface charge of the red blood cells by treatment with either neuraminidase (removal of charges) or poly-lysine (masking of charges) increased the binding to macrophages. This was thought to be due to the decreased electrostatic repulsion between the negatively charged membranes of the red cells and the macrophages (Bongrand et al., 1981). This seems to conflict with the in vivo observation of reduced binding for non-charged particles and increased binding and RES clearance for charged particles (Wilkins and Myers, 1966), especially negatively-charged ones. Surface charges only hamper the particle-cell interaction at short distances. Crosslinking of the particle and the macrophage by a large molecule (e.g. immunoglobulin in receptor mediated uptake) reduces the influence of charge (Bongrand et al., 1981). Increased immunological recognition due to the charge and consequently increased receptor-mediated uptake could explain the increased uptake of charged particles observed in vivo. In cell cultures containing serum an increased binding with increased particle surface charge has been described, e.g. for liposomes (Schwendener et al., 1984). These results indicate that the electrostatic interactions between colloidal particles as described by the DLVO theory (Rupprecht, 1975; Lagaly, 1984) are negligible for the receptor-mediated phagocytosis of drug carriers.
Investigations of the effect of carrier charge on RES uptake are hampered by the fact that changing the charge on particles may change other equally important factors such as size and surface hydrophobicity. The total effect on RES uptake is due to all of these factors which leads to contradicting reports in the literature. Singer et al. (1967) describe a higher RES clearance for latex particles when prepared in the presence of non-ionic Tween 80. However, the non-ionic Tween creates less charged particles and should therefore lead to a reduction but not an increase in the clearance. In order to reduce the RES clearance non-charged carriers need to be used.

Charge determination

The reduction in charge can be achieved by coating the particles with non-ionic polymers (Müller, R.H. et al., 1986a). Measurement of the extent of charge reduction can be used as a criterion for selection of the most suitable polymers for use in drug targeting (Mak et al., 1988). The non-ionic polymers coat the particles and shift the plane of shear from the outer Helmholtz plane to the outer boundary of the polymer coating layer (Müller, R.H. et al, 1988e; Koopal et al., 1988). The thickness of the coating-polymer layer can be determined by measuring the extent of reduction in the zeta potential (Müller, R.H. et al. 1988e). These measurements are only possible if the adsorbed polymer does not form a new interface at which the formation of new Stern and diffuse layers occur, as has been described for the adsorption of cationic surfactants onto silica gel (Rupprecht, 1975).

Charge measurements of drug carriers in serum can be used to determine their interaction with charged blood components (Müller et al., 1986b, Lherm et al., 1988). On exposure to serum, standard particles are heavily opsonized and possess a zeta potential of about -15 mV, whereas particles coated with a hydrophilic polymer such as Poloxamine 908 are less opsonized and possess a zeta potential of about -5 mV (dysopsonic effect of the coating).

3.3.1 Laser Doppler Anemometry

3.3.1.1. Theory

Most particles (solid particles or emulsion droplets) are charged in aqueous dispersion media. The charge can be due either to the process of dispersing the particles in water, charged groups on the surface and/or adsorption of ions from the dispersion medium. In salt solutions the particles possess an adsorbed monolayer of ions on their surface (Fig. 3.3.1./1). This layer consists of fixed, dehydrated and in most cases negatively charged ions (inner Helmholtz layer). These negative ions increase the surface potential Ψ_0 (Nernst potential) to the potential of the inner Helmholtz plane Ψ_i. The next monolayer (outer Helmholtz plane) consists of fixed but hydrated positive ions reducing the potential to Ψ_δ, the potential of the Stern plane, whereby δ is the thickness of the Stern plane. In the diffuse layer the potential drops towards zero. During the movement of the particle a part of the diffuse layer will be stripped to reveal a potential at the surface of shear; the so called zeta potential -

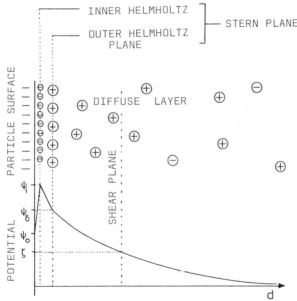

Fig. 3.3.1./1: Formation of Stern plane and diffuse layer on particle surface (Ψ_0 - surface or Nernst potential, Ψ_i - potential of inner Helmholtz plane, Ψ_δ - Stern potential, δ - thickness of Stern plane, ZP - zeta potential at surface of shear). Course of potential in dependence on the distance d from the particle surface.

ZP (Ney, 1973; Hunter, 1981). As the height of the zeta potential depends on the Nernst potential, zeta potential measurements can be taken as an indirect measure of the surface charge.

The zeta potential can be measured by determination of the velocity of particles in an electric field (electrophoresis measurements). Conventional instruments use a light microscope to observe the particle movement (Zetameter by Rank Brothers). Modern zetameters use Laser Doppler Anemometry (Cummins and Pike, 1977; Müller, R.H. and Merz, 1985) to determine the particle velocity (Zetasizer II, Malvern Instruments, Malvern, UK).

A Laser Doppler Anemometry (LDA) set up consists of a laser, a beam splitter and a lens which focusses the beams into the measuring volume, forming a beam crossover (Fig. 3.3.1/2). The particles move through the beam crossover and scatter laser light. The scattered laser light is detected in the forward direction and projected by collecting optics onto a photomultiplier. The frequency of the laser light scattered by the particles differs from the frequency of the incident beam. This frequency shift is caused by the Doppler effect and is a function of the particle velocity. The Malvern Zetasizer uses the photomultiplier signal to calculate a correlation function which is transferred via a Fourier transform to the frequency spectrum of the scattered light.

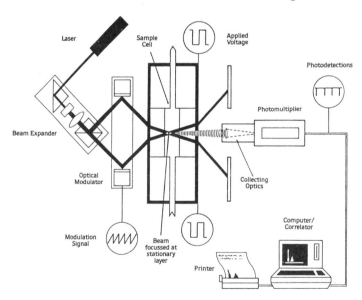

Fig. 3.3.1./2: Diagram of Malvern Zetasizer II (after Malvern Instruments product information PB021 9-84, 1984).

The particle velocity v is expressed in relation to the electrical field strength E as electrophoretic mobility μ (μm/s)/(V/cm):

$$\mu = \frac{v}{E}$$

v - particle velocity

E - field strength

The electrophoretic mobility μ can be converted to a zeta potential by using the equations of Helmholtz, Henry or Debye-Hückel (Riddick, 1968; James, 1979, Müller, R.H., 1983). In the presented work only the equation by Helmholtz has been applied:

$$ZP = \frac{4 v \pi n}{E \epsilon}$$

n - viscosity of dispersion medium

E - field strength

ϵ - dielectric constant

For water at 25°C, with a dielectric constant of 80, one can simply multiply the electrophoretic mobility μ (um/s)/(V/cm) by a factor of 12.8 to obtain the Smoluchowski zeta potential (mV). For the zeta potential measurements a Malvern Zetasizer II was used. For the measurements at low ionic strength (up to 0.01 M buffer) a large bore capillary cell (4 mm diameter), at high ionic strength (physiological salt concentration) a small bore capillary cell (0.7 mm diameter) was employed.

3.3.1.2 Charge measurements of uncoated model carriers

Zeta potential-pH profiles were determined for the series of standard latex particles in 0.01 M phosphate buffer at pHs ranging from 6.0 to 8.0 (Fig. 3.3.1./3 and 4)(Müller, R.H. and Mak, 1985; Müller, R.H. et al, 1986a, Müller, R.H. 1986-1988). The zeta potentials found ranged from about -50 mV (PSF) to almost -90mV (PS-OH). A lower potential of about -65 mV was obtained for small polystyrene particles (PS-0.06) compared to the larger ones (PS-0.14 and PS-0.90). Although they were of the same polymer (polystyrene) they exhibited different zeta potentials indicating more charged groups on the surface of the larger polystyrene latex particles. The latex with additional functional groups attached to their surface possessed an even higher charge than the unmodified polystyrene particles.

Zeta potential - pH profiles of standard latex

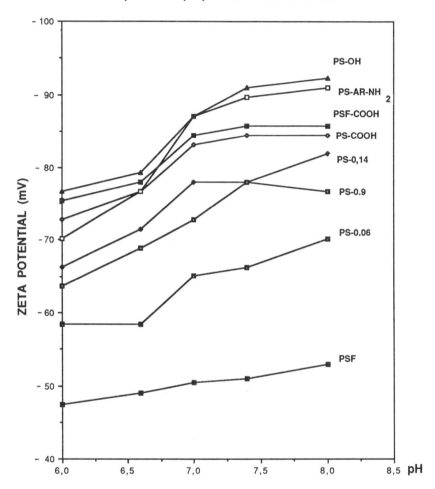

Fig. 3.3.1./3: Zeta potential/pH profile of standard latex particles in 0.01 M phosphate buffer.

3.3.1.3 Charge measurements of coated model carriers

Coating of the particles with polymers leads to the formation of adsorbed coating layers up to 150 Å which will cover part of the diffuse layer and protect it against removal. The plane of shear is shifted to a greater distance from the particle resulting in a reduction of the measured zeta

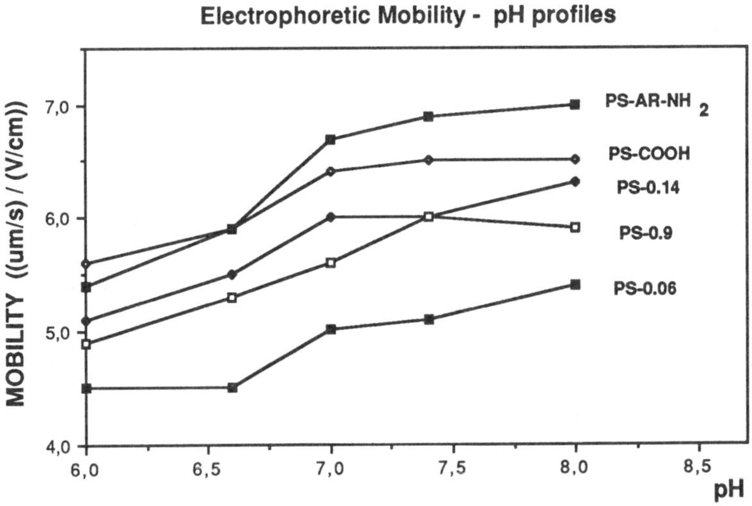

Electrophoretic Mobility - pH profiles

Fig. 3.3.1./4: Electrophoretic mobility/pH profile of standard latex particles in 0.01 M phosphate buffer.

potential (Fig. 3.3.1./5) (Müller, R.H. et al., 1986a, Müller, R.H., 1986-1988). If the coating layer is sufficiently thick to cover (and protect) the whole diffuse layer, the measured zeta potential will be approximately zero. The particles are now uncharged; this is one of the requirements in reducing RES clearance of particulates.

The thickness of the coating layer required to protect the diffuse layer against removal depends on the extent of the diffuse layer itself, and in turn its thickness depends on the concentration and valency of ions present in the dispersion medium. The amount of decay of the potential in the diffuse layer depends on the salt concentration (Fig. 3.3.1./6). The layer is larger than 300 Å in salt solutions below 10^{-4} M (1:1 electrolyte), but only 8 Å in physiological salt solution (0.9% NaCl). This means that even coating polymers creating a thin coating layer will lead to particles being uncharged in the body fluids. Zeta potential-pH profiles of coated 60 nm polystyrene particles were determined over a pH range from pH 2 to pH 10. The pH was adjusted with HCl and NaOH.

The zeta potential of the uncoated PS-0.06 was approximately -50 mV and nearly constant over the whole pH range. Coating of the particles led to a reduction in the potential which depended on the coating layer thickness. The coating layer thicknesses of the particles used in the zeta potential measurements were determined in parallel by Photon Correlation Spectroscopy (PCS). The layer thickness was investigated at every pH used for the potential measurements (Table 3.3.1./1). The uncoated latex possessed an

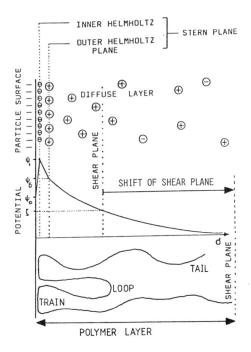

Fig. 3.3.1./5: Shift of the plane of shear after coating with polymers. The polymer adsorption layer covers part of the diffuse layer and protects it against removal. The plane of shear shifts to a greater distance to the particle and the zeta potential is reduced.

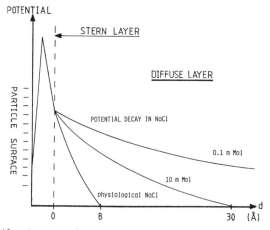

Fig. 3.3.1./6: Decay of the potential in the diffuse layer in different electrolyte concentrations.

Table 3.3.1./1: Thickness of coating layer on 60 nm latex at different pH values (pH adjusted with HCl or NaOH), determined by Photon Correlation Spectroscopy (* on 76.1 nm latex).

Coating Material	Average Molecular weight	coating layer thickness (A)				mean (A)
		pH 2.1	pH 3.0	pH 5.5	pH 9.5	
Poloxamer 181	2000	17	15	17	16	16
182	2500	18	18	18	19	18
184	2900	22	20	29	23	24
331	3800	48	-	-	-	48
402	5000	61	53	57	58	57
Poloxamer 234	4200	28	27	29	31	29
235	4600	33	31	35	40	35
333	4950	54	54	58	66	58
335	6500	51	49	53	57	53
Poloxamer 108	5000	58	57	60	58	58
188	8350	77	73	80	74	76
217	6600	58	56	60	57	58
237	7700	81	80	85	73	80
238	10800	156	159	160	158	158
238*		-	-	132	-	132
288	13500	126	129	130	136	130
338	14000	172	171	168	170	170
388*		-	-	154	-	154
407	11500	123/114	(98)	(95)	(100)	119
407*		-	-	154	-	154
Poloxamine 908	27000	133	134	137	131	134
colominic acid		27	-	-	-	27
sialic acid		31	-	-	-	31

almost constant potential over the whole pH range, indicating no changes in the number and kind of charged groups on the surface. It was expected that the coating layer thickness of the nonionic Poloxamers and Poloxamine 908 was constant and not pH dependent. However, with polymethylmethacrylate particles carrying amino groups on the surface, a dependence of the coating layer thickness of Poloxamine 908 on the pH was observed (Lynn, R. et al. 1988).

Coating of particles with water insoluble Poloxamers (cloud point below room temperature) was performed by dissolving the polymers in 96% ethanol and adding the ethanolic solution to a diluted latex dispersion (30 µl of 2.5% latex stock dispersion in 10 ml water). Addition to the concentrated 2.5% latex led to particle coagulation due to the ethanol. The coating layers were very thin (appr. 20 Å) for Poloxamer 181 and 182 and approximately 50 Å for Poloxamer 331. When compared to the poor zeta potential reduction obtained for the coated particles, this values seemed to be too high; it might possibly be due to slight coagulation in the sample. Poloxamer 181 and 182 reduced the zeta potential by about 50% (Fig. 3.3.1./7). This strong reduction can be explained by the logarithmic decay of the potential in the diffuse layer. The thin coating protects the first part of the diffuse layer in which a strong potential decay occurs.

Coating of particles with water soluble Poloxamers led to a stronger zeta potential reduction (Fig. 3.3.1./8-10). Below pH 6 and above pH 7, two potential plateaus were observed. Such plateaus were less distinct in the pH profile of the uncoated latex (PS-0.06). A possible explanation for the drop in the zeta potential of the coated latex at pH 10 might be the influence of the added NaOH. The pH of the distilled water was around 4 - 5 requiring a large amount of NaOH to adjust at pH 10. Low ionic concentrations can lead to a zeta potential increase (visible as an enhancement of the plateau formation above pH 7), whereas higher concentrations cause a zeta potential drop (ZP drop at pH 10).

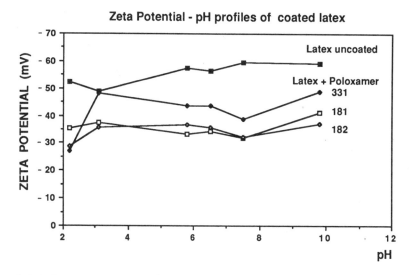

Fig. 3.3.1./7: Zeta potential/pH profiles of coated 60 nm polystyrene latex particles, pH adjusted with HCl and NaOH.

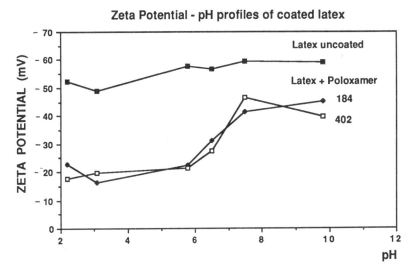

Fig. 3.3.1./8: Zeta potential/pH profiles of coated 60 nm polystyrene latex particles, pH adjusted with HCl and NaOH.

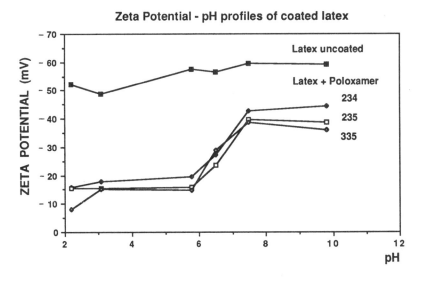

Fig. 3.3.1./9: Zeta potential/pH profiles of coated 60 nm polystyrene latex particles, pH adjusted with HCl and NaOH.

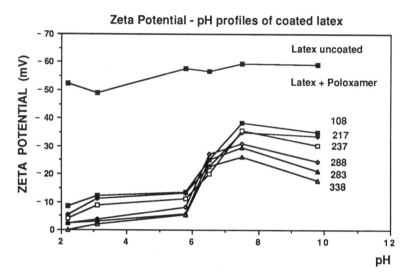

Fig. 3.3.1./10: Zeta potential/pH profiles of coated 60 nm polystyrene latex particles, pH adjusted with HCl and NaOH.

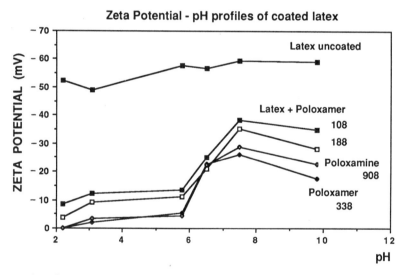

Fig. 3.3.1./11: Zeta potential/pH profiles of 60 nm polystyrene latex particles coated with Poloxamer 108, 188, 338 and Poloxamine 908 (pH adjusted with HCl and NaOH).

Adjustment of the pH using HCL and NaOH causes little or no compression of the diffuse layer but has the disadvantage of creating a different ion concentration at each pH. The ion concentration effect can interfere with any potential reduction due to the coating process. The ion concentration can be kept more stable by using 0.01 M buffer. The ion concentration of 0.01 M buffer will vary slightly due to the changes in the dissociation of the salts at different pH values, but, no difference was found in systems where the 0.01 M buffer was replaced by a buffer with constant ion concentration.

Fig. 3.3.1/11 shows the profiles of particles coated with polymers of special interest for drug targeting. Poloxamer 108 belongs to the group of hydrophilic polymers with a high HLB (30.5) but the lowest molecular weight. Despite the thin coating layer of about 58 Å obtained with Poloxamer 108, a distinct zeta potential reduction was created. Coating with Poloxamer 188 forms a layer of 76 Å and it has been shown in vivo to lead to a reduction of the liver uptake of particles (Illum and Davis, 1984). There is however, not much difference in the zeta potential reduction achieved using 108 and 188. Coating polymers with more pronounced effect on liver uptake (Poloxamer 338, Poloxamine 908) formed coating layers of about 130 Å, but produced only a slightly more significant reduction of the zeta potential. The reason for this can be seen in the large extent of the diffuse layer in dispersion medium of low ionic strength (>300 Å) which is above the protective adsorbed layers. Even polymers with a thin adsorbed coating layer are able to cover the part of the diffuse layer in which the steepest potential decay occurs (<50 Å). A thicker coating (e.g. 130 Å) does not lead to further distinct reduction.

Differences can be seen by compressing the diffuse layer to about 100 Å by using 0.01 M buffer. Coating polymers which create adsorbed layers of more than 100 Å will cover and protect the whole diffuse layer and the zeta potential will be almost zero (Poloxamer 338 and Poloxamine 908). Polymers with a coating layer thickness below 100 Å (e.g. Poloxamer 188: 76Å) protect only a part of the diffuse layer and lead to a zeta potential reduction (Fig. 3.3.1./12).

The coating layers of Poloxamer 338 and 407 and Poloxamine 908 on 130 nm polystyrene latex were found to be slightly thinner than on the 60 nm particles (c.f. chapter 8). Zeta potential-pH profiles in 0.01 M citrate phosphate buffer showed a slight charge above pH 6 due to less protection of the diffuse layer (Fig. 3.3.1./13 and 14). The coating efficiency of Poloxamine 1508 is similar to 908, as indicated by a similar reduction in the zeta potential, Poloxamine 1307 and 1107 coat much less effectively and the particles still possess a distinct zeta potential (Fig. 3.3.1./14).

Decreasing the buffer concentration to 0.001 M increased the thickness of the diffuse layer and made the coating Polymers Poloxamer 188 and 407 and

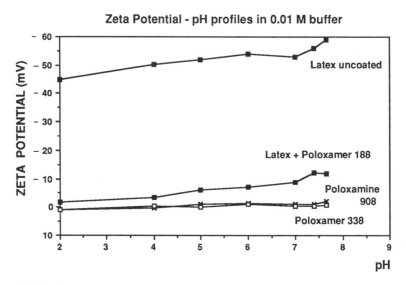

Fig. 3.3.1./12: Zeta potential/pH profiles of 60 nm polystyrene latex particles coated with Poloxamer 188 and 338 and Poloxamine 908 (0.01 M phosphate citrate buffer).

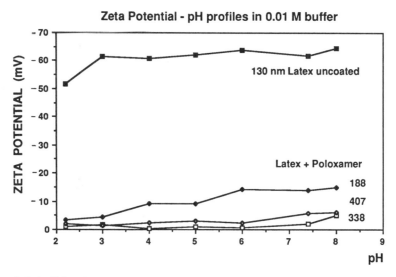

Fig. 3.3.1./13: Zeta potential/pH profiles of 130 nm polystyrene latex particles coated with Poloxamer 188, 338 and 407 (0.01 M phosphate citrate buffer).

70

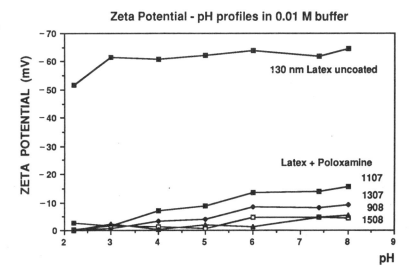

Zeta Potential - pH profiles in 0.01 M buffer

Fig. 3.3.1./14: Zeta potential/pH profiles of 130 nm polystyrene latex particles coated with Poloxamine 908, 1107, 1307 and 1508 (0.01 M phosphate citrate buffer).

Poloxamine 908 less effective in reducing the zeta potential (Fig. 3.3.1./15 and 16). The adjustment of the diffuse layer thickness by varying the ionic concentration can be used to distinguish between similar coating polymers which produce different coating layer thicknesses but comprise a sufficiently thick layer to eliminate the zeta potential in 0.01 M buffer. To investigate further the correlation between the length of the ethylene oxide chain and the resulting coating layer thickness (charge and zeta potential reduction), Antarox CO, Antarox DM, Gafac RE960 and Mulgofen ON870 were used to coat 130 nm polystyrene latex (Table 3.3.1./2). The Antarox surfactants are available with EO chains ranging from 5 to 100 units. Due to the large extent of the diffuse layer surrounding the particles, there is only a slight charge reduction for latex suspended in distilled water using surfactants with short EO chains (< 30 units). Only surfactants with longer EO chains lead to a distinct zeta potential reduction. A zeta potential reduction takes already place with surfactants up to 9 EO units (reduction by 7.6 mV with Antarox CO660). Doubling the length of the EO chain (Antarox CO850) does not double the zeta potential reduction (reduction by 9.2 mV). This can be explained by the fact that there is not a linear but an exponential decay of the potential in the diffuse layer.

Larger differences in the coating properties of the various Antarox

71

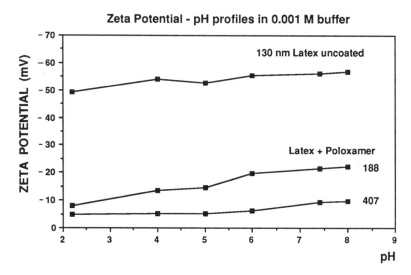

Fig. 3.3.1./15: Zeta potential/pH profiles of 130 nm polystyrene latex particles coated with Poloxamer 188 and 407 (0.001 M phosphate citrate buffer).

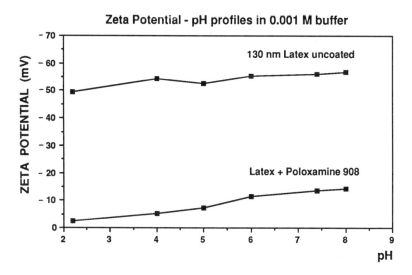

Fig. 3.3.1./16: Zeta potential/pH profiles of 130 nm polystyrene latex particles coated with Poloxamine 908 (0.001 M phosphate citrate buffer).

72

Table 3.3.1./2.: Zeta potentials of coated 130 nm polystyrene latex in distilled water and 0.01M phosphate citrate buffer pH 5. (*percentage of ethylene oxide in molecule). Poloxamer and Poloxamine coatings were used as 'internal standard' to assess the coating efficiency of the other surfactants.

coating surfactant	number of EO chains	EO units per chain	zeta potential (mV) water	buffer
no coating	-	-	- 59.1	- 62.2
Antarox CO630	1	5	- 53.6	- 37.4
CO660	1	9	- 51.5	- 35.3
CO730	1	10	- 50.5	- 34.8
CO850	1	20	- 49.9	- 28.9
CO880	1	30	- 50.2	- 31.1
CO890	1	40	- 45.3	- 20.6
CO970	1	50	- 45.8	- 17.1
CO990	1	100	- 43.9	- 10.3
Antarox DM530	1	5	- 45.6	- 24.5
DM970	1	150	- 39.0	- 2.7
Gafac RE960	1	50	- 43.2	- 37.7
Mulgofen ON870	1	20	- 47.7	- 29.3
Poloxamer 188	2	75	- 43.4	- 9.2
338	2	128	- 36.5	- 0.9
407	2	98	- 35.4	- 3.0
Poloxamine 1107	4	70%*	- 40.4	- 9.0
1307	4	70%*	- 37.6	- 4.2
1508	4	80%*	- 35.9	- 0.7
908	4	80%*	- 35.5	- 2.0

polymers could be seen using a 0.01 M phosphate citrate buffer. Antarox CO 990 proved to be less effective than Poloxamer 407 and Poloxamine 908 and is comparable to Poloxamer 188 (c.f. chapter 8, in vivo distribution).

Antarox CO970 contains 50 EO units and reduces the zeta potential from -62.2 to -17.1 mV. Gafac RE960 has an identical structure to Antarox CO970 apart from having a phosphoric acid group at the end of the EO chain. It is a nonionic surfactant with a charged group attached to it. Most likely due to the charged group which is phosphoric acid, it has a relatively high potential of -37.7 mV in 0.01 M citrate buffer.

A very promising candidate for in vivo investigations is Antarox DM970 which causes a potential reduction similar to Poloxamine 908 and Poloxamer 407. The Antarox DM series is based on a dinonyl phenol structure (Antarox CO nonyl phenol) which might lead to a higher affinity for the latex

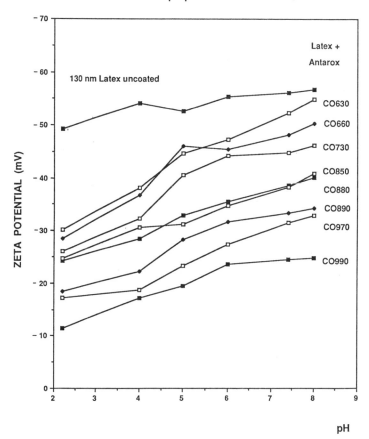

Fig. 3.3.1./17: Zeta potential/pH profile of Antarox CO coated 130 nm latex in 0.001 M phosphate citrate buffer.

surface and therefore a thicker and more closely packed coating layer. This coating film covers the particle surface better than the film by Antarox CO990. Mulgofen ON870 seems to offer no advantage in coating properties compared to Antarox CO850, both comprising EO chains of 20 units.

The full zeta potential/pH profiles of the coated carriers from table 3.3.1./2 are given in the figures 3.3.1./17-21. In general the potential reduction is less distinct in 0.001M than in 0.01M buffer. The Antarox DM970 profile is very similar to Poloxamine 908.

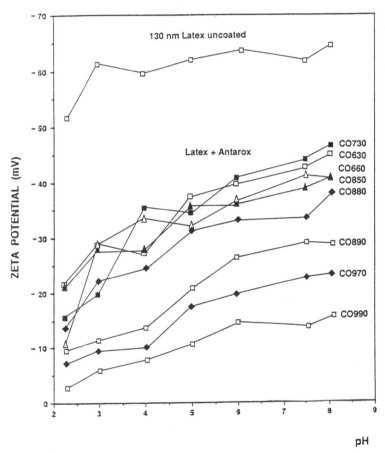

Fig. 3.3.1./18: Zeta potential/pH profile of Antarox CO coated 130 nm latex in 0.01 M phosphate citrate buffer.

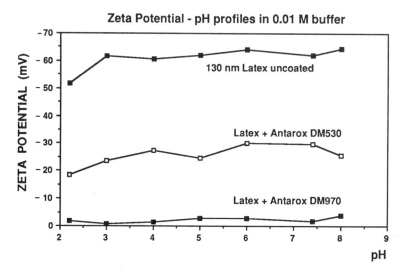

Fig. 3.3.1./19: Zeta potential/pH profile of Antarox DM coated 130 nm latex in 0.01 M phosphate citrate buffer.

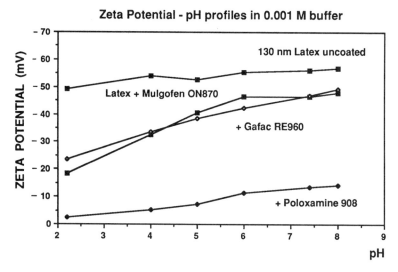

Fig. 3.3.1./20: Zeta potential/pH profile of Gafac RE960, Mulgofen ON870 and Poloxamine 908 coated 130 nm latex in 0.001 M phosphate citrate buffer.

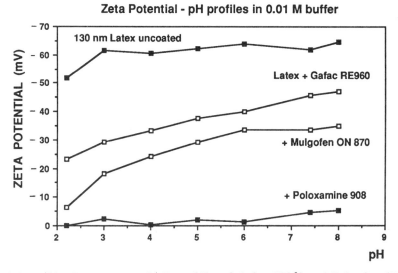

Fig. 3.3.1./21: Zeta potential/pH profile of Gafac RE960 and Mulgofen ON870 coated 130 nm latex in 0.01 M phosphate citrate buffer.

The potential of coated carriers depends not only on the molarity of the buffer used but also on the type of buffer (the concentration·of ions, the type of salts, the extent of ionic dissociation, and the interaction of particles with buffer components). In 0.01 M Tris buffer and in 0.01 M phosphate buffer at pH 7.4, small differences in the zeta potential reduction achieved after coating were found. Slightly positive potentials were even obtained for some Poloxamers (and Poloxamine 908) (Table 3.3.1./3 and 4). Larger differences in the potential were found for uncoated latex particles and particles coated with egg lecithin, colominic acid (neuraminic acid) and sialic acid (N-acyl-neuraminic acid). However, the general tendency was the same in all the buffers and buffered NaCl solutions.

In physiological salt solutions the diffuse layer is around 8 Å thick and even thin surface coatings lead essentially to uncharged particles. In buffered 0.9% NaCl solution all the coating polymers produced latex with practically zero-charge (Table 3.3.1./3). The small zeta potential reduction obtained with the Poloxamer 181 coated latex in phosphate buffer might be due to its low solubility in the dispersion medium.

With uncoated undialysed and dialysed latex particles similar zeta potentials were obtained in salt solutions (0.01M buffer, buffer with 0.9% NaCl), but in distilled water the potential of the undialysed particles was much higher. This might be due to electrolytes present in the undialysed

Table 3.3.1./3: Zeta potentials of latex in distilled water (pH adjusted with NaOH), 0.01 M phosphate buffer and 0.01 M phosphate buffer in physiological NaCl solution (0.9% w/v) (coating on dialysed 60 nm polystyrene latex).

coating material	coating layer thickness (A)	zeta potential (mV)		
		dist. water pH 7.5	phosphate buffer pH 7.4 0.01M without	with NaCl 0.9%
no coating				
latex undialyzed	-	- 59.1	- 48.3	- 70.2
latex dialysed	-	- 50.9	- 48.3	- 70.6
Poloxamer 181	16	- 32.0	- 33.4	- 17.4
182	18	- 32.1	- 24.5	- 4.2
184	24	- 41.6	- 12.0	- 0.8
331	48	- 38.7	- 21.3	- 5.0
402	57	- 46.4	- 4.8	- 2.5
234	29	- 42.6	- 4.9	- 2.6
235	35	- 39.6	- 3.9	- 3.0
333	58	- 40.0	- 1.1	- 1.2
335	53	- 38.6	+ 0.2	- 0.7
108	58	- 38.4	+ 0.6	- 2.5
188	76	- 35.4	+ 2.1	- 0.7
217	58	- 35.1	+ 1.1	- 1.5
237	80	- 35.6	+ 2.5	- 0.7
238	132	- 29.6	+ 4.0	- 0.9
288	130	- 24.3	+ 4.5	- 0.9
338	154	- 17.6	+ 4.9	- 0.3
407	119	- 21.8	-	-
Poloxamine 908	134	- 28.9	+ 5.4	- 0.3
colominic acid		- 61.0	- 50.6	- 80.4
sialic acid		- 46.0	- 53.5	- 75.2
egg lecithin		- 45.0	- 22.3	- 35.8

sample. Low electrolyte concentrations of around 10^{-4} to 10^{-5} M can lead to a zeta potential increase. Both latex particles (undialysed and dialysed) possessed a potential of only -48.3 mV in 0.01 M buffer, but a potential of -70 mV in buffer with added NaCl. However, the measurements were repeated twice and the zeta potential values could be reproduced.

Table 3.3.1./4: Zeta potential of latex in distilled water (pH adjusted with NaOH), 0.01 M Tris buffer and 0.01 M Tris buffer in physiological NaCl solution (0.9% w/v) (coating on dialyzed 60nm polystyrene latex).

coating material	coating layer thickness (A)	zeta potential (mV)		
		dist. water pH 7.5	Tris buffer pH 7.4 without	0.01M with NaCl 0.9%
no coating				
latex undialyzed	–	− 59.1	− 44.9	− 62.9
latex dialysed	–	− 50.9	− 43.6	− 56.3
Poloxamer 181	16	− 32.0	− 27.1	− 17.8
182	18	− 32.1	− 20.7	− 14.5
184	24	− 41.6	− 4.2	− 3.6
331	48	− 38.7	− 17.1	− 12.8
402	57	− 46.4	− 1.5	− 1.5
234	29	− 42.6	− 2.0	− 1.7
235	35	− 39.6	− 1.2	− 1.6
333	58	− 40.0	− 1.5	− 1.1
335	53	− 38.6	− 1.8	− 0.7
108	58	− 38.4	+ 1.6	+ 0.5
188	76	− 35.4	+ 1.9	− 0.3
217	58	− 35.1	− 0.3	− 0.3
237	80	− 35.6	+ 3.2	− 0.4
238	132	− 29.6	+ 4.0	− 0.5
288	130	− 24.3	+ 4.3	− 0.3
338	154	− 17.6	− 0.2	− 0.0
407	119	− 21.8	–	–
Poloxamine 908	134	− 28.9	+ 4.3	− 1.0
colominic acid		− 61.0	− 45.8	− 59.9
sialic acid		− 46.0	− 47.6	− 61.6
egg lecithin		− 45.0	− 19.9	− 63.9

3.3.1.4 Measurement of the surface charge of latex particles after coating with serum

After intravenous injection, particles acquire a charge due to the adsorption of blood components. Irrespective of their charge before injection, most of the particles acquire a charge of about -15 mV (zeta potential calculated using the Helmholtz equation). Uncoated and coated latex particles were incubated with serum (5 minutes incubation time) and their potential was determined directly in serum (Müller, R.H. et al., 1986b; Müller, R.H. 1986-1988). Due to the high salt concentration of serum the current was too high to use the standard electrophoresis capillary of the Malvern Zetasizer. Therefore the methyl cellulose coated, small diameter (0.7mm) capillary cell was used.

After exposure to serum, the uncoated latex particles acquired a zeta potential of -14.9 mV (Table 3.3.1./5). Coating of the particles with Poloxamer and Poloxamine polymers led to a lower zeta potential, indicating a reduction in the amount of adsorbed (charged) serum components. There may also be a difference in the nature of adsorbed serum components. Determination of the adsorbed components by Polyacrylamide gel electrophoresis

Table 3.3.1./5: Zeta potential of coated latex in water at pH 5.8 and in serum (* soluble in water with strong Tyndall effect due to cloud point of 19C).

coating material (in order of decreasing hydrophobicity)	coating layer thickness (A)	zeta potential (mV) in water pH 7.5	serum	HLB
uncoated latex	none	- 50.9	- 14.9	-
Poloxamer 184	24	- 41.6	- 16.0	15
234	29	- 42.6	- 12.5	14
235	35	- 39.6	- 11.4	16
333	58	- 40.0	- 8.5	9
335	53	- 38.6	- 8.7	15
108	58	- 38.4	- 14.4	30.5
402	57*	- 46.4	- 10.0	4
217	58	- 35.1	- 11.4	25
188	76	- 35.4	- 9.6	29
237	80	- 35.6	- 9.7	24
238	132	- 29.6	- 6.7	28
288	130	- 24.3	- 6.5	28
407	119	- 21.8	- 4.6	22
338	154	- 17.6	- 5.2	27
Poloxamine 908	134	- 28.9	- 5.2	30.5

Surface charge of latex particles after coating with serum

(PAGE) or immunoblotting may lead to a better understanding of the factors responsible for RES recognition or the avoidance thereof.

After exposure to serum, the lowest zeta potentials were obtained for polymers with the thickest coating layer (Poloxamer 338 and 407, Poloxamine 908). These polymers have been shown to reduce (Poloxamer 338) or avoid (Poloxamer 407 and Poloxamine 908) liver and spleen clearance. It is however thought that the reduced uptake is not a function of the thickness of the coating layer but of its hydrophilicity (Müller, R.H. and Koosha, 1988).

It cannot be concluded, that a low zeta potential, measured after exposure of latex particles to serum, indicates that these particles may avoid RES recognition after i.v. injection. The particles fulfill only one of the requirements (low uptake of serum components) to reduce RES uptake. Therefore such measurements cannot be used to make a positive selection of suitable coating polymers. However, the measurements can be used to eliminate unsuitable polymers. A coated particle which acquires a high charge in serum is very likely to be cleared by the body macrophages - irrespective of that it might comprise a hydrophilic surface.

3.3.1.5. Summary

Zeta potential measurements of standard polystyrene latex and polystyrene latex after chemical modification of its surface by introduction of functional groups revealed large differences in surface charge. Polystyrene latex particles of different sizes had different surface charges (from zeta potential measurements), of those measured, 60 nm latex possessed the lowest zeta potential. The increased number of charged and hydrated groups on the larger latex particles is believed to be one factor responsible for the poor coating of these particles with Poloxamer and Poloxamine (c.f. chapter 8).

Coating of the particles led to a reduction in the measured zeta potential. The adsorbed coating polymer layer covers part of the diffuse layer surrounding the particles and protects it against removal. The plane of shear is shifted to a larger distance (c.f. Fig. 3.3.1./5).

Zeta potential reduction on coating depends on the extent of the diffuse layer (as determined by the ionic concentration) and how much of the diffuse layer is covered by the polymer coating film (i.e. thickness of adsorbed coating layer):

- In distilled water the particles are surrounded by a large diffuse layer and therefore zeta potential reductions of at maximum 40% percent were obtained.

- The reduction in zeta potential on coating was more distinct in 0.001 M

buffer solutions. Due to the electrolytes present, the diffuse layer is thinner and the polymer coatings can cover it to a larger extent.
- After further compression of the diffuse layer using 0.01 M buffer, the polymers which reduce or avoid RES recognition after i.v. injection (producing a coating layer thickness > 100 Å) lead to uncharged particles.
- In physiological salt solution, the diffuse layer is compressed to about 8 Å and even coating polymers producing only thin coating films, create uncharged latex.
- Coating surfactants containing charged groups (e.g. Gafac RE960) produced coated particles with a higher charge than particles coated with nonionic polymers comprising a similar coating layer thickness (Antarox CO990, Poloxamer 188).

The adjustment of the coating layer thickness by varying the salt concentration (using 0.001 and 0.01 M buffers) can be used to distinguish between polymers of similar coating properties (e.g. Poloxamine 908, 1107, 1307 and 1508) with regard to their efficiency in particle charge reduction.
The measurement of zeta potential can be employed to assess potential charge-reducing polymers. Well characterized particles coated with Poloxamers (188,338,407) and Poloxamine 908 could be used as a kind of 'internal standard'.
Zeta potential measurements of coated particles in serum showed a reduction in the adsorption of charged serum components. The degree of reduction increased with increasing thickness and decreasing hydrophobicity of the coating film. However, the reduced interaction is a function of the surface hydrophobicity and not the coating layer thickness (compare studies with Poloxamine 908 coated PHB/SDS carriers). Coating polymers which reduced or eliminated RES uptake of particles possessed the lowest zeta potential in serum (appr. -5 mV compared to uncoated particles of -15 mV).

A high efficiency of charge reduction in aqueous media and a low uptake of charged components in serum, are, however, not the only properties required for a suitable coating polymer.

3.3.2. Amplitude Weighted Phase Structuration (AWPS)

3.3.2.1. Theory of AWPS

Amplitude Weighted Phase Structuration (AWPS) is a laser light scattering technique for the determination of particle velocities (Schätzel and Merz, 1984; Merz, 1985; Müller, R.H., 1983; Müller, B.W. et al., 1985; Müller R.H. and Merz, 1985). It can be applied to electrophoresis measurements similar to Laser Doppler Anemometry (LDA). The major advantage when compared to LDA is the ability to perform zeta potential measurements at low electrical field strengths.

The optical set-up (Fig. 3.3.2./1) is a symmetrical real fringe system identical to that used in LDA. It consists of a laser light source and a beam splitter dividing the laser light into two beams of the same intensity and frequency. The two beams pass through Bragg cells which create a frequency shift of 1 kHz between them. A lens focusses the two beams to a beam crossover. The beam crossover forms a fringe system moving with 1 kHz due to the 1 kHz frequency shift of the two laser beams. The scattered light from particles moving through the fringe system is detected by an Avalanche diode.

The major difference between AWPS and LDA is in the signal processing and the theoretical treatment. The signal processing electronics determine the amplitude and phase of the scattered light. The phase is measured with a resolution of $2\pi/4096$. In LDA, only a phase resolution of 2π can be achieved because the passed fringes of the interference fringe system are counted. The product of the phase and integrated amplitudes is used to

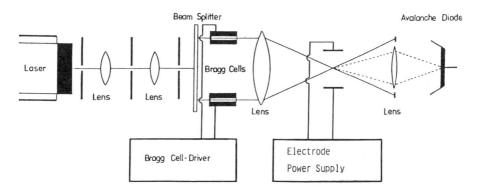

Fig. 3.3.2./1: Principal set up of AWPS (explanations compare text, after Müller, R.H. et al., 1986).

calculate a 64 channel structure function $S(\tau)$:

$$S(\tau) = q^2 \; \frac{\pi}{4} \; \langle A^2 \rangle \; (\; v_c\tau^2 + (\mu \; E/w_E)^2 \; (1-\cos w_E\tau) \;) \; + \; q^2 \langle A^2 \rangle 2D\tau$$

q - $2\pi/d$
d - fringe distance
A - amplitude of the Doppler signal
v_c - a constant collective velocity, e.g. the thermal convec-
   ,   tion component parallel to the direction of the electric
      field
τ - relaxation time
μ - electrophoretic mobility (particle velocity/field
     strength)
E - field strength
w_E - oscillation frequency of the electrical field
D - diffusion constant

The structure function $S(\tau)$ consists of three terms, containing a constant collective velocity (e.g. convection in the cell), the electrophoretic mobility μ and the diffusion constant D which allows the calculation of the particle size by the Einstein equation:

$$R = \frac{K \; T}{6 \; \pi \; n \; D}$$

R - particle radius
K - Boltzmann constant
T - absolute temperature
n - viscosity of dispersion
    medium

The structure function is a straight line if there is no convection and no electrophoretic mobility in the sample (Fig. 3.3.2./2, A). It has a parabolic form if convection is present (Fig. 3.3.2./2, B) and a sinusoidal shape if there is additionally a particle motion (Fig. 3.3.2./2, C: particle velocity = 4 µm/s; Fig. 3.3.2./2, D: particle velocity = 90 µm/s). Information about aggregates or the presence of larger particles in the sample can be obtained from the amplitude distribution of the scattered light. For a monodisperse sample, the intensity shows a Raleigh-type distribution (Fig. 3.3.2./3, A). The presence of larger particles in the monodisperse bulk population results in distortion of the Raleigh distribution (Fig. 3.3.2./3, B).
Determination of convection in the cell parallel to the direction of the electrical field can be used to correct the measured electrophoretic

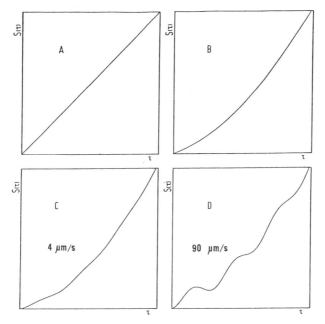

Fig. 3.3.2./2: Different forms of structure functions: A - straight line (no convection and no particle motion) B - parabolic form (convection present, but no particle motion) C,D - parabolic form with sinusoidal shape (convection present, particle velocity 4 μm/s and 90 μm/s)

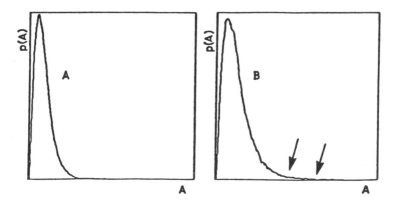

Fig. 3.3.2./3: A - Raleigh distribution of the scattering intensity of a monodisperse particle population (A - amplitude, p(A) - probability of A). B - Raleigh distribution with distortions due to large particles.

mobility, in order to eliminate disturbances due to convection. In combination with the high resolution of the method, low particle velocities can be determined and therefore low electrical field strengths are sufficient (e.g. 2 V/cm). LDA requires that the particles pass a minimum number of fringes. which means that a higher particle velocity is needed for the LDA measurement. To achieve this particle velocity, field strengths in the range of 10 to 20 V/cm are used.

The AWPS option of simultaneous size measurement is useful to detect changes in the sample during the application of an electrical field. AWPS can be applied to particles up to a few micrometer in size and requires only a field strength of 2-4 V/cm. However, polydisperse samples cannot be measured by AWPS because of the distortions caused to the structure functions by the intense light scattering of the larger particles present. LDA is suitable for particles up to 10 µm and can be used on polydisperse samples, but it requires a higher field strength, which can damage sensitive samples.

3.3.2.2. Zeta potential determinations of standard latex

Zeta potential measurements of different sized polystyrene latex particles have been performed using LDA in electric fields ranging in strength from 2 V/cm to 30 V/cm (Fig.3.3.2./4 and 5). Below about 12 V/cm, the obtained zeta potentials show stronger fluctuations for 1 µm latex than for 60 nm latex. Using AWPS, a linear relationship between measured particle velocity V_E and field strength could be obtained over a field strength range from 2 to 20 V/cm (Fig. 3.3.2./6, Eudragit™ dispersion). Due to a non-optimized cell design (flat, parallel metal electrodes) a high convection velocity v_c was present in the sample. As AWPS allows the separate calculation of convection, the measured particle velocity could be corrected accordingly and this therefore caused no problems. Recently, the design of the measuring cell has been optimized, using a 4mm diameter capillary. This has led to a drastic reduction in measured v_c. To investigate, if both methods lead to similar results and to validate AWPS, zeta potential/pH profiles of the series of standard latex have been determined by AWPS (Müller, R.H., 1986-1988) and LDA (Müller, R.H., 1986-1988; Müller, R.H. et al. 1987c). The potentials were very similar in phosphate buffers between pH 6.0 and pH 8.0 (Fig. 3.3.2./7 and 8). Very similar profiles, differing by only a few mV were found in phosphate citrate buffers between pH 2 and pH 8 (Fig. 3.3.2./9-12). These results show that LDA and AWPS are comparable techniques, which yield similar results. However, the measurement of latex suspensions with high degree of aggregation led to distortions in the structure function, and could therefore not be measured by AWPS.

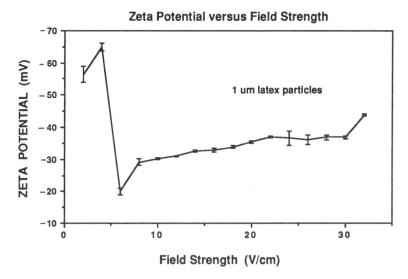

Fig. 3.3.2./4: Zeta potential of 1 µm polystyrene particles determined at different field strengths (Malvern Zetasizer II).

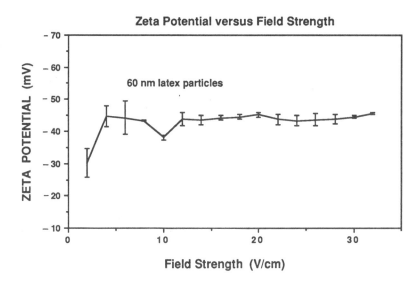

Fig. 3.3.2./5: Zeta potential of 60 nm polystyrene particles determined at different field strengths (Malvern Zetasizer II).

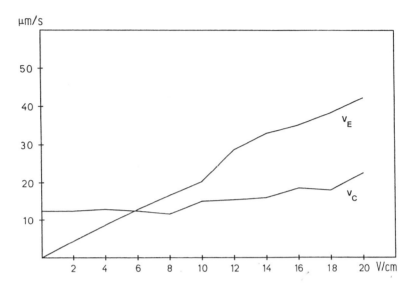

Fig. 3.3.2./6: Particle velocity v_E and convection velocity v_C in an Eudragit dispersion in dependence on an increasing field strength (0 V/cm to 20 V/cm) determined by AWPS (Müller, B.W. et al, 1985).

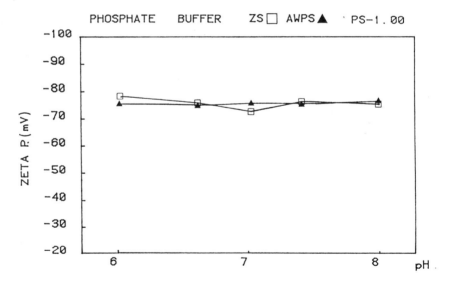

Fig. 3.3.2./7: Zeta potential/pH profile of 1 µm polystyrene latex (PS-1.00) in 0.01 M phosphate buffer determined by LDA using a Zetasizer (ZS ☐) and by AWPS (Δ).

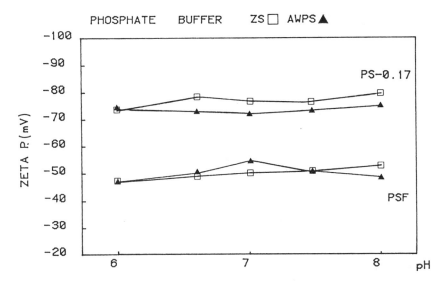

Fig. 3.3.2./8: Zeta potential/pH profiles of 0.17 μm polystyrene latex (PS-0.17) and fluorescently labelled polystyrene latex (PSF) in 0.01 M phosphate buffer determined by LDA using a Zetasizer (ZS □) and by AWPS (Δ).

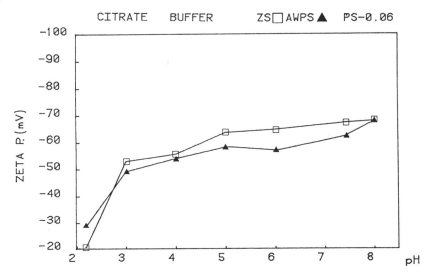

Fig. 3.3.2./9: Zeta potential/pH profile of 0.06 μm polystyrene latex (PS-0.06) in 0.01 M citrate phosphate buffer determined by LDA using a Zetasizer (ZS □) and by AWPS (Δ).

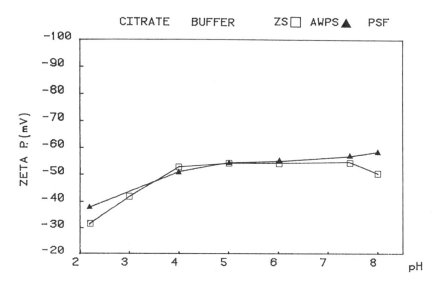

Fig. 3.3.2./10: Zeta potential/pH profile of fluorescently labelled poly-styrene latex (PSF) in 0.01 M citrate phosphate buffer determined by LDA using a Zetasizer (ZS □) and by AWPS (Δ).

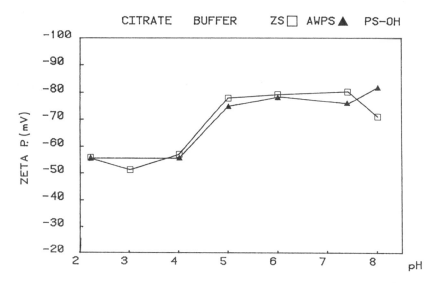

Fig. 3.3.2./11: Zeta potential/pH profile of hydroxylated polystyrene latex (PS-OH) in 0.01 M citrate phosphate buffer determined by LDA using a Zetasizer (ZS □) and by AWPS (Δ).

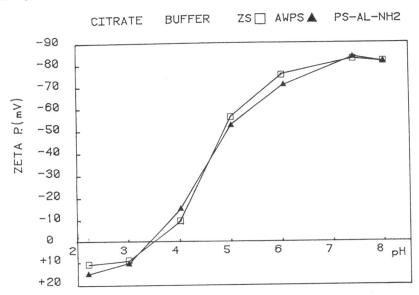

Fig. 3.3.2./12: Zeta potential/pH profile of polystyrene latex surface modified with aliphatic amino groups (PS-AL-NH$_2$) in 0.01 M citrate phosphate buffer determined by LDA using a Zetasizer (ZS □) and by AWPS (Δ).

3.3.2.3 Zeta potential measurements of potential drug carriers

AWPS has been employed to measure the zeta potentials of a range of potential drug carrier systems, e.g. parenteral fat emulsions, liposomes, polymer carriers (poly lactic acid, alkyl-cyanoacrylates) and albumin particles (Müller, R.H. et al, 1986).

The advantage of measurements at low electric field strengths was demonstrated for sensitive samples such as parenteral fat emulsions. Properties of these emulsions were changed by exposure to strong electrical fields (e.g. 20 V/cm). Fig. 3.3.2./13 shows the frequency peak obtained by LDA for a soya bean oil emulsion. With increased exposure to the electric field (20 V/cm) the frequency peak split and two maxima occurred. After further exposure to the field, the peak split into two separate peaks of a lower and higher mean frequency than the original peak. This indicated the presence of two sub-populations different in charge. The mean zeta potential of the two peaks was however identical to the zeta potential of the undamaged emulsion. Lowering the field strength (to 15 V/cm) and shortening the exposure time avoided splitting the emulsion into two

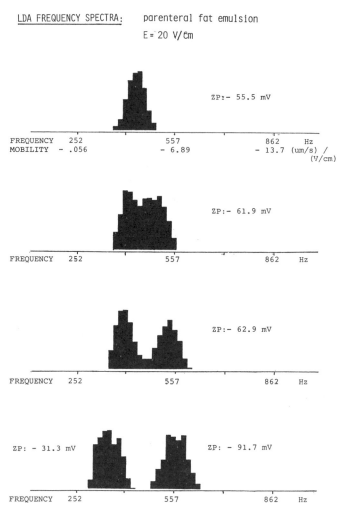

LDA FREQUENCY SPECTRA: parenteral fat emulsion

E = 20 V/cm

ZP:- 55.5 mV

FREQUENCY   252   557   862   Hz
MOBILITY   - .056   - 6.89   - 13.7 (um/s) /
                                                (V/cm)

ZP:- 61.9 mV

FREQUENCY   252   557   862   Hz

ZP:- 62.9 mV

FREQUENCY   252   557   862   Hz

ZP: - 31.3 mV   ZP: - 91.7 mV

FREQUENCY   252   557   862   Hz

Fig. 3.3.2./13: LDA frequency peaks obtained from a parenteral fat emulsion
exposed to a field of 20 V/cm. The field damages the sample indicated by
the splitting up and finally separation of the peak into two peaks with
increasing exposure time to the field.

populations of different charge. Such damaging effects were not observed
using AWPS.
Positively and negatively charged liposomes were kindly prepared by the
Department of Physiology and Pharmacology, Medical School, University of
Nottingham. The positive liposomes contained dipalmitoyl phosphatidyl-

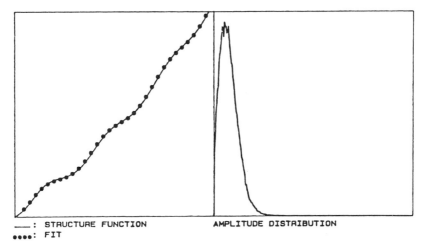

———: STRUCTURE FUNCTION   AMPLITUDE DISTRIBUTION
••••: FIT

Fig. 3.3.2./14: Structure function S(τ) and amplitude distribution of the
scattered light from positively charged liposomes (zeta potential: +38.0
mV, dispersion medium: isotonic phosphate buffer diluted with distilled
water by ten, field strength: 5.0 V/cm).

choline (DPPC), cholesterol and stearylamine (molar ratio 5:2:1) and the
negative liposomes DPPC, cholesterol and dicetyl phosphate (5:2:1). Both
preparations were dispersed in isotonic phosphate buffer. For measurements,
they were diluted 1/10 in distilled water in order to increase their zeta
potential. For the positively charged liposomes, the obtained structure
function showed a medium sinusoidal shape and resulted in a zeta potential
of +38.0 mV and a mean size of 80 nm. The amplitude distribution of the
scattered light is Raleigh type and shows no distortions, indicating a
monodisperse sample (Fig. 3.3.2./14. The AWPS version used for the
measurements was still equipped with parallel flat electrodes in a cubic
cell. Due to this electrode design and the salts present in the dispersion
medium, a Joule heating occurred, leading to a convection velocity of 4.6
µm/s (particle velocity: 21.9 µm/s). Diluting the liposomes with water by
40 resulted in an increase in the zeta potential up to +49.4 mV, due to the
lower compression of the diffuse layer in low salt concentrations (Fig.
3.3.2./15).The amplitude distribution again shows no distortions at higher
amplitudes. With the negative charged liposomes (dilution of the isotonic
phosphate buffer 1/10 with water) a potential of -59.9 mV and a liposome
diameter of 84 nm were obtained.
Poly lactic acid (PLA) particles (kindly supplied by Boots Company plc,
Nottingham) were produced by grinding of the polymer and not by a solvent
evaporation technique. The particles were dispersed in water and after

93

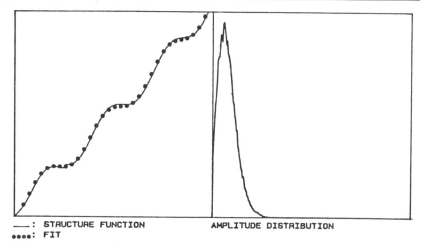

<pre>___: STRUCTURE FUNCTION   AMPLITUDE DISTRIBUTION
••••: FIT</pre>

Fig. 3.3.2./15: Structure function S(τ) and amplitude distribution of the scattered light from positively charged liposomes (zeta potential: +49.4 mV, dispersion medium: isotonic phosphate buffer diluted with distilled water by forty, field strength: 5.0 V/cm).

settling of the larger particles, the supernatant was taken for the measurement of the zeta potential. The supernatant contained a bulk particle population with a mean size of 1.7 μm. The structure function (Fig. 3.3.2./16) possessed a distinct sinusoidal shape, corresponding to a field velocity of 27.3 μm/s (zeta potential -52.8 mV). The convection velocity in the direction of the applied field (E=5 V/cm) was 3.7 μm/s. In comparison to the PLA particles produced by solvent evaporation, the potential of the ground particles was relatively high. The amplitude distribution showed no distortions by particles much larger than the bulk population.

Albumin particles were produced by an emulsion technique using different dispersion media (Saunders, 1988). The particle size distribution within a sample was relatively broad, ranging from 1 to about 10 μm (determined by Laser Diffractometry). So, for the measurement of the zeta potential by AWPS, the supernatant was taken after a few hours settling time. A zeta potential of -24.4 mV was obtained for albumin particles produced in olive oil (Fig. 3.3.2./17), -27.2 mV for those produced in Cyclohexane (Fig. 3.3.2./18). The production in different media did not create a difference in the potential. The amplitude distribution showed distinct distortions and a peak due to amplitude overflow at higher amplitudes. This indicates the polydispersity of the sample.

Butylcyanoacrylate particles (Wright, 1988) with a diameter of 34 nm were measured in 0.01 M HCL. Due to the ions present in the acid medium, a

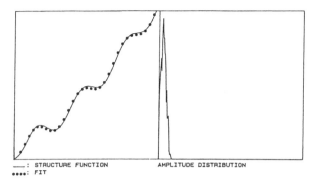

: STRUCTURE FUNCTION   AMPLITUDE DISTRIBUTION
: FIT

Fig. 3.3.2./16: Structure function $S(\tau)$ and amplitude distribution of the scattered light from Poly lactic acid particles produced by grinding of the polymer (diameter 1.7 um, particle velocity 27.3 µm/s, zeta potential -52.8 mV)

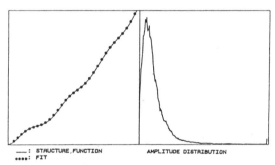

: STRUCTURE,FUNCTION   AMPLITUDE DISTRIBUTION
: FIT

Fig. 3.3.2./17: Structure function $S(\tau)$ and amplitude distribution of albumin particles produced in olive oil (mean diameter 1.57 µm, zeta potential -24.4 mV).

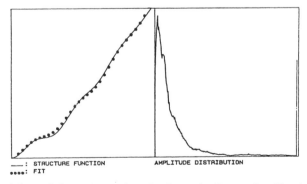

: STRUCTURE FUNCTION   AMPLITUDE DISTRIBUTION
: FIT

Fig. 3.3.2./18: $S(\tau)$ and amplitude distribution of albumin particles produced in cyclohexane (mean diameter 1.76 µm, zeta potential -27.2 mV).

convection velocity of 4.6 μm/s was measured, and as a result of the low zeta potential of the particles (-5.9 mV) a particle velocity of 3.0 μm/s was obtained. This resulted in a more parabolic structure function where the shape is dominated by the convection (Fig. 3.3.2./19B). The function shows no distinct sinusoidal shape any more. Fig. 3.3.2./19A shows the structure function without application of an electric field resulting in a measured potential of 0 mV. The function is however not a straight line but is slightly parabolic, indicating that a convection velocity is present in the cell. The measurements show that AWPS is capable of eliminating distortions of the measurement by convection, even when the convection velocity is in the range of the observed particle velocity. A correction was no longer found to be possible when the convection velocity was a

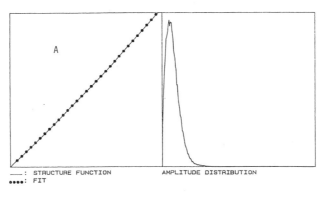

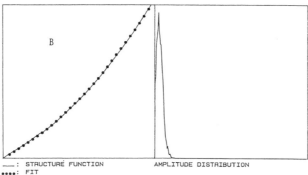

Fig. 3.3.2./19: Structure function S(τ) and amplitude distribution of butylcyanoacrylate particles of 30 nm in diameter. A - without application of an electric field. B - with application of an electric field (zeta potential: -5.9 mV, particle velocity 3.0 μm/s, convection velocity 4.6 μm/s).

multiple of the particle velocity. The objective should therefore be to chose a cell design which reduces convection, instead of eliminating it at a later stage by a mathematical process. This has been done in the latest AWPS model by introducing a capillary cell instead of the cubic cell with parallel flat electrodes. The measurements (even in the presence of a high convection) do however demonstrate very nicely the potential of the AWPS technique.

3.3.2.4. Summary

AWPS is a laser light scattering technique which allows the simultaneous determination of particle size and electrophoretic mobility (zeta potential). Other special features are the correction of the zeta potential for convection in the measuring cell and the ability to measure at low electric field strengths.

Zeta potential measurements of standard latex using LDA and AWPS showed that both methods yielded comparable results.

Measurements on a range of potential drug carriers ranging in size from 30 nm to about 2 µm, demonstrated the applications of AWPS. The possibility of using low field strengths proved to be very advantageous in the investigation of sensitive samples such as parenteral fat emulsions.

With LDA, strong variations in the measured zeta potential were obtained below a field strength of 10 V/cm. However, for AWPS a linear relationship was found for particle velocity and electric field strength. This means, that the measured zeta potential is independent on the applied field strength.

3.4. Surface Hydrophobicity

3.4.0 Importance of surface hydrophobicity for drug carriers

The surface hydrophobicity is a parameter determining the surface modification of carriers by polymer adsorption, the interaction of carriers with cells in vitro and their in vivo distribution. The coating of particles by adsorption of polymers depends on the affinity of the polymers to the particle surface. The polymers are bound by hydrophobic interactions which means that a less hydrophobic particle surface will lead to a reduced affinity of the coating polymers. This results in a thinner or no coating layer at all (c.f. 2.0.). The surface properties of a thinner film might be different from thick adsorbed layers and subsequently lead to a change in the in vivo distribution.

The hydrophobicity of bacteria surface is important for the interaction with phagocytes (van Oss et al., 1975 and 1984). An increase in surface hydrophobicity leads to increased hydrophobic interaction with phagocytes and enhanced phagocytosis. The phagocytosis of yeast particles correlated with their contact angle, that means an increase in surface hydrophobicity led to enhanced adherence and ingestion by the phagocytes, opsonization increased the surface hydrophobicity and subsequently the ingestion of the yeast particles (Dahlgren and Sunquist, 1981). Albumin particles surface modified with hydrophilic polyethylene glycol showed a reduced uptake in cultures of mouse peritoneal macrophages compared to the more hydrophobic non-modified particles (Artursson et al., 1983). The particles rapidly phagocytosed in the cell cultures exhibited a rapid clearance from the blood in vivo.

The in vivo clearance of bacteria from the blood stream is determined by their surface hydrophobicity. Increasing the surface hydrophobicity of Salmonella typhimurium 395 MS by coupling of dinitrophenyl ligands to the surface led to an enhanced RES clearance after intravenous injection (Edebo and Richardson, 1985). The hydrophobicity of the bacteria was determined by Hydrophobic Interaction Chromatography, the same technique is used in the presented work to measure the surface hydrophobicity of drug carriers.

The hydrophobicity of the surface determines the interaction with blood components leading to opsonization and subsequent removal by the RES (c.f. 1.2.). Hydrophobic bacteria adsorb aspecifically immunoglobulin G (IgG) and subsequently they are bound to the Fc receptors on phagocytes leading to phagocytosis (van Oss et al., 1984). More hydrophilic bacteria can reduce the unspecific adsorption but will be coated with specific antibodies of the IgG-class (van Oss et al., 1984).

Hydrophilisation of particles by coating with hydrophilic polymers reduces

99

the RES clearance. A relationship between the reduction in surface hydrophobicity of coating films as determined by contact angle measurements and RES clearance was described by Tröster and Kreuter (1988). Contact angle measurements cannot be applied to the hydrated polymer particle in its original dispersion medium. Uncoated particles need to be compressed to form a tablet or the polymer particles need to be dissolved in an organic solvent to cast a polymer film for the contact angle measurement. Coated particles cannot be measured at all. The surfactants used for the particle coating need to be coated on a film or a plate of the polymeric particle material and to be dried before the measurement (Tröster and Kreuter, 1988). The properties of the surfactant film adsorbed and dried on this flat polymer film might differ from the properties of a film adsorbed on a strongly curved particle surface. In addition, the surfactant adsorbed on the particle is still hydrated by the surrounding dispersion liquid. Hydrophobic Interaction Chromatography determines the hydrophobicity of the adsorbed surfactant layer on the particle in its original dispersion medium and is therefore regarded to be more suitable than contact angle measurements.

3.4.1. Rose Bengal binding methods

3.4.1.1. Rose Bengal adsorption isotherms

The binding constant of Rose Bengal to the surface of the standard polystyrene latex particles was used as measure of surface hydrophobicity (Müller, R.H. et al, 1986c; Mak et al, 1986; Davis et al, 1986). Adsorption isotherms were measured in 0.1 M phosphate buffer (pH 7.4). The latex was incubated with Rose Bengal (3 hours at room temperature), centrifuged for 1 - 2 hours at 20.000 rpm to spin down the particles and the concentration of free Rose Bengal in the supernatant determined spectrophotometrically at 542.7 nm. Due to the high affinity of Rose Bengal for polymer surfaces (e.g. centrifuge tubes) control samples were run in each experiment. The saturated adsorption of Rose Bengal to the latex particles was achieved within the incubation time of three hours. No increased adsorption was found in samples after 24 hours incubation. The binding constant was calculated using a Scatchard plot according to the equation:

$$r/a = KN - Kr$$

r - amount of Rose Bengal adsorbed $(\mu g/\mu m^2)$ $(\mu g/mg)$
a - equilibrium concentration of Rose Bengal $(\mu g/ml)$
K - binding constant $(ml/\mu g)$
N - maximum amount bound $(\mu g/\mu m^2)$, $(\mu g/mg)$

Fig. 3.4.1./1 shows the adsorption isotherms obtained using polystyrene latex particles of different sizes (PS-0.06, PS-0.17 and PS-0.90) and surface properties (modified by the introduction of additional amino groups (PS-AR-NH$_2$)). The amount adsorbed per mg latex (dry weight) was plotted against the equilibrium concentration of Rose Bengal for the latex suspensions of different mean particle sizes. The adsorption plateaus are located at very different concentrations of Rose Bengal due to the large difference in the surface area between 0.06 μm and 0.90μm particles. Plotting the amount of Rose Bengal adsorbed per unit surface area $(\mu g/\mu m^2)$ reduced the difference in plateau levels (Fig 3.4.1./2). The difference in the slopes of the adsorption isotherms indicates the different affinity and binding constants of Rose Bengal for the different surfaces. Plotting the data from the slope of the adsorption isotherms using the Scatchard equation (r/a against r) led to straight lines (Fig. 3.4.1./3) whereby the slope gives the binding constant K (Table 3.4.1./1).
Different binding constants were obtained for the small polystyrene latex (0.06μm) and the larger latices of 0.14μm and 0.9 μm mean particle size. The small latex were more hydrophobic (K=0.40 ml/μg) than the larger

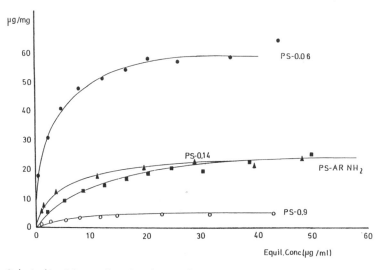

Fig. 3.4.1./1: Adsorption isotherm of Rose Bengal on polystyrene particles
of 0.06 μm, 0.14μm, 0.90 μm (PS-0.06, PS-0.14 and PS-0.90) and on
polystyrene particles carrying aromatic amino groups on the surface (PS-AR-
NH^2). The amount of Rose Bengal adsorbed is given per mass polymer (mg)

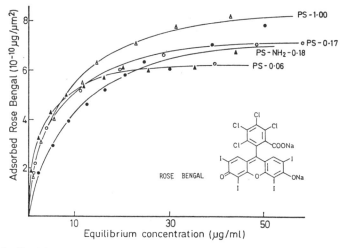

Fig. 3.4.1./2: Adsorption isotherm of Rose Bengal on polystyrene particles
of 0.06 μm, 0.14μm, 0.90 μm (PS-0.06, PS-0.14 and PS-0.90) and on
polystyrene particles carrying aromatic amino groups on the surface (PS-AR-
NH^2). The amount of Rose Bengal adsorbed is given per unit of surface area
(μm^2).

102

Table 3.4.1./1: Binding constants K, maximum amount bound N per mg latex and per unit surface area for the standard latex particles obtained from Rose Bengal adsorption isotherms.

Latex particles	binding constant K (ml/mg)	maximum amount N bound per	
		mass polymer (µg/mg)	unit surface $(10^{10}µg/µm^2)$
PS-0.06	0.40	63.0	6.6
PS-0.14	0.29	24.1	5.9
PS-0.90	0.28	4.5	7.0
PSF	0.12	22.3	5.5
PS-AL-NH$_2$	0.23	20.9	6.9
PS-AR-NH$_2$	0.14	24.3	7.6
PSF-COOH	0.27	22.5	6.3
PS-COOH	0.06	3.1	1.0
PS-OH	0.04	4.1	1.8

particles (K=0.29 and 0.28 ml/µg respectively). This is of importance for the coating of particles with polymers. Despite the fact that the particles of different sizes are made of the same material, they have different surface properties. This is likely to influence their adsorption of polymers, and consequently the thickness and hydrophobicity of the resulting coating layer. The latex with a higher mean particle diameter have a larger number of charged groups on the surface (c.f. chapter 3.3.1). Zeta potential measurements gave a potential of about -65 mV for PS-0.06 but potentials in the range of -75 to -80 mV for the larger latex. The number of charged groups depends on the production conditions used by the manufacturer. The proof that an increased number of surface charged groups reduces the surface hydrophobicity can be seen from the Rose Bengal binding constants obtained for latex after surface chemical modification by the introduction of additional carboxyl groups (PS-COOH) or hydrophilic functional groups (PS-OH, PS-AR-NH$_2$). These latices possess higher zeta potentials and binding constants below 0.28 ml/mg.

Such differences in the surface hydrophobicities of polystyrene latices are important for phagocytosis studies in cell cultures. Cell cultures are being used for the testing of potential coating polymers which are able to protect against in vivo phagocytosis (c.f. chapter 7.1). Polystyrene latex PS were coated with polymers, and the number of coated particles taken up

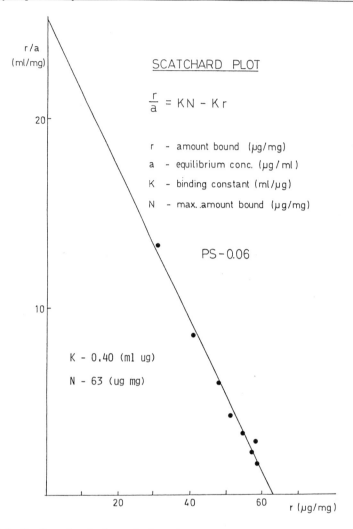

Fig. 3.4.1./3: Scatchard plot of the adsorption isotherm of Rose Bengal on 0.06 μm polystyrene particles (PS-0.06).

by the macrophages in the cell culture is compared to an uncoated control. In previous studies (Illum et al., 1987), in order to make detection of the phagocytosed particles easier, 5 μm latex which can be visualised by light microscopy were used. The results obtained in these studies were transferred directly to 60nm latex. Because of the difference in the surface hydrophobicities of the latex preparations, the properties of the coating layers are likely to differ. The extrapolation of results obtained with 5 µm particles to 60 nm particles is therefore not necessarily valid (cp. chapter 8).

Fluorescent polystyrene particles are produced by attachment of hydrophobic fluorescent dyes to the naked particle surface. For such fluorescently labelled particles it was expected that the Rose Bengal binding constant would be around 0.30. Such a high binding constant could be found for the fluorescent labelled carboxylated particles PSF-COOH. The attachment of the hydrophobic dye yellowish green increased the binding constant from K=0.06 for the unlabelled PS-COOH to K=0.27 for PSF-COOH (batch A). However, a purchased second batch of PSF-COOH (batch B) was much less hydrophobic than the first batch indicated by a low binding constant (K=0.13 ml/mg). From the Rose Bengal measurements this result could not be explained. Only investigation of the two batches by Hydrophobic Interaction Chromatography (c.f. chapter 3.4.2.2.) could explain the observed differences in surface hydrophobicity.

The introduction of functional groups to the particle surface led to a reduction in the surface hydrophobicity and the measured binding constant K. Attachment of aromatic and aliphatic amino groups on the surface reduced K to 0.23 and 0.14 respectively, while introduction of carboxyl and hydroxyl groups reduced K even further, to 0.06 and 0.04 ml/µg respectively. It is thought that the small reduction in K for the particles after attachment of amino groups, might be due to the fact that the groups are attached via an aliphatic chain or an aromatic ring. This might bring about an increase in the surface hydrophobicity which compensates the decrease produced by the attached functional groups. An explanation as to why the particles with the aliphatic amino groups were more hydrophobic than the ones with the aromatic amino groups could not be given because of the lack of information available from the supplier Polysciences about the chemical modification process.

The objective of the characterization of the latex was to find suitable methods for the detection of differences in surface hydrophobicities. Knowledge of the reasons for the observed differences in hydrophobicity was not essential for the development of a suitable measuring technique. For further studies on the differences in polymer coatings, it was essential to have a detailed knowledge of the production method and the chemicals involved. Contamination of the particles by adsorbed detergents is important as this may effect coating by Poloxamer and Poloxamine. It was shown that commercial latices contained surfactants despite the fact that they were sold as surfactant free (c.f. chapter 3.5.).

3.4.1.2. Rose Bengal partitioning method

The determination of adsorption isotherms is time consuming, so a faster partitioning method was investigated (Müller, R.H. et al. 1986c). The latex suspension is regarded as a two phase system, whereby the surface of the particles is one phase and the dispersion medium is the second. Rose Bengal partitions between these two phases and a partition quotient PQ can be determined:

$$PQ = \frac{\text{amount Rose Bengal bound on surface}}{\text{amount Rose Bengal in dispersion medium}}$$

For the partitioning experiments, the concentration of Rose Bengal was kept constant and the concentration of latex particles was varied. Increasing the latex concentration leads to an increase in the surface area and consequently the partition quotient should increase linearly. Plotting PQ against the particle surface area will therefore yield a straight line from which the slope S can be taken as a measure of hydrophobicity.

For a partitioning analysis, suspensions with constant Rose Bengal concentration (20 µg/ml) but increasing latex particle concentrations were

Table 3.4.1./2: Characterization data from both Rose Bengal methods (after Müller, R.H. et al., 1986c; Davis et al., 1986).

Particles (figure = size in µm)	k (ml/µg)	N (µg/mg)	total surface area (µm²/ng) x E10	max. amount bound/unit surf. area (µg/µm²) x E10	slope from part.exp. (ml/µm²) S
PS-0.06	0.40	63.0	9.52	6.61	9.124 E-11
PS-0.14	0.29	24.1	3.36	7.18	6.39 E-11
PS-0.9	0.28	4.5	0.63	7.02	6.023 E-11
PSF-0.19	0.12	22.3	3.01	7.43	2.335 E-11
PS-AR-NH₂-0.18	0.14	24.3	3.21	7.58	2.723 E-11
PS-NH₂-0.19	0.23	20.9	3.01	6.94	5.29 E-11
PSF-COOH-0.21	0.27	22.5	2.72	8.27	5.56 E-11
PS-COOH-0.19	0.06	3.1	3.01	1.02	5.131 E-13
PS-OH-0.25	0.04	4.1	2.29	1.82	1.42 E-12

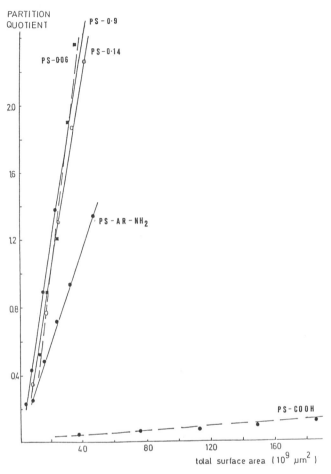

Fig. 3.4.1./4: Rose Bengal partitioning method. Plot of the partition
quotient versus the total surface area of the particles. The slope S of the
straight line is a measure of the surface hydrophobicity of the latex
(Müller, R.H. et al., 1986c).

prepared. The suspensions were incubated for three hours, the particles
centrifuged at 20.000 rpm and the amount of free Rose Bengal in the
supernatant was determined spectrophotometrically at 542.7 nm.
Plotting of PQ against the total surface area of the latex gave a line with
a very steep slope for the most hydrophobic polystyrene latex (PS-0.06, PS-
0.14 and PS-0.9), when compared to the relatively hydrophilic carboxylated
latex PS-COOH (Fig. 3.4.1./4). A good correlation was found between the

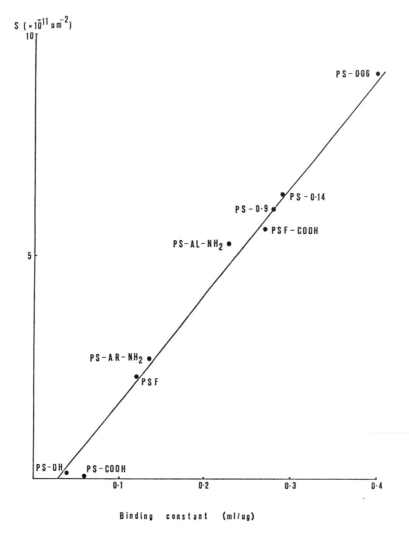

Fig. 3.4.1./ 5: Plot of the slope S (from the partitioning method) versus the binding constant K (from the adsorption isotherms) for the series of standard latex. The latex are placed in order of increasing surface hydrophobicity (Müller, R.H. et al., 1986c).

binding constants K, obtained from the Rose Bengal adsorption isotherms, and the slopes S obtained by the partitioning method. Plotting S versus K produced a straight line. The particles are placed in order of increasing hydrophobicity (Fig. 3.4.1./5). The distinct difference in surface hydrophobicity between PS-0.06 and the larger polystyrene latices (0.14 and 0.90) could be confirmed. Table 3.4.1./2 gives an overview of the data obtained using both Rose Bengal methods.

Hydroxylated and Carboxylated latex are at the lower edge of the surface hydrophobicity range. The affinity of Rose Bengal for their surfaces is very low. Consequently, high concentrations of Rose Bengal had to be used for the determination of their adsorption isotherms and large quantities of particles were required for the partitioning experiment in order to obtain a detectable amount of Rose Bengal adsorbed onto the particle surface. This shows the limitations in the application of the method to particles which are more hydrophilic than PS-OH and PS-COOH.

3.4.1.3 Summary

Rose Bengal is a suitable probe to measure the surface hydrophobicity of uncoated model carriers. Determination of the binding constant of a range of particles (via the production of adsorption isotherms) showed an increased adsorption with increasing particle hydrophobicity. The Rose Bengal binding constants were used to place the particles in order of increasing surface hydrophobicity. The same result could be obtained using a quicker dye-partitioning method.

Differences in the surface hydrophobicity of particles made from the same material (polystyrene) but differing in size (over the range 60 nm to 0.9 µm) were found. This questions the validity of interpreting results obtained with larger particles (in surface coating and phagocytosis studies) in respect of small latex particles.

Large differences between batches of latex were found. This was especially true for surface modified particles (fluorescent label on surface). Obviously differences in the chemical reaction for the surface modification led to particles very different in hydrophobicity. The variations in hydrophobicity between particles of different sizes or between batches show the importance of characterization of model latices. Otherwise observed effects in an experiment due to between batch differences in surface properties might lead to wrong conclusions.

A limitation of the Rose Bengal methods is that the calculated binding constant K or the slope S are only average measures of the hydrophobicity of the particles. They do not give any information about possible subpopulations, which may differ in surface hydrophobicity. Furthermore, the methods are not applicable to particles less hydrophobic than PS-COOH or PS-OH and to particles coated with hydrophilic polymers (Poloxamer).

3.4.2. Hydrophobic Interaction Chromatography (HIC)

3.4.2.0. Applications of HIC

Hydrophobic Interaction Chromatography (HIC) is a column chromatography which separates substances or particulates on the basis of differences in their hydrophobic interaction with a hydrophobic gel matrix. To avoid an overlapping of ion-exchange, charge and hydrophobic effects the matrices need to be composed of a neutral gel, such as alkyl-Sepharose CL-4B. The separation achieved depends on the hydrophobicity of the solute, the hydrophobicity of the matrix and the interactions with and between the solvent water molecules. Any perturbation which effects one of these components (e.g. ionic strength of the water and temperature) changes the separation achieved, providing a great degree of flexibility in the design of the experimental conditions. Addition of salts can promote or reduce the hydrophobic interactions between matrix and solute. Addition of anions such as Cl^- and even more so PO_4^{3-} increase hydrophobic interactions ("salting out" effect), whereas the addition of cations such as Ca^{2+} and Ba^{2+} disrupts the structure of water ("chaotropic" effect) and leads to a relative decrease in interactions (von Hippel and Schleich, 1969; Pahlmann et al., 1977). Solutes can be bound to the matrix in the presence of a high ionic strength (e.g. 4M NaCl) and eluted by lowering the salt concentration or changing to an ion with a lower salting out effect. Alternatively, non-ionic detergents such as Triton X-100 can be used. The hydrophobic region of the detergent molecule binds to the matrix and displaces the solutes or particulates bound to the matrix.

3.4.2.1. Experimental

The apparatus used for HIC consisted of a column (bed volume 10 ml), an arrangement of two solvent pumps and a UV spectrometer connected to a chart recorder for detection of the particles (at 400nm) (Fig. 3.4.2./1). To create a surfactant gradient, 0.1% Triton X-100 was pumped from the reservoir (R) to the mixing container (M) at a flow rate of 0.3 ml/min. Before the start of the experiment, the column was equilibrated with buffer (0.02 M phosphate buffer in 0.3 M NaCl). Latex particles (15 µl of a 2% w/v suspension) were loaded onto the column and eluted at a flow rate of 0.3 ml/min. Washing of the column was performed using a sequence of different solutions: 10 ml of 0.1% Triton X-100 in water, then 10 ml of distilled water, 10 ml of 10% ethanol, 20 ml of 5% butanol and finally equilibration with 10 ml of distilled water (flow rate 0.3 ml/min).
Gel matrices with increasing hydrophobicity (increasing length of the

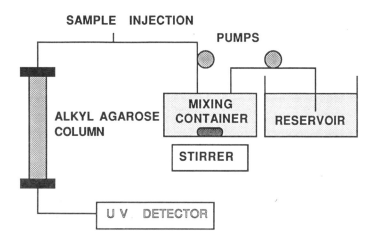

Fig. 3.4.2./ 1: Hydrophobic Interaction Chromatography apparatus. In order
to create a Triton X-100 gradient, 0.1% surfactant solution was pumped from
the reservoir (R) to the mixing container (M).

coupled alkyl chain) have been employed:

        Sepharose CL-4B (neutral agarose)
        Agethane (ethyl-agarose)
        propyl-agarose (propylamine-agarose)
        butyl-agarose (butylamine-agarose)
        pentyl-agarose (pentylamine-agarose)
        hexyl-agarose (hexylamine-agarose)
        octyl-agarose (octylamine-agarose)

The model carriers (polystyrene latex particles) were loaded onto the
column in 0.3 M NaCl adjusted to pH 6.8. Higher salt concentrations led to
flocculation of the uncoated particles on the column as shown by PCS
determinations of the eluted particles. A Triton X-100 gradient proved to
be suitable for the elution of uncoated model drug carriers (latex). Coated
latex showed a weaker interaction with the matrix and were eluted with the
buffered saline. The elution volume increased with increasing hydrophobicity of the coating. To differentiate between coatings of similar low
hydrophobicity, the hydrophobicity of the matrix was increased.

3.4.2.2. Characterization of uncoated carriers

To investigate the suitability of HIC for the characterization of unmodified (i.e. non-coated) drug carriers, the series of standard latices were used (Müller, R.H. et al, 1986b). The particles were loaded onto the column in the presence of buffer. The carboxylated (PS-COOH) and the hydroxylated particles (PS-OH) could be eluted (Fig. 3.4.2/2) without using Triton X-100. Both passed down the column without any interaction (elution volume of appr. 4 ml which is equal to the void volume of the column). The other particles were bound to the gel matrix and could only be eluted by using 0.1% Triton X-100. This indicates that the hydroxylated and carboxylated latex had less hydrophobic surfaces.

To be able to detect differences between the surface hydrophobicity of PS-OH and PS-COOH, a more hydrophobic matrix (ethyl-agarose) was used. The more hydrophobic ethyl-matrix was able to bind these particles due to increased hydrophobic interaction. The elution of the particles was performed using a Triton X-100 gradient (0% - 0.025%).

The chromatogram obtained from polystyrene latex (PS-0.14) showed a broad peak from an elution volume of 27-40 ml (Fig. 3.4.2/3) indicating that there are differences in surface properties within the particle population. The hydroxylated and the carboxylated particles gave a main peak at 20.0 ml and 22.6 ml respectively (Fig. 3.4.2/3). This indicates only a slight difference in surface hydrophobicity as detectable by HIC. There is however a second peak at 32.0 ml for PS-OH and a long, distinct tail for PS-COOH. That proves that within the particle population there is a relatively hydrophilic fraction and a second fraction similar in surface hydrophobicity to the unmodified polystyrene particles (PS-0.14). These results can be easily explained by looking at the production method of these particles, as employed by Polysciences. The polystyrene latices are firstly polymerised and then the surface is modified by the chemical introduction of additional hydroxyl or carboxyl groups. This reaction will of course not lead to surface modification of all particles to the same extent. The second peak at around 32.0 ml can therefore be attributed to polystyrene latex particles with little or no surface modification.

The efficiency of the chemical surface modification seemed to vary from batch to batch, as in different batches a varying ratio of the main 20 ml peak to the minor peak (at around 32 ml) was obtained. An extremely large batch to batch variation was found during the investigation of two batches of fluorescent-labelled carboxylated latex (PSF-COOH) (Mak et al, 1986). The chromatograms also exhibited two peaks; the first peak can be attributed to a hydrophilic fraction and the second to a much more hydrophobic fraction. Bat h A shows the main peak at 31.4 ml and a minor peak at 16.3 ml (Fig. 3.4.2/4). However the main peak of batch B is located

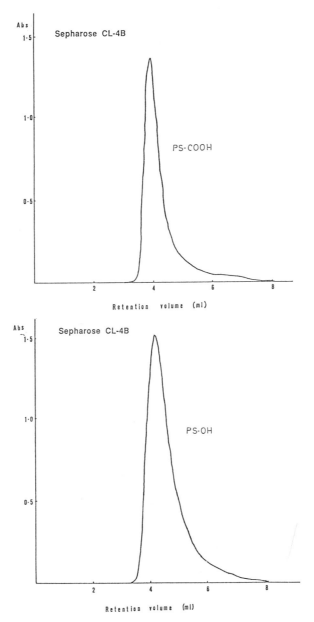

Fig. 3.4.2./2: Chromatogram of carboxylated (PS-COOH) and hydroxylated (PS-OH) polystyrene latex particles on Sepharose CL-4B. The latex pass down the column without interaction (elution volume = void volume).

113

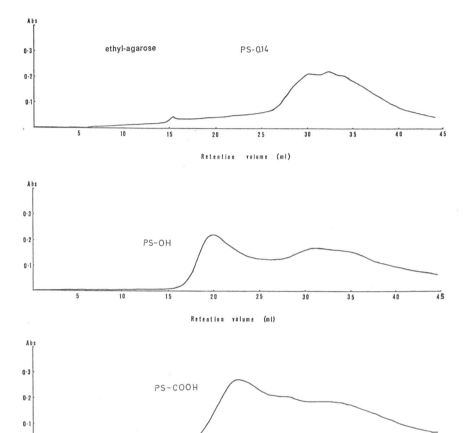

Fig. 3.4.2./3: Chromatograms of latex on ethyl-agarose gel: polystyrene (PS-0.14), hydroxylated polystyrene (PS-OH) and carboxylated polystyrene (PS-COOH) particles. Elution was performed using a Triton X-100 gradient.

at 16.3 ml indicating that batch B is less hydrophobic than A. The coupling reaction of the hydrophobic dye yellowish green with the latex was more successful in batch A than in batch B. In the Rose Bengal adsorption studies, a low binding constant was obtained for the more hydrophilic batch B. It was expected to find a higher binding constant due to the attachment of the hydrophobic dye on the particle surface. Such expected high binding constant could only be found for batch A. These differences in the binding

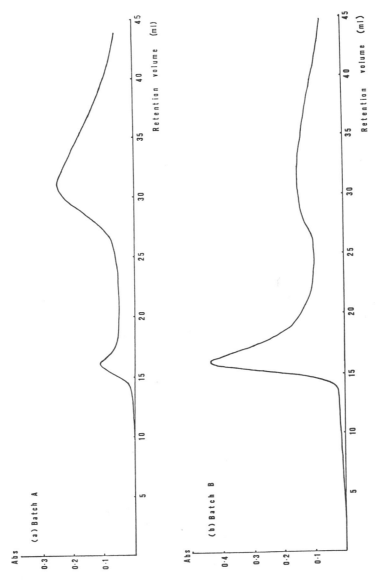

Fig. 3.4.2./4: Chromatogram of 2 batches (A and B) of fluorescently labelled carboxylated polystyrene (PSF-COOH) particles on ethyl-agarose. Elution was performed with a Triton X-100 gradient. The two batches contain a relatively hydrophilic (at 16 ml) and a more hydrophobic particle subpopulation (at 31 ml elution volume) respectively but in different proportions.

115

constants and related surface hydrophobicity of the particles found from the Rose Bengal studies could not be explained. A binding constant, as determined by the Rose Bengal method, is only an average value of hydrophobicity, whereas HIC contains information of possible subpopulations within the particle populations differing in surface hydrophobicity. HIC could therefore explain the observed phenomenon.

The data shows the importance of having suitable characterization methods available and of characterizing particles before the performance of further experiments. The observed variations in the surface hydrophobicity are likely to be of great importance. For example when using latices for studies of phagocytosis in cell cultures, the phagocytosis will be enhanced if a batch of latex is more hydrophobic than the previous one. This might explain to some extent, the variations observed in cell culture studies when using a new batch of standard particles. Cell culture results are much more reproducible within one batch of particles.

The HIC placed the particles in the same order of hydrophobicity as the Rose Bengal adsorption studies (Table 3.4.2/1). Binding constants and elution volumes obtained by HIC are in good agreement.

Table 3.4.2/1: Binding constants obtained by Rose Bengal adsorption studies and elution volumes obtained by HIC for standard latices.

Particles	binding constant K (ml/µg)	elution volume (ml)
PS-0.14	0.29	32.46
PSF-COOH batch A	0.27	31.35
PS-AL-NH$_2$	0.23	30.34
PSF	0.12	29.98
PS-COOH	0.06	22.62
PS-OH	0.04	20.00

3.4.2.3. HIC of coated carriers

Polystyrene latex (PS-0.14) was coated with a series of water soluble Poloxamers and with Poloxamine 908. The hydrophobicity of the polymer coatings was investigated using HIC (Mak et al, 1988 and 1988a). All the coated particles passed down HIC columns prepared from Sepharose CL-4B without any interaction. Fig. 3.4.2/5 shows a chromatogram obtained with Poloxamine 908 coated latex whereby the elution volume of 4.5 ml is equal to the void volume of the column.

The Sepharose column was used to investigate the influence of particle size on the elution volume. Larger particles might be eluted earlier. Therefore polystyrene latex of mean size 0.9 µm was coated with Poloxamine 908 and passed down the column. No difference was found in the elution volume compared to the 0.14 µm latex and therefore, for the study a size effect could be excluded. The size difference between the investigated particles was relatively small (0.14 µm - 0.25µm).

The Sepharose matrix was not suitable to resolve differences in hydrophobicity between the coating materials. Employing the more hydrophobic ethyl-agarose matrix led to a differentiation between the more hydrophobic Poloxamers (low HLB). Poloxamer 101 coated particles appeared to bind strongly to the matrix (Fig. 3.4.2/6), Poloxamer 184 showed a slight interaction as indicated by the fact that its elution volume was slightly higher than the void volume of the column. Poloxamer 234, 282 and the more hydrophilic polymers (Poloxamer 338 and 407, Poloxamine 908) passed again without interaction.

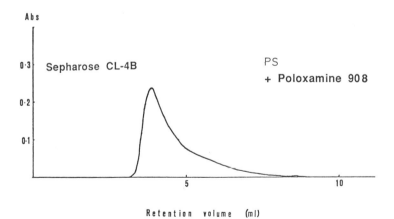

Fig. 3.4.2./5: Chromatogram of polystyrene latex particles (PS-0.14) coated with Poloxamine 908 on a Sepharose CL-4B matrix. Elution with buffered saline (0.3 M NaCl) without Triton X-100 gradient.

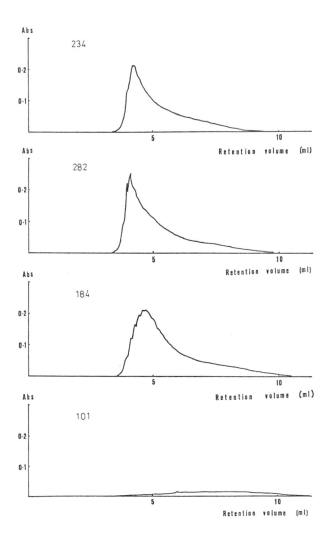

Fig. 3.4.2./6: Chromatograms of polystyrene latex particles (PS-0.14) coated with Poloxamers 234, 282, 184 and 101 on ethyl-agarose matrix. The Poloxamer coating with 101 is the most hydrophobic and the particles are mostly retained on the column.

Increasing the hydrophobicity of the matrix by using propyl-agarose led to the binding of the Poloxamer 234 and 282 coated particles (Fig. 3.4.2/7). The coating was too hydrophobic for the particles to elute with the void volume. A good differentiation in elution volume could be observed between

118

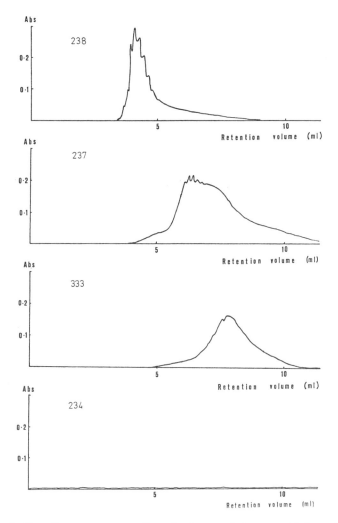

Fig. 3.4.2./7: Chromatograms of polystyrene latex particles (PS-0.14) coated with Poloxamers 238, 237, 333 and 234 on propyl-agarose matrix. The surface hydrophobicity of the coatings increases from Poloxamer 238 to 234 indicated by the increase in the elution volume. The Poloxamer 234 coated latex was too hydrophobic to be eluted and was retained on the column.

the particles coated with Poloxamers 333, 237 and 238, whereby the latter passed again without any interaction. The propyl-agarose column proved to be suitable to place most of the Poloxamer coatings in an order of decreasing hydrophobicity (Table 3.4.2/2).

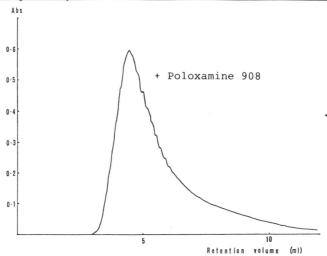

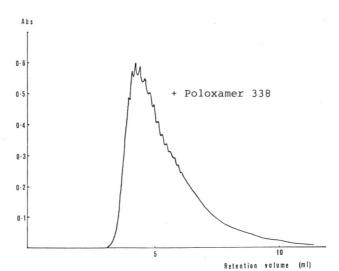

Fig. 3.4.2./8: Chromatograms of polystyrene latex particles (PS-0.14) coated with Poloxamine 908 and Poloxamer 338 on pentyl-agarose matrix. Both coated particles passed down the column without interaction.

The latex coated with the high molecular weight (>10,000) Poloxamers 238, 288, 338 and 407 and Poloxamine 908 still passed down the column without interaction. A differentiation in the hydrophobicity of the coatings was not possible. By increasing the hydrophobicity of the matrix further using pentyl-agarose, it was hoped to detect differences in surface hydropho-

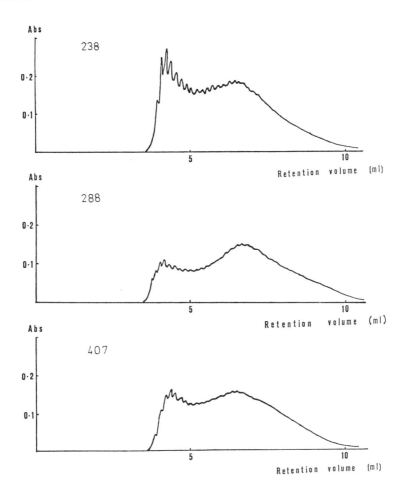

Fig. 3.4.2./9: Chromatograms of polystyrene latex particles (PS-0.14) coated with Poloxamers 238, 288 and 407 on pentyl-agarose. Two peaks were obtained. The second peak represented a particle subpopulation with a more hydrophobic surface.

bicity. The latex coated with Poloxamer 338 and Poloxamine 908 again were eluted with the void volume (Fig. 3.4.2/8). However, the Poloxamer 238, 288 and 407 coated latex exhibited two peaks (Fig. 3.4.2/9). This indicates a broader distribution in surface properties whereby the first eluted peak (at around 4.5 ml) belongs to particles similar in surface hydrophobicity to those coated with Poloxamer 407 and Poloxamine 908. The second peak represents more hydrophobic particles.

Table 3.4.2/2: Elution volumes of polystyrene latex particles (PS-0.14) coated with a series of Poloxamers and Poloxamine 908 on propyl-agarose. (Void volume of the column is 4.50 ml)

coating polymer	coating layer thickness (Å)	elution volume (ml)
Poloxamer 338	154	no interaction
407	119	no interaction
288	130	no interaction
238	132	no interaction
237	81	6.22
188	77	6.53
217	58	7.12
L122	61	7.20
108	58	7.23
335	51	7.53
333	54	7.84
235	33	7.97
234	28	retained
184	22	retained
Poloxamine 908	133	no interaction

Particles coated with Poloxamer 407 and Poloxamine 908 passed down even a hexyl-column without interaction. There were slight differences in the retention volumes for Poloxamine 908 (4.94 ml) and Poloxamer 338 (5.28 ml). In further investigations it could be shown, that a fraction of the coated particles was retained by the column (c.f. chapter 8). The ratio of the number of particles eluted to the number of particles bound can be used as a further characterization parameter to distinguish between such hydrophilic coatings.

3.4.2.4. Summary

Hydrophobic Interaction Chromatography (HIC) is a suitable method to distinguish between the surface hydrophobicity of uncoated drug carriers. This could be shown by using standard polystyrene particles with different surface properties as model carriers. A differentiation can be obtained by loading the particles on columns with alkyl-sepharose and eluting them with a Triton X-100 gradient.
The importance of such a characterization could be demonstrated by the detection of large batch to batch variations in surface properties of "standard" latex particles. Such variations can lead to reproducibility problems in investigations where surface hydrophobicity plays an important role (e.g. particle phagocytosis in cell cultures).
Coated model drug carriers were characterized by using the elution volume as a parameter, without the application of a Triton X-100 gradient. To resolve differences between very hydrophilic coatings, the hydrophobicity of the matrix was increased by using alkyl-sepharoses with increasing alkyl chain length. A series of Poloxamer coatings could be placed in order of decreasing surface hydrophobicity. Poloxamine 908 and Poloxamer 338 and 407 coatings proved to be least hydrophobic indicating their potential to reduce phagocytosis by the RES.
The Rose Bengal methods give a binding constant as a measure of hydrophobicity. This is an average parameter and can only be applied on uncoated particles. HIC provides information on subpopulations with different surface hydrophobicities (resolution into different elution peaks) and can be applied to coated particles. HIC is however much more time consuming than Rose Bengal measurements (esp. the Rose Bengal partitioning method, 3.4.1.2.).

3.4.3. Aqueous two-phase partitioning

3.4.3.1. Theoretical and Experimental

The mixing of dextran and polyethylene glycol (PEG) solutions will above certain concentrations of the two polymers result in a two phase system (Albertsson, 1971). For very large polymers, the interaction energy between the molecules themselves tends to dominate over the entropy of mixing per mole. Therefore the result of mixing depends on the type of interaction between two different polymers. If the interaction is repulsive in character and the molecules prefer to be surrounded by their own kind, two phases will result. The system is in the favoured energetic state when the two polymers are separated. The dextran/PEG system will separate into a PEG-rich upper phase and a dextran-rich lower phase. On this basis there is no difference between the phase separation mechanism of polymer solutions and the classic water/octanol partition system. Polymer solutions can be ranked in a hydrophobic ladder. This ladder falls within a very narrow part of the conventional solvent spectrum which lists the solvents according to their hydrophilic-hydrophobic character (Fig. 3.4.3./1). Partitioning between two phases is an established method for the separation of macromolecules, bacteria, cells etc. (Walter and Selby, 1967; Walter et al., 1968; Shanbag and Axelsson, 1975; Eriksson et al., 1976; Walter and Krob, 1976; Magnusson and Johansson, 1977; Magnusson et al., 1977; Albertsson, 1978; Eriksson and Albertsson, P.-A., 1978; Miörner et al., 1980; Miörner et al, 1982; Sharpe and Warren, 1984).

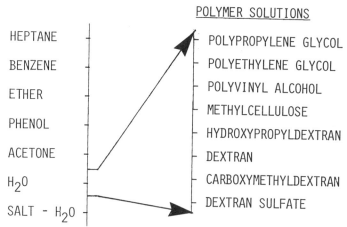

Figure 3.4.3./1: Hydrophobic ladder of aqueous polymer solutions (after Albertsson, P.-A., 1971)

Aqueous two-phase partitioning - Theoretical and experimental

Because of the surface properties of a partitioning material, it will have a greater affinity for one of the two phases. The forces which determine the rate and extent of distribution of particles are the Brownian motion and the interfacial tension. Brownian motion will distribute the particles randomly throughout the whole system. The interfacial force will move them to the phase where they have the lowest interfacial free energy. A particle in a two-phase system can be located in the lower (bottom) phase, in the interface or in the upper (top) phase. Its position will depend on the interfacial tensions between the particle and the upper and lower phase and the interfacial tension between the two phases (Albertsson, 1958, 1971). A system containing 0.11 M sodium phosphate buffer will result in a positive top phase with a potential difference of about 3 mV to the bottom phase (Reitherman et al., 1973).

Two phase-partitioning is a sensitive technique which can be applied to detect changes in the surface properties of polymeric or emulsion carriers by comparing the partitioning behaviour of uncoated and coated carriers or modified emulsions. However, only little attention has been given to the partitioning of polymeric particles (Albertsson, 1958). In the reported systems the polymeric particles moved only to one phase. To measure differences in the partitioning before and after coating of particles, a partitioning between two phases is desirable. Using two-phase systems of different composition, the partitioning of polymeric model drug carriers (polystyrene particles) and emulsions varying in surface properties was studied (Müller, R.H. et al., 1989).

A range of dextrans (mw 20,000, 100,000 and 500,000) and polyethylene glycols (mw 2,000, 6000, 10,000, 20,000 and 35,000) were used for the preparation of the two-phase system. Two-phase systems with relatively low and high polymer concentrations were prepared and tested for particle partitioning between top and bottom phase (= two phases). However, in all the systems the particles partitioned mostly to one phase (top phase), with only a few percent accumulating in the interface. The proportion at the interface increased with standing (settling) time of the system. This increase was found to vary with the nature of the particles. For most experiments a settling time of 2 to 4 hours was chosen.

The handling of the more concentrated polymer systems proved to be too complicated because of their high viscosity. They had no advantage over the less viscous low concentrated systems which were used for most of the investigations. High molecular weight dextrans had no advantage in obtaining a more even partitioning between two phases, so the cheaper dextran 20 (mw 20,000) was used. The final optimized composition of the aqueous two phase system was 16.0% dextran 20, 12.0% PEG 2,000, 0.01 M phosphate buffer and 0.05 M NaCl. The systems were allowed to settle by gravity and readings were taken after 2 or 4 hours' settling time. The particulate carrier concentration in each phase was determined by absorption measurements at 400 nm in a spectrometer.

Particles were coated with Poloxamer polymers, Poloxamine 908 and phospholipids (Nattermann):

Soya-PE-H	- Phosphatidylethanolamine (PE, 92.2%), hydrogenated
Egg-PC-H	- Phosphatidylcholine (PC, 99.9%), hydrogenated (H)
Egg-PG	- Phosphatidylglycerol (PG, 96-98%)
DPPC	- Dipalmitoylphosphatidylcholine (97.7%)
NC95	- soya PC (90-96%),
Infusol	- soya lecithin, PC (60-80%), PE (8-15%)

3.4.3.2. Partitioning of polymeric carriers

To investigate the partitioning of uncoated polymeric carriers and to study the influence of different surface groups, the range of polystyrene standard particles was used. The surface hydrophobicity of these particles was characterized by Rose Bengal adsorption studies (c.f. chapter 3.4.1.). The binding constant K, obtained from the Rose Bengal studies, was used to place them in order of increasing hydrophobicity (Table 3.4.3./1). In the partitioning experiments employing a dextran 20/PEG 2,000 system, no distinct, reproducible differences between the particles in their distribution between the two phases could be found (Table 3.4.3./1). Even the relatively hydrophilic hydroxylated polystyrene particles partitioned into the top PEG-rich phase. It may be that they are still too hydrophobic to

Table 3.4.3./1: The standard polystyrene latices listed in order of increasing surface hydrophobicity (increasing Rose Bengal binding constant K) and their partitioning in a dextran 20/PEG 2,000 two-phase system.

polystyrene particles	binding constant K (ml/µg)	percentage in		
		top phase	interface	bottom phase
PS-OH	0.041	86.1	13.9	0
PSF	0.120	92.1	7.9	0
PS-AR-NH$_2$	0.135	97.3	2.7	0
PS-1.00	0.279	96.8	3.2	0
PS-0.14	0.289	87.5	12.5	0
PS-0.06	0.400	95.0	5.0	0

have partitioning properties significantly different from the other latices. Furthermore, aggregation of the particles in the PEG-rich phase was observed.

This could well influence the partitioning process and will interfere with the absorption assay to some extent. The interactions of the particles with the polymers making up the two-phase system and the time-dependent tendency to form aggregates were investigated using Photon Correlation Spectroscopy (PCS). Particles dispersed in the PEG-rich top phase showed a slight increase in size with time (Table 3.4.3./2):

Table 3.4.3./2: Size of coated and uncoated latices in top (PEG-rich) phase - time depending.

time (h)	uncoated latex 145nm (PS-0.14)		Poloxamine coated latex	
	size	polydispersity	size	polydispersity
0.25	161	0.10	180	0.07
0.5	174	0.13	-	-
1.0	175	0.15	181	0.08
2.0	182	0.14	184	0.07
5.0	188	0.24	183	0.07
9.0	205	0.24	186	0.05

There was a slight but steady increase in particle size for the uncoated latex over a period of 9 hours. Simultaneously the polydispersity index increased to 0.24 indicating the formation of particle aggregates. As there was only limited coagulation during the first few hours, the interference with the absorption assay was considered to be small. Coating with the steric stabilizer Poloxamine 908 protected the particles against coagulation and constant sizes and a low polydispersity were obtained over the whole observation period.

To investigate which polymer of the two-phase system (dextran or PEG) is responsible for the observed aggregation, latex particles (PS-0.06) were incubated with PEG and dextran solutions of different concentrations. The mean particle size was measured by PCS in order to determine coating layer thicknesses and/or particle aggregation. A coating layer of PEG 2,000 on 60 nm latex is too thin to be detected by PCS, so to make the adsorbed layer more easily detectable, a high molecular weight PEG (mw 35,000) was used. An adsorption of PEG could be detected above polymer concentrations of

Table 3.4.3./3: Adsorption layer thicknesses of PEG 35,000 onto 60 nm latex particles (PS-0.06) determined by PCS.

PEG 35,000 conc. (%)	adsorption layer thickness (Å)	polydispersity index
0.00001	5	0.08
0.0001	4	0.07
0.001	44	0.08
0.05	52	0.08
0.1	41	0.09
1.0	62	0.12

Table 3.4.3./4: Size increase and aggregation of 60 nm polystyrene latex (PS-0.06) in 0.005% solutions of different molecular weight dextrans.

dextran mol. weight	size increase (nm)	polydispersity index
20,000	0.2	0.06
500,000	1.5	0.07
700,000	0.9	0.06
2,000,000	34.4	0.12 (0.25 h)
	36.4	0.14 (0.50 h)

0.001% and adsorption layers of 40 to 60 Å were found (Table 3.4.3./3). The polydispersity index (a measure of the polydispersity of the sample) was almost constant (0.08) over the whole concentration range, making it unlikely that PEG caused the previously observed aggregation.

In dextran solutions of 0.005%, no adsorption could be detected for the molecular weights 20,000, 500,000 and 700,000, and a low polydispersity index was found (Table 3.4.3./4). However mixing with dextran mw 2,000,000 led to an increase in size of the latex of 35 nm and in the polydispersity index from 0.07 to 0.14 indicating particle aggregation. Mixing of latex with dextran-rich bottom phase led to immediate formation of aggregates larger than 5 µm. The system has most likely the most favourable energetic

Table 3.4.3./5: Partitioning of PS-0.14 latex coated with Poloxamer polymers and Poloxamine 908 in a dextran 20/PEG 2,000 system.

Polymer coating	percentage of coated particles in		
	top phase	interface	bottom phase
Poloxamer 188	98.3	1.7	0
Poloxamer 338	93.9	6.1	0
Poloxamer 407	93.2	6.8	0
Poloxamine 908	96.5	3.5	0

state when the hydrophobic latex particles aggregate reducing the interfacial area which is in contact with the hydrophilic dextran.

Coating of PS-0.14 latex with hydrophilic block co-polymers from the Poloxamer and Poloxamine series did not alter its partitioning (Table 3.4.3./5). This is thought to be due to a specific interaction between the ethylene oxide units of the PEG in the PEG-rich top phase and the ethylene oxide chains comprising the Poloxamer and Poloxamine structure. For particles coated with such polymers, a PEG-free two phase system is required. The PEG/dextran system is suitable only for obtaining qualitative information on coating polymer adsorption which is indicated by a reduction in particle aggregation within the system. In contrast to naked particles, the coated latex did not form aggregates in the two-phase system probably due to the steric stabilization effect provided by the polymers (Napper, 1983).

Particles more hydrophilic than the hydroxylated latex, or those coated with hydrophilic polymers cannot be characterized by the Rose Bengal method due to a lack of adsorption of the hydrophobic dye. For these particles the aqueous two-phase partitioning method was found to be more suitable. Coating of the model latex with phospholipids altered their partitioning behaviour (Table 3.4.3./6). For most phospholipids, the percentage of coated particles partitioning into the top phase could be reduced from 80-100% to 40%. With two coating materials (Infusol, NC 95), no particles partitioned into the top phase.

As a comparison, aqueous dispersions of the phospholipids were partitioned. In contrast to uncoated latex which accumulate in the top phase, the phospholipid dispersion partitioned only between bottom phase and interface. Theoretically, if particles are completely coated with a phospholipid, they should partition in a similar way to the aqueous dispersion of the phospholipid. However, in contrast to the behaviour of the phospholipid dispersions, some phospholipid coated particles partitioned to a large

Table 3.4.3./6: Partitioning of pure aqueous phospholipid dispersions and phospholipid coated model carriers (polystyrene latex PS-0.14).

phospholipid	aqueous phospholipid dispersion (%)			phospholipid coated carrier (%)		
	top	inter	bottom	top	inter	bottom
Soya-PE-H	0	71.5	28.5	80.7	12.5	6.8
Egg-PC-H	0	67.9	32.1	86.1	4.0	9.9
Egg-PG	0	68.9	31.1	39.8	52.3	7.9
DPPC	0	71.2	28.8	45.7	29.4	24.9
NC 95	0	87.4	12.6	0	55.4	44.6
Infusol	0	83.7	16.3	0	75.6	24.4

proportion into the top phase (particles coated with Soya-PE-H, Egg-PC-H, Egg-PG and DPPC). This indicates that the particles partitioning into the top phase did not have an intact phospholipid coat. The affinity of the phospholipid to the particle surface seems to be too low to form a coating layer with complete coverage of the particle surface. However, two coatings (Infusol 95, NC 95) performed well as indicated by a similar partitioning of coated particles and the pure phospholipid dispersion. Thus the aqueous two-phase partitioning could be a suitable test for the quality (extent of surface coverage) of coating films on polymeric carriers. It should be noted that in contrast to the two-phase system employed here and the solid phospholipid dispersions, phospholipid vesicles behave differently in other systems (e.g. dextran 500/PEG 6,000).

3.4.3.3. Partitioning of emulsion carriers

As possible carriers for drugs, parenteral fat emulsions have also been investigated. The emulsion droplets have a hydrophilic surface provided by the phospholipid emulsifying agent (lecithin). These systems are of particular interest because of their low clearance by the reticuloendo-thelial system following intravenous injection. The partitioning of emulsions did not lead to any coalescence of droplets and a good reproducibility of the partitioning could be obtained (Table 3.4.3./7). The partitioning process was time dependent. With increasing standing time of

Table 3.4.3./7: Partitioning of parenteral fat emulsions in an aqueous two phase system dextran 20/PEG 2,000 (2 hours, 3 experiments).

fat emulsion	top phase (%)	interface (%)	bottom phase (%)
Intralipid 20%	0	67.9	32.1
	0	64.5	35.5
	0	63.5	36.5
Venolipid 20%	0	64.8	35.2
	0	66.6	33.4
	0	63.7	36.3

Table 3.4.3./8: Dependence of the partitioning of Intralipid 20% on the standing time of the two-phase system (mean of 3 experiments).

standing time (hours)	percentage in		
	top phase	interface	bottom phase
1	0	36.5	63.5
2	0	64.5	35.5
3	0	78.7	21.3

Table 3.4.3./9: Partitioning of parenteral fat emulsions from various suppliers in an aqueous two-phase system dextran/PEG 2,000 (2 hours standing time, n=3).

fat emulsion	supplier	top phase (%)	interface (%)	bottom phase(%)
Lipofundin S 10%	B. Braun	0	49.0	51.0
Lipofundin S 20%		0	50.0	50.0
Lipofundin MCT10%		0	41.0	58.9
Endolipide 10%		0	50.4	49.6
Intralipid 20%	KabiVitrum	0	65.5	34.7
Venolipid 20%	Morishita	0	65.1	34.9

the two-phase system the emulsion droplets accumulated in the interface
(Table 3.4.3./8).

Differences in the partitioning of fat emulsions obtained from various
suppliers were found (Table 3.4.3./9). These differences are attributed to
variations in the nature of the natural lecithins used as stabilizing
agents. Lipofundin S contains soya lecithin, whereas other emulsions
contain egg lecithin. The two Lipofundin S emulsions are only different in
the concentration of the oil content, but not in their ingredients.
Therefore similar surface properties of the oil droplets were expected and
were confirmed by a similar partitioning. The incorporation of drugs into
fat emulsions can change the surface hydrophilicity of the oil droplets and
subsequently might greatly alter the in vivo organ distribution. Quantification of these effects should be possible by two-phase partitioning.

3.4.3.4. Summary

Because of small or no differences in partitioning, aqueous two-phase
partitioning is not suitable for the characterization of hydrophobic
polymeric drug carriers. In addition, interaction of the carriers with the
polymers of the two-phase system (dextran) leads to the formation of
aggregates.

Coating of the particles with sterically stabilizing polymers (Poloxamer,
Poloxamine) avoids this aggregation. Poloxamer coated particles could
therefore be used as a standard particle for two-phase partitioning.

The method allows the characterization of more hydrophilic carriers such as
phospholipid coated polymeric particles and emulsions. The change in
partitioning after modification of the carrier (coating, drug
incorporation, sterilization etc.) is an indication of the extent of the
change in surface properties (e.g. extent of polymer coating, amount of
drug in emulsion interface).

However, correlation between measured changes in the partitioning and the
in vivo organ distribution of the carriers needs further investigation.

To characterize Poloxamer and Poloxamine coated carriers, a PEG-free system
is required in order to avoid the interaction between the PEG in the top
phase and the ethylene oxide chains in these block co-polymers.

Further possible applications of the method to drug carriers include the
assessment of detergent residues (from the particle production process) on
the surface of polymeric drug carriers and the effect of sterilization
(gamma-irradiation) on the surface hydrophobicity of the polymer particles.

3.5. Chemical analysis of the carrier surface

3.5.1. Static Secondary Ion Mass Spectrometry (SSIMS)

The characterization methods mentioned above provide information about size, charge, surface properties, coating layers, degree of surface modification and interaction of carriers with serum components. However, the information about the chemical composition of the surface is of importance in the detection of contaminants on standard latex particles or detergent residues from the production process in biodegradable polymeric drug carriers. Knowledge of the chemical composition may explain some phenomena observed during the surface modification of carriers (e.g. coating) or their in vivo distribution.

Recently developed techniques for surface analysis are X-ray photoelectron spectroscopy (XPS or ESCA) (Briggs, 1983) and Static Secondary Ion Mass Spectrometry (SSIMS) (Davies and Brown, 1987; Briggs, 1987). The first XPS spectra of polymer surfaces were published in 1971 (Clark and Kilcast) and the first SSIMS spectra in 1980 (Gardella and Hercules). In XPS the surface of a sample is bombarded with high energy x-rays leading to the expulsion of core electrons from the atoms present. The kinetic energy of the ejected electrons is measured and used to calculate the binding energy of the

SECONDARY ION MASS SPECTROMETRY (SSIMS)

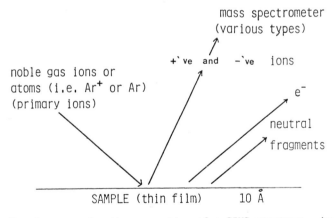

Fig. 3.5./1: Process for the generation of a SIMS spectrum. Argon ions bombard the surface leading to the ejection of negative and positive mass fragment ions which are analysed in a mass spectrometer (negative and positive SIMS spectrum)(figure by courtesy of M.C. Davies).

electron. In XPS a spectrum of binding energies is obtained whereby each binding energy is highly characteristic for the molecular state of each element. From the spectrum the nature of the elements and their relative amounts (semi-quantitative) can be determined. SIMS is more molecularly specific than XPS. The SIMS technique involves the generation of a mass spectrum which can be analysed using conventional mass spectrometry rules. The sample is placed in a vacuum and bombarded with noble gas ions or atoms (Fig. 3.5./1). The bombardment leads to the ejection of elements, fractions of molecules and even intact molecules (charged and non-charged). The ejected secondary ions are analysed in a quadropole mass spectrometer. While SIMS is a surface destructive technique, the ion dose employed in SSIMS is sufficiently low to ensure that the surface remains undamaged during the analysis - i.e. "static SIMS" conditions. The information obtained refers to the chemical composition of a surface layer of 10Å in depth. Dynamic SIMS penetrates deeper into the samples and the spectrum might show changes with increasing depth of the beam (different chemical composition below the surface, damage to the sample). To obtain maximum information, SSIMS can be used in conjunction with XPS analysis (Davies et al., 1988a; Wright, 1988). The maximum molecular weight of ions which can be detected by SSIMS is in the range of 400 to 600 D. A higher mass range can be covered by Time-of-Flight SSIMS (Davies et al., 1988a).

3.5.2. SSIMS analysis of carriers

Surface analysis of the range of polystyrene particles has been performed to investigate the presence of different surface groups and possible contaminants. The PS-0.06 particles comprised a clean polystyrene spectrum. However, the larger PS-1.00 were contaminated by sodium dodecyl sulphate (Davies, 1986). Further cleaning of PS-0.06 latex suspension by dialysis using a low purity dialysis tube resulted in contamination of the particles. Plasticizer (phthalate) was released from the tubing and adsorbed on the latex surface (Roberts, 1988). These examples demonstrate, that SSIMS is a powerful method for the chemical analysis of surfaces.

A range of Polyhydroxybutyrate (PHB) particles has been produced (Koosha and Müller, R.H., 1988a and 1988b) and characterized by SSIMS (Müller et al., 1987a, Müller et al., 1987b). Among the surfactants used in the production process were sodium dodecyl sulphate (SDS) and polyvinyl alcohol (PVA). SSIMS spectra were obtained using a VG SIMSLAB instrument consisting of an ion gun, a secondary ion energy analyser and a quadropole mass spectrometer (VGMM 12-12, 0-1200 Daltons).

The PHB particles produced using sodium dodecyl sulphate (PHB-SDS) were investigated by SSIMS before and after cleaning by dialysis using a high

Before Cleaning

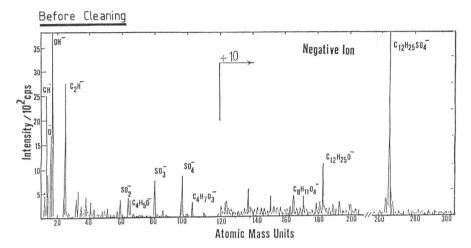

Fig. 3.5./2: Negative SSIMS spectrum of Polyhydroxybutyrate carriers produced with sodium lauryl sulphate (PHB-SDS). The spectrum is dominated by fractions of the SDS molecule indicating the heavy surface contamination with SDS (spectrum above 120 mass units reduced by a factor 10) (Davies, M.C. et al., 1987)

purity tubing (Spectra/Por™). The spectrum obtained before cleaning shows the contamination of the carrier surface by SDS (Fig. 3.5./2). There is a very large peak from the dodecyl sulphate anion (at 265 atomic mass units) and many peaks from fractions of the molecule ($C_{12}H_{25}O^-$, SO_4^-, SO_3^- and SO_2^-) which dominate the negative spectrum. The peaks from the PHB (fractions and intact molecular ion, multiples of molecular ion, e.g. $C_4H_5O^-$, $C_4H_7O_3^-$, $C_8H_{11}O_4^-$) are relatively small compared to the intensities from the SDS fractions. In addition it has to be noted that the intensities of fragments of higher than 120 atomic mass units are reduced by a factor 10 (Fig. 3.5./2).

Cleaning of the particles should remove most of the SDS by desorption with time but some is likely to remain due to physical entrapment into the particle surface (Fig. 3.5./3, Davies et al., 1987). In the SSIMS analysis of the dialysed particles, the peak due to the dodecyl ion $C_{12}H_{25}SO_4^-$ is completely absent (spectrum only given up to 180 mass units) and the dominant ions throughout the spectrum relate to the PHB molecule. Some sulphate species were detected, indicating a residual surface presence of SDS. The SDS surfactant concentration is not sufficiently high to statistically yield enough molecular ions for quantification. The results just give a qualitative indication of the changes in SDS surfactant concentration. As a comparison the spectrum of PHB is given in Fig. 3.5./4.

After Cleaning

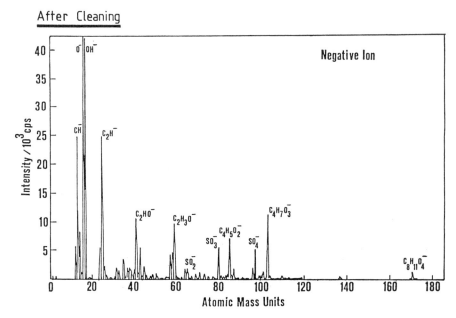

Fig. 3.5./3: Negative SSIMS spectrum of Polyhydroxybutyrate carriers from Fig. 3.5./2 after cleaning by dialysis. The fractions from the PHB polymers dominate the spectrum (Davies, M.C. et al., 1987).

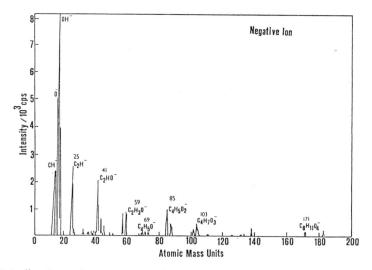

Fig 3.5./4 Control spectrum of pure Polyhydroxybutyrate without any contamination (reference spectrum to Fig. 3.5./2 and 3).

PHB carriers produced using PVA (PHB-PVA) had a substantial amount of the non-ionic PVA incorporated into their surface. Charge measurements revealed that the particles were uncharged in distilled water and comprised interaction with charged serum components to an extent as low as Poloxamine 908 coated latex model carriers. Determination of the surface hydro-phobicity by Hydrophobic Interaction Chromatography (c.f. chapter 9.4.) revealed an even less hydrophobic surface than the coated 60 nm latex carriers. These results indicating the presence of PVA on the PHB carrier surface were confirmed by SSIMS analysis (Davies et al., 1988c).

3.6. Determination of CFT of coated carriers

3.6.1. Theoretical and Experimental

The steric stabilization effect of coating polymers depends on the amount of polymer adsorbed per unit surface area and the coating layer thickness.These factors are influenced by the molecular weight of the polymer, its affinity to the particle surface, temperature, the electrolyte concentration in the dispersion medium and the solvency of the dispersion medium for the stabilizing moiety. Addition of salts (salting out effect) or increases in temperature reduce the solvency and lead to a thermodynamically unstable dispersion. Stabilizing polymers containing EO chains flocculate at increased temperatures. The hydrogen bonds between the polymeric ether oxygens and the water molecules break down (Tadros and Vincent, 1980). This temperature is the so called Critical Flocculation Temperature (CFT) of the dispersion. The CFT depends on the nature of the polymer and the kind of electrolyte added. For covalently bound EO chains the CFT is correlated to the θ temperature of the stabilizing moiety in the bulk solution. The CFT is below the θ temperature (Napper, 1970 and 1977) but approaches the θ temperature with increasing length of the EO chain (Cowell, et al., 1978). For physically adsorbed polymers the CFT depends on the degree of coverage (Lambe et al., 1978; Dobbie et al., 1973). The CFT of Poloxamer coated polystyrene latex is below the θ temperature of the EO chain at <u>low</u> coverage (EO chains are adsorbed in a <u>loop/train</u> conformation)(Tadros and Vincent, 1980). In contrast, the CFT of latex stabilized by adsorbed polystyrene/PEO polymer exceeds the θ temperature of PEO at low coverage (Dobbie et al., 1973). In both cases, at <u>high</u> surface coverage the CFT approaches the θ temperature (EO chains are more extended and possess more <u>tail</u> conformation). The adsorbed co-polymer adopts the conformation whereby most of the EO chains are exposed to the aqueous phase. Therefore with increasing coverage the CFT approaches the θ temperature (cloud point) for free EO in solution (appr. 68°C in 0.2 M sodium sulphate solution). Comparing the measured CFT with the θ temperature of free EO chains in solution should provide some information about the coverage and conformation (loops, trains) of the adsorbed polymers.
Latex particles were coated by mixing equal volume of coating polymer solution (2% w/v) and latex dispersion (2.5%) and incubating overnight. For the CFT determination the coated particles (0.15 ml) were mixed with 1.0 M sodium sulphate solution (0.6 ml) and distilled water (2.25 ml) giving a final concentration of 0.2 M sodium sulphate. The salt addition should reduce the solvency of the dispersion medium to allow a CFT determination in water. The cloud points of the investigated block co-polymers are above 100°C and no flocculation of the coated latex dispersions could be observed

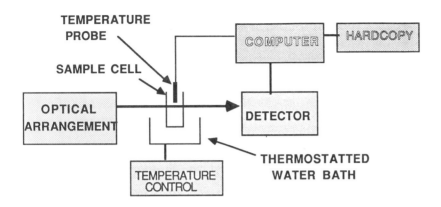

Fig. 3.6./1: Set up of the CFT apparatus by C. Washington (Pharmacy Department, Nottingham University)

without electrolyte addition. A control was prepared by using the same procedure but replacing the sodium sulphate solution with distilled water. Some of the CFT determinations were performed using an SP 1800 Pye-Unicam spectrophotometer connected to a temperature programming unit (Pye-Unicam SP 867). The temperature was raised by $1°C$/min and the turbidity measured at 450 nm. The other CFT apparatus used was developed in the Pharmacy Department at Nottingham University (Dr. C. Washington)(Fig. 3.6./1). The samples were placed in a temperature controlled cell and the temperature raised at a rate of $2°C$/min. The absorption of the sample was measured at 3 different wavelengths simultaneously and given as the total absorption at these three wavelengths. Measured absorption and temperature were relayed to a BBC microcomputer and analysed to determine the onset of the flocculation.

3.6.2. Results of CFT determinations

Most of the CFT values obtained for a range of Poloxamer polymers and Poloxamine were at about $70°C$ (Pye-Unicam 1800, Illum et al., 1987). The CFT is approaching the θ temperature of free EO chains in solution. This indicates a high surface coverage by the polymers and the exposure of mainly EO chains on the surface (more tail formation). Only Poloxamer 184 with a thin coating layer of 24 Å possessed a much lower CFT. The molecule is the least water soluble of the Poloxamer range with a high propylene oxide content. The CFT can therefore only be compared with the θ

139

temperature of free polyethylene oxide in water to a limited extent. The CFT of Poloxamer 188 is well below the θ temperature indicating a low surface coverage and the presence of a mainly loop/tail conformation. The loops expose propylene oxide chains to the continuous, aqueous phase resulting in a more hydrophobic coating. This is in good agreement with the surface hydrophobicity determinations.

Plotting the CFT versus the coating layer thickness of the polymers shows that above a thickness of about 50 Å the CFT levels at approximately 70°C (Illum et al. 1987). Therefore the CFT data indicate no differences in the stabilizing effect of longer chained poloxamers. Such differences could be used to assess the importance of steric stabilization in biological behaviour of coated polymeric carriers, such as the reduced uptake by macrophages. Stability determinations of parenteral fat emulsions stabilized by low (Poloxamer 188) and high molecular weight polymers (Poloxamer 338 and 407, Poloxamine 908) indicated no difference in the stabilizing capacity between these polymers. This confirms the results of CFT measurements.

CFT measurements were performed to characterize Antarox CO and Gafac surfactants (using the CFT apparatus at the Pharmacy Department, Nottingham). The CFT of Poloxamers 188 and 407 and Poloxamine 908 were determined for comparison. Only slightly higher values were obtained compared to the previous measurements (appr. 75°C). Antarox CO990 (with 100 EO units) and Gafac RE960 (50 EO units) behaved similar to the ABA block co-polymers (Table 3.6./1). The reason for the slightly higher CFT values might be the use of a different batch of 60nm latex particles. It has been shown that there are batch to batch variations in the surface hydrophobicity of such

Table 3.6./1: CFT of polymer coatings with various length of the EO chains and coating layer thickness (* percentage of EO per molecule).

coating polymer	number of EO units per molecule	coating layer thickness (H_2O) (Å)	CFT (°C)
Antarox CO 630	5	12	34.4
Gafac RE960	50	68	72.8
Antarox CO990	100	73	75.0
Poloxamer 188	75	76	75.6
Poloxamer 407	98	120	75.8
Poloxamine 908	80*	134	74.9

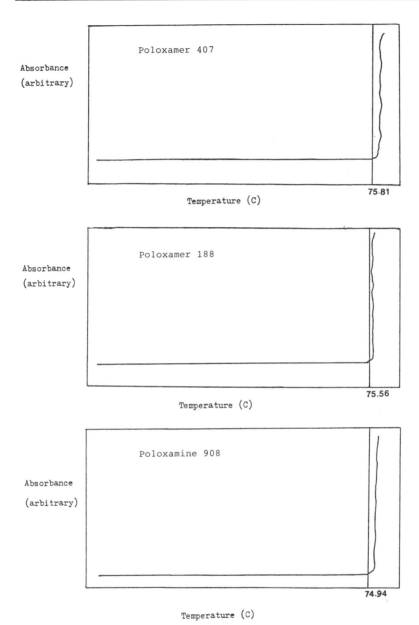

Fig. 3.6./2: Plots of the absorbance versus temperature obtained in CFT
measurements for Poloxamer 407 and 188, and Poloxamine 908. The vertical
lines in the plot give the determined CFT.

141

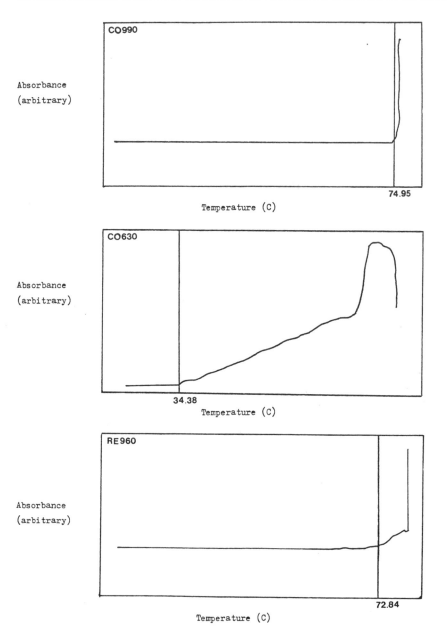

Fig. 3.6./3: Plots of the absorbance versus temperature obtained in CFT measurements for Antarox CO990 and CO630, and Gafac RE960. The vertical lines in the plot give the determined CFT.

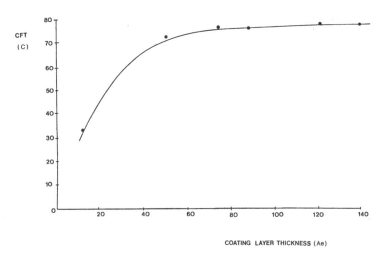

Fig 3.6./4: The influence of the coating layer thickness of Antarox, Gafac, Poloxamer and Poloxamine polymers on the CFT temperature of coated 60 nm polystyrene latex (in 0.2 M Na_2SO_4).

particles. A less hydrophobic second batch would lead to lower surface coverage resulting in an increase of the CFT.

Antarox CO630 with a thin coating layer of appr. 12Å (5 EO units) shows an even lower CFT than Poloxamer 184 (coating layer 24 Å, 13 EO units). It confirmed that only with polymers carrying short EO chains differences in the CFT can be found. The plots of absorbance versus temperature show a steep increase in absorbance for Poloxamer, Poloxamine and Antarox CO990 at the CFT (Fig. 3.6./2 and 3). For Gafac RE960 a slight increase in absorbance at the CFT was monitored before heavy flocculation took place. For the shorter chained Antarox CO630 this effect is much more distinct. The slow increase in absorbance starts at 34.4°C and proceeds steadily up to appr. 70°C when the very steep increase occurs as observed with the other coating polymers. Plotting the CFT versus the coating layer leads to a plateau at 75°C above appr. 50 Å coating layer (Fig. 3.6./4).

3.6.3. Summary

The Critical Flocculation Temperatures (CFT), as measures for the stabilizing capacity, are similar for all polymers which produce a coating layer thickness larger than 50 Å. The CFT values can be used to characterize the coating polymer layer in vitro. Comparison of the CFT with the θ temperature can give information about the surface coverage and the ratio of loops to tails. The tails are strongly solvated creating a hydrophilic surface to the coated particle. This hydrophilicity has been shown to be important for avoidance of RES uptake.

The CFT measurements cannot differenciate between polymers with long EO chains. However, differences in the CFT were found with the same polymer adsorbed onto different batches of latex indicating a different surface coverage. This needs further investigation and CFT measurements might be applicable to the measurement of differences in surface coverage and conformation of polymer layers on larger polystyrene latex. The fact that larger polystyrene latex coated with Poloxamine 908 was cleared by the RES is most likely due to a poor coverage of the surface by Poloxamine 908 (c.f. chapter 8).

The results obtained do not support the theory that steric stabilization is an important factor in the reduced uptake of particles coated with polymers to a layer thickness >100Å. In vitro polymers with shorter coating layers provide the same stabilizing effect as Poloxamine 908 or Poloxamer 338 and 407.

144

```
┌─────────────────────────────────────────────────────────────────────┐
│                                                                       │
│   4. NON-BIODEGRADABLE MODEL CARRIERS                                 │
│                                                                       │
└─────────────────────────────────────────────────────────────────────┘
```

4.0. Problems associated with the use of model carriers

For basic investigations of the targeting of drugs using colloidal
çarriers, it is advantageous to use non-biodegradable model carriers. For
animal studies, model carriers should be non-biodegradable to avoid an
overlapping of organ distribution of the particles and biodegradation
effects after injection. Particles used as model carriers should be well
characterized and their production should not be subjected to variation
between batches.

Polystyrene particles have been chosen as model carriers for a number of
reasons:

1. They are commercially available from a number of sources in a range of
nominal particle sizes, and can be obtained surface modified with different
attached chemical groups or fluorescently labelled (which facilitates easy
analysis by a Fluorescence Activated Cell Sorter - FACS).

2. They can be easily labelled with radioactive iodine by a simple process
of mixing the particles with radioactive NaI and gamma-irradiating them to
a total dose of 10^4 Gy.

3. The particles possess a relatively hydrophobic surface which strongly
adsorbs coating polymers.

4. After in vivo administration, the particles will not degrade and there
is no interference of organ distribution effects with a degradation process
(e.g. release of radioactive marker during biodegradation of particles).

5. The commercial particles with different surface properties could be used
to develop suitable characterization methods for drug carriers (c.f.
chapter 3).

However, one of the results of developing these methods was the realization
that the quality of the commercial products was often not sufficiently high
for the required purposes. Minor points were the wrong nominal particle
sizes quoted for most of the investigated Polysciences latices. More
serious were:

- the broad polydispersity of 'monodisperse' latex (PCS polydispersity
index of 0.20 instead of 0.05) which made them unsuitable for the
determination of a coating layer thickness
- contamination by surfactants in 'surfactant-free' latex   (Roberts et al,
1988)
- batch to batch variations in surface hydrophobicity
- batch to batch differences in the labelling efficiency (and simultaneously surface hydrophobicity) of fluorescently marked latex
- the poor information provided about the manufacturing conditions and the

chemicals involved (e.g. surfactants).

To avoid the problems associated with commercially available latices, polystyrene particles were produced under controlled conditions for use in some experiments (e.g. determination of coating layer thickness).

4.1. Production of polystyrene model particles

4.1.1. Materials

Aquacide 11: Sodium salt of carboxymethylcellulose, mw 500,000
Chloroauric acid (Hydrogen tetrachloroaurate): $HAuCl_4$
Potassium persulphate: $K-O-SO_2-O-O-SO_2-O-K$ (initiator)
Sodium citrate: $Na_3C_6H_5O_7$ dihydrate
Sodium styrene sulphonate: $CH_2=CH-C_6H_5-SO_3Na$ (co-monomer, SO_3Na
Styrene: $CH_2=CH-C_6H_5$ (monomer)

4.1.2. Material purification

Styrene was distilled prior to use at 5mm Hg pressure and at $36°C$ to remove the stabilizer. The stabilizer is a free radical inhibitor (o-hydroxy-p-tert-butylphenol). Reduced pressure was necessary because in the absence of inhibitor, styrene polymerises above $40°C$ in the presence of oxygen. Even at the lower distillation temperature, a nitrogen atmosphere is required to prevent polymerisation. After distillation, the styrene was kept under nitrogen in an aluminium foil covered vessel to protect it from light (styrene is light sensitive) and stored at $4°C$.

The potassium persulphate was recrystallized twice from double distilled water prior to use. A saturated solution was prepared at room temperature and left for nine hours at $4°C$ to recrystallize. The twice recrystallized potassium persulphate is light sensitive and was stored light protected in a dessicator at room temperature.

4.1.3. Particle Production

The polymerisation was performed in a three-necked round bottomed flask placed in a thermostatically-controlled heater/stirrer oil bath (at $80°$ C). 50 ml of water were placed in the flask and degassed by bubbling with nitrogen for 15 minutes, 0.2 to 0.6 ml of styrene was added and dispersed by stirring using a glass coated magnetic follower. After dispersion of the styrene (ca. 5 minutes) 10 ml of a preheated aqueous potassium persulphate solution (80° C) was added (0.2 to 1.0 g potassium persulphate in 10 ml). The reaction was then allowed to proceed for 6 hours (stirred under a slow positive nitrogen flow) (after Goodwin, 1973; Goodwin et al., 1974; Chainey et al., 1982).

4.2. Influence of production parameters on latex size

A range of factors influence the resulting particle size, e.g. monomer content, initiator concentration, pH, ionic strength and stirring rate. Due to the large number of factors influencing the production process it is difficult to keep the production conditions constant and therefore particle size reproducibility is affected. Varying the initiator concentration from 0.02 to 0.12 g/ml led to particles in the range of 110 nm to about 200 nm. The polymerisations were performed in duplicate. The particle size could be reproduced very closely in some cases (about 5 nm difference between two batches) but in others a difference in the mean diameters up to 40 nm was obtained. This might be due to a small change in the production parameters (e.g. the pH and ionic concentration of distilled water). The size of the particles was measured by PCS. The presence of a few aggregates in a sample will have more of an effect on the PCS diameter than it will on the number diameter. The PCS diameter is based on the intensity of the scattered light and therefore emphasizes the larger particles in a population. From the

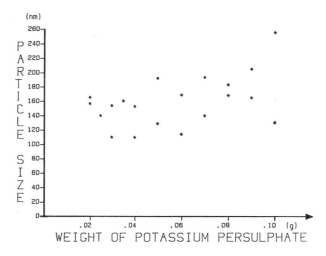

Fig. 4./1: Particle size (PCS data) obtained by producing polystyrene latex with varying amounts of initiator (reaction mixture: 50 ml dist. water + 0.2 ml styrene + 0.02-0.12 g potassium persulphate in 10 ml water).

data obtained, there was no linear relationship found between mean particle size and initiator concentration (Fig. 4./1). The smallest size obtained with this method was close to 100 nm using an initiator concentration of about 0.03 to 0.04 g/ml. This seemed to be an optimum concentration to obtain the smallest latex and is in accordance with the literature. Above 0.1 g/ml the particle size did not further increase but reached a plateau at about 270 nm.

Increasing the monomer concentration but keeping a constant ratio of initiator to monomer led to an increase in particle size. The particles proved to be stable at least over 3 weeks (monitored period) without the need for additional stabilization (Table 4./1). In the absence of bacterial contamination, the latex dispersions are stable for more than 1 year indicated by constant PCS size and polydispersity index (Roberts, 1988).

The use of a lower monomer concentration (0.20 ml) led to only slightly smaller latex but increased the polydispersity to 0.30 which is a relatively broad distribution. The best preparations, with a small mean particle diameter and a low sample polydispersity were obtained with the addition of 0.30 ml monomer. The latex proved to be stable over the monitored period of 3 weeks. The latex dispersions produced had a particle

Table 4./1: Particle sizes obtained with different monomer concentrations but constant ratio of initiator to monomer (amounts of initiator and monomer are given as total per 60 ml reaction medium). Change in particle size during storage of latex (6 hours = size measurement after termination of polymerisation).

amount of		time	PCS results	
initiator (g)	monomer (ml)	(h)	diameter (nm)	polydispersity index
0.02	0.20	6	124	0.30
		24	121	0.29
		500	121	0.32
0.03	0.30	6	114	0.04
		24	113	0.05
		500	111	0.02
0.04	0.40	6	159	0.02
		24	163	0.02
		500	160	0.06

Table 4./2: Size, standard deviation of size (SD) and polydispersity index (polydisp. index) of latex after concentration process using different methods.

method for particle concentration	Photon Correlation Spectroscopy data			
	size (nm)	SD (%)	polydisp. index	water removed
no concentration = original sample	115	0.7	0.01	none
rotary evaporator	118	1.2	0.02	95%
thermostated vacuum oven	125	4.7	0.08	40%
Aquacide™ 11	129	8.5	0.14	60%
evaporation in freeze dryer	138	9.4	0.18	60%

concentration of about 0.3-0.5% w/v (dependent on polymerisation conditions) which was below that of commercially available latices (usually 2.5 - 10.0 % w/v). For some applications, a higher latex concentration is required (e.g. i.v. injection into rabbits). To increase the polymer content the water content was reduced using the following methods:

1. Thermostated vacuum oven: $40°C$, 600 mm Hg
2. Rotary evaporator: $33°C$, vacuum adjusted to stay below the BP of water
3. Dialysis using Aquacide™ 11
4. Water evaporation in freeze dryer

Ideally, removal of the water from the sample should not lead to particle coagulation. PCS measurements were performed to monitor changes in sample size and polydispersity during water removal (Table 4./2). Rotary evaporation proved to be the best method to concentrate the latex dispersion without causing particle aggregation. However, it is time consuming because the vacuum has to be adjusted to ensure that boiling of the water does not occur.

The polymerisations were performed in only 60 ml of reaction medium, therefore producing 60 ml of latex dispersion. To increase the amount of particles produced, production on a ten times larger scale was performed (500 ml of water, 2.5ml/3.0 ml styrene, 0.3 g potassium persulphate in 100 ml of water, total reaction volume: 600 ml). The stirring speed was increased to create a strong vortex in order to adequately disperse the added styrene. Despite of the increased stirring speed, about 10-15% of the styrene was left partially polymerised around the stirrer. As expected, the particles obtained were larger than in the small scale production, but of a

149

Table 4./3: Size, standard deviation of size (SD) and polydispersity index
of particles from large scale production (PCS data). Amounts of initiator
and monomer are given as total per 600 ml reaction medium. Change in
particle size during storage of latex (6 hours = size measurement after
termination of polymerisation).

amount of styrene (ml) added	time (hours)	Photon Correlation Spectroscopy data		
		size (nm)	SD (%)	polydisp. index
2.5 ml	6	252	1.4	0.05
	24	257	1.7	0.08
	500	258	2.5	0.11
3.0 ml	6	262	3.2	0.06
	24	259	1.3	0.04
	500	261	1.1	0.02

high quality (low polydispersity) and stable over the monitored period of 3
weeks (Table 4./3).
However, different conditions lead to different particle sizes. A size
reduction was observed when preparing 300-400 nm latex on a larger scale
(Roberts, 1988). A similar size reduction was unlikely in the preparations
performed here because the particles prepared on a small scale were already
in the range of the smallest size which can be obtained with this method
(ca. 100 nm).

4.3. Incorporation of colloidal gold in latex model carriers

The density of the polystyrene particles is too low to follow their uptake
into cells by TEM. The incorporation of colloidal gold into the core of the
particles could be used as an electron dense marker. Also, radioactive
colloidal gold could be introduced, to be used as marker for micro-
autoradiography. Iodine-131 can be used to label easily polystyrene
particles but the level of radioactivity is too high to enable exact
location of the particles within a cell compartment. Radioactively labelled
colloidal gold particles can be obtained by producing them in the presence
of radioactive gold salts.
Colloidal gold was prepared by mixing of 1 ml of Chloroauric acid (1%
$HAuCl_4$ in water) and 50 ml of distilled water. After the solution was

heated to boiling, 0.5-5.0 ml of a 1% sodium citrate solution was added and the boiling continued for a further 5 minutes. After 20-30 seconds the solution darkened to a purple colour due to the precipitation of colloidal gold. The amount of sodium citrate solution added has little influence on the resultant mean particle size (Wright, 1988). However, little fluctuations in PCS size measurements and the lowest polydispersity index were obtained for the sample prepared with 1 ml sodium citrate solution (36 nm, polydispersity index 0.35).

The fact that colloidal gold tends to aggregate necessitates the addition of a stabilizer to commercially produced colloidal gold products (e.g. Poloxamer 188). The high aggregation tendency of colloidal gold solutions and the presence of unwanted stabilizers in commercial products were the reasons for the self-production.

To incorporate the colloidal gold, polystyrene was polymerised in the presence of colloidal gold particles, which act as reaction core around which the styrene polymerises (similar to the 'shot-growth' technique) (Chainey et al, 1982). The ratio of the number of colloidal gold particles to styrene monomer (calculated as theoretical number of polymerised polystyrene particles) was varied. With increasing ratio of colloidal gold to monomer, the size of the produced particles decreased (Table 4./4).

The amount of styrene added to the reaction medium was kept constant throughout. Only the number of colloidal particles was increased in

Table 4./4: Latex particle size in dependence on the ratio number of gold particles : number of polymerised polystyrene particles.

ratio gold/ polystyrene particles	time (hours)	Photon Correlation Spectroscopy data		
		size (nm)	SD (%)	polydisp. index
2:1	6	183	2.5	0.04
	24	180	0.8	0.03
	500	185	1.5	0.03
5:1	6	165	0.8	0.03
	24	160	0.4	0.02
	500	164	2.6	0.05
10:1	6	132	0.7	0.02
	24	135	0.9	0.02
	500	131	1.6	0.04

relation to the theoretical number of polystyrene particles which would have been obtained without colloidal gold addition. The size decrease with an increasing number of reaction cores suggested the incorporation of the gold into the polystyrene particles. This could be confirmed by TEM. The polydispersity index of the polystyrene-gold particles was extremely low, another effect of the incorporation. A similar incorporation was performed during the production of cyanoacrylate particles (Wright, 1988).

4.4. Production of latex particles of a mean size below 100nm

The above surfactant-free styrene polymerisation technique could not produce latex particles smaller than 100 nm. To target to the bone marrow,

Table 4./5: Particle sizes, standard deviation of the size (SD) and polydispersity index of latex produced using styrene and varying amounts of the co-monomer styrene sulphonate (high styrene concentration, 0.6ml per 60ml reaction medium).

sodium styrene sulphonate (g/60ml medium)	time (h)	Photon Correlation Spectroscopy data		
		size (nm)	SD (%)	polydisp. index
0.010	6	96	1.4	0.08
	24	100	4.1	0.12
	500	91	1.2	0.10
0.012		104	3.6	0.16
		108	2.9	0.12
		98	2.1	0.07
0.014	6	92	3.1	0.07
	24	93	4.5	0.08
	500	90	1.0	0.05
0.016	6	97	2.3	0.03
	24	89	1.3	0.05
	500	89	1.5	0.06
0.018	6	105	1.1	0.05
	24	107	2.2	0.08
	500	103	1.5	0.06

particles need to be in a size range of 60 to 70 nm. After coating with Poloxamine 407 the size will be increased to around 80 to 90 nm but the coated model carriers will still be capable of passing through the fenestrations in the sinusoids of the bone marrow. Therefore investigations into the production of latex particles below 100 nm using a co-monomer, sodium styrene sulphonate, were carried out.

The polymerisation was performed as described above but using a different reaction medium composition (50 ml distilled water + 0.6 ml/0.3 ml styrene + 0.01 to 0.018 g sodium styrene sulphonate and 0.03 g potassium persulphate in 10 ml distilled water). The sodium styrene sulphonate was dissolved together with the potassium persulphate in the 10 ml of distilled water. The charge on the co-monomer increases the resultant particle charge, leading to increased charge stabilization of the formed particles and to a smaller size.

By increasing the co-monomer concentration, a decrease in size could be achieved but not as much as was expected (Table 4./.5). The styrene monomer

Table 4./6: Particle sizes, standard deviation of the size (SD) and polydispersity index of latex produced using styrene and varying amounts of the co-monomer styrene sulphonate (low styrene concentration, 0.3ml per 60ml reaction medium).

sodium styrene sulphonate (g/60ml medium)	time (h)	Photon Correlation Spectroscopy data		
		size (nm)	SD (%)	polydisp. index
0.010	6	94	1.5	0.04
	24	94	0.8	0.04
	500	96	1.8	0.06
0.012	6	78	1.5	0.07
	24	77	0.7	0.05
	500	77	0.7	0.05
0.014	6	66	1.0	0.05
	24	66	1.3	0.07
	500	67	1.4	0.10
0.018	6	63	0.5	0.04
	24	63	0.9	0.04
	500	66	1.3	0.07

concentration of 0.6 ml was probably too high. Changing the co-monomer concentration had little effect on the resultant particle size, possibly because of the narrow concentration range investigated.

A particularly small size could be produced by reducing the amount of styrene by 50% to 0.3ml per 60 ml reaction medium (Table 4./6). After this reduction in the monomer concentration, an increase in the amount of the co-monomer led to a distinct decrease in size. Particles with lowest size and smallest size distribution (low polydispersity index of about 0.05) were obtained with 0.018 g of sodium styrene sulphonate per 60 ml reaction medium.

4.5. Summary

Surfactant-free polystyrene latex particles in the size range of 100 nm to 270 nm were produced under controlled conditions for use as model carriers. A knowledge of the production conditions and the chemicals involved is essential to explain effects observed with the model carriers during their surface modification or after their in vivo administration (organ distribution). To optimize particle production, the polymerisation parameters were varied (monomer and initiator concentration/ ratio initiator to monomer) and large scale productions were performed.

As higher model latex particle concentrations are required for some applications, e.g. i.v. administration to animals, methods of concentrating the model suspensions were investigated. Rotary evaporation at low vacuum proved to be the most effective means of removing excess water without adversely affecting the latex stability.

Colloidal gold was produced and incorporated into polystyrene particles by polymerising styrene in its presence. The colloidal gold can be used as electron dense marker for TEM investigations. Radioactive colloidal gold can be incorporated as a radioactive label, e.g. for micro-autoradiography. Model particles for bone marrow and hepatocyte targeting have been produced. The particles have to be in the range of 60 to 70 nm to be able to leave the blood circulation via fenestrations in the sinusoids. The production of particles of such a small size could be achieved by the use of the co-monomer sodium styrene sulphonate.

5. BIODEGRADABLE POLYMERIC CARRIERS

5.0. Biodegradable polymers for drug carriers

For practical application polymeric drug carriers need to be composed of degradable or biodegradable materials. Strictly, biodegradation can be defined as a degradation which occurs more rapidly in vivo than in vitro. A polymer which is degraded by a hydrolytic process in vitro and is only degraded by the same process with a similar velocity in vivo, is degradable. However, if the degradation velocity in vivo is increased, the polymer is biodegradable.

Natural materials such as albumin (Gallo et al, 1984; Burger et al., 1985), polysaccharides (Artursson et al, 1986 and 1987) and gelatin (Yoshioka et al, 1981) can be used in the preparation of carriers. Disadvantages are that they are poorly chemically characterized. Adverse immunological reactions have also been described after administration in vivo. Materials such as human serum albumin (HSA) are of limited availability and are expensive.

Therefore, the use of synthetic, chemically well defined, non-immunological polymers, which are available in larger quantities and are relatively cheap is more practical. Polyalkylcyanoacrylate particles have been studied (Couvreur, 1988; Verdun et al., 1986; Kreuter, 1983) but are not in use therapeutically because they release toxic degradation products. However, clinical trials are at present underway on the use of cyanoacrylate particles for the delivery of cytotoxic drugs (Couvreur, 1988a).

Polymers such as poly(lactic acid) (PLA) and its co-polymers with glycolic acid (PLA/GA) and poly(hydroxybutyric acid) (PHB) are toxicologically more acceptable. Other polyesters such as poly(β-malic acid) (Braud and Vert, 1984; Braud et al, 1985), polyorthoesters (Heller and Himmelstein, 1985) and polyanhydrides (Mathiowitz and Langer, 1987) are investigated as materials for polymeric drug carriers.

PLA and PLA/GA have been used in the formulation of a large variety of compounds, such as peptides (Sanders et al, 1985 and 1985a), antimalarial drugs (Wise et al., 1976 and 1978), contraceptives (Beck et al, 1983), narcotic antagonists (Schwope et al, 1975), antibiotics (Ikada et al, 1985), corticoids (Spilizewski et al, 1985), local anaesthetics (Wakiyama et al., 1981) and hormones (Wise et al, 1980). Latices based on these polymers will chiefly be used for the delivery of potent drugs (Gurny et al, 1981). PLA and PLA/GA are in use as surgical sutures and implants because they are biodegradable, biocompatible (Wise et al., 1979) and physically strong. Lactic acid exhibits a stereoirregularity of the C atom in β-position and exists in both D and L forms. It can therefore form

D, DL and L polymers. The D,L polymer form is more suitable for particle production because it is less crystalline than the L form.

$HO-CH_2-COOH$

glycolic acid

$HO-CH-COOH$
   |
   CH_3

lactic acid
$(L(+), D(-))$

$HO-CH-CH_2-COOH$
   |
   CH_3

β-hydroxybutyric acid

$HO-(CH-CO-O-CH-CO-O-)_nH$
   | |
   R   R

poly(lactic/glycolic acid)

$(R = H$ or $CH_3)$

$HO-(CH-CH_2-CO-O-)_nH$
   |
   CH_3

poly(β-hydroxybutyric acid)

Lactic acid is a natural metabolite of carbohydrate metabolism and the end product of the anaerobic metabolism of glucose and glycogen. It is a naturally occurring compound which should therefore cause no toxic side-effects. The polymer therefore seems suitable for use as a matrix in drug delivery systems. PLA and its co-polymer can be prepared by chemical synthesis (Kitchel and Wise, 1985) and therefore have advantages over less well defined natural products. PLA and PLA/GA degrade by bulk hydrolysis, undergoing random, non-enzymatic chain scission of the ester linkages. The degradation leads to the formation of lactic and glycolic acid which are normal metabolic compounds. The homopolymers degrade more slowly than their co-polymers. The complete degradation of PLA takes about one year, whereas the co-polymer containing 50% GA only takes 3 to 6 weeks to degrade. Co-polymers with less or more GA, approach again the degradation velocity of the homopolymer.

PHB is a naturally occurring, optically active (D-) polyester produced by various bacteria such as Bacillus megaterium, Rhodospirillum rubrum, Bacillus cereus and Pseudomonas vibrio. The polymer was first isolated by Lemoigne (1925, 1926 and 1927) and serves as a carbon and energy source in the bacteria. PHB can be extracted from the bacterial cells using solvents such as methylene chloride (Baptist, 1962), chloroform (Lundgern et al, 1965) and propylene carbonate. Alternatively it can be chemically synthesized by the polymerisation of β-butyrolactone (Agostini, 1971) leading to a product which is identical to the natural polymer but without its optical activity. PHB has a melting point in the range 162-180°, is a relatively crystalline polymer (crystallinity 80%) and has a glass transition temperature of about 0° C. The high degree of crystallinity and its tendency to form crystals cause problems in the production of spherical drug carriers. A less crystalline polymer would be more suitable. The degree of crystallinity can be reduced by copolymerisation with β-hydroxyvalerate (HV) leading to a co-polymer PHB/HV (Holmes et al, 1981 and 1984).

In bacterial cells PHB is metabolised to carbon dioxide and energy. The hydrolytic system for PHB degradation consists of an activator (e.g. trypsin), a thermolabile depolymerase and an esterase which converts oligomers to monomers (Merrick and Doudroff, 1964). In Bacillus cereus, a heat stable disruptase system was described in addition to the depolymerase (Barber, 1973). More relevant for the use of PHB as a drug carrier is its degradation in humans, that means the question of its hydrolytic and enzymatic degradation. In vitro investigations by Holland et al. (1987) showed enhanced degradation at pH values above 10 and at 70° C. Little enzymatic degradation was observed on blood-contact; the incorporation of the co-monomer HV accelerated the degradation. Other reports could however not confirm the degradation-accelerating effect of HV in studies with subcutaneous implants, but did confirm in blood-contact studies that degradation is not faster in vivo than in vitro (Williams and Miller, 1987; Miller and Williams, 1987). This means that in the strictest sense the material is not biodegradable. The polymer is degraded in vivo by a hydrolytic process which was shown in vitro to cause random chain scission of the polymer (Majid et al, 1987).

The hydrolytic process is very slow and in vitro no decrease in molecular weight was found after six months (Gilding, 1981). However, in vivo degradation after 8 weeks was reported (Kronenthal, 1974). Evidence for a slow in vivo degradation was reported by Korsatko (1983) who observed a weight loss in subcutaneously implanted tablets. Our own preliminary studies with subcutaneous implanted tablets in rats gave no evidence for any in vivo degradation over a period of 6 months (Müller, R.H., Pouton, C.W., and Koosha, F., unpublished data). In the hydrolytic degradation of the polymer, which is most likely a surface erosion process (Pouton, C.W. et al, 1988), the surface area of the implant will be the dominant factor in determining the rate of degradation. Tablets provide a small surface area leading to the observation of little or no degradation over a period of months. PHB is therefore not a suitable polymer for use in larger sized (bio)degradable implants. PHB microspheres and nanoparticles create a larger surface area which should enhance the rate of hydrolytic degradation. Biodegradation studies with such carriers (C14 labelled) are currently underway (Müller, R.H. and Kreuter, J.). It can be assumed that the degradation of PHB is influenced by a range of factors such as the crystallinity (which is reduced by HV incorporation), surface area, polymer compaction (e.g. in tablets), porosity and of course the biological environment (e.g. the presence of body fluids).

In contrast to the bulk hydrolysis of PLA/GA carriers, PHB cannot absorb water and hydrolysis therefore only takes place on the exposed surface. This surface degradation phenomenon could make PHB suitable for the design of controlled release formulations of peptides and peptide drugs. The release is determined by the rate of surface erosion of the polymer, giving PHB a high potential as carrier material in controlled drug delivery. The combination of a large surface and an increased amorphous fraction of PHB in the carriers should provide a sufficiently high in vivo degradation.

In the last few years there has been growing interest in the use of PHB and the co-polymer PHB/HV in drug carriers. The polymers have been used for the production of implant tablets (Korsatko 1983 and 1983a) and oral dosage forms (Gould et al, 1987) but mainly for the production of microcarriers (Bissery et al, 1984; Juni et al, 1986; Brophy and Deasy, 1986, Koosha et al., 1987 and 1988a). A detailed review of PHB as a polymer for drug carriers is given by Koosha et al. (1989).

5.1. Materials and methods

For particle production, a range of Polyhydroxybutyrate polymers with different molecular weights and obtained from two suppliers were used:

molecular weight of PHB	supplier	solubility in chloroform (%w/v)
3,000	Chemie Linz	-
21,500	ICI (Marlbrough)	10.7
68,000	Chemie Linz	3.06
255,000	Chemie Linz	0.01
500,000	Chemie Linz	0.16
800,000	ICI (Marlbrough)	1.06

A high solubility in chloroform is important for obtaining a good yield in the particle production. The solubility of most of the Chemie Linz polymers was too low for our purposes; it may be due to differences in the extraction process of the PHB. ICI use chloroform in the extraction, and the degradation of high molecular weight PHB (e.g. 800,000) to low molecular weight polymer (e.g. 20,000). It is likely that this explains the good chloroform solubility of their PHB polymers.

PHB with a molecular weight of 3,000 was found not to be suitable for particle production. Instead of spherical particles a flaky product was obtained. Therefore (unless otherwise stated) PHB mw 21,500 ICI was used.

Poly(D,L-lactic acid) (PLA) and its co-polymer with glycolic acid (PLA/GA) were provided by Boehringer Ingelheim (FRG). The inherent viscosities were 1.0 and 0.7 respectively.

Chloroform and methylene chloride were used as organic solvents for the polymers during the production process. Different detergents were used as stated to optimize the production process.

Emulsions for particle production were prepared using a Silverson homogenizer, sonic probes (Dawe, type 7532B with 100 W and type 7532A with 150 W; Labsonic 2000, B. Braun Melsungen) and a Microfluidizer (Microfluidics Corp.).

5.2. Production of carriers

5.2.1. Emulsification evaporation technique

Polymeric particles can be produced by emulsion polymerisation of the corresponding monomer (e.g. styrene) or by emulsification evaporation of a preformed polymer dissolved in an organic solvent (e.g. polyhydroxy-butyrate). The emulsion polymerisation from monomers can produce relatively small particles but it has the disadvantage that possibly toxic monomer and initiator (catalysts) residues are present. In addition, the method is not applicable to polymers such as polyesters and elastomers such as cis-polyisopyrene (Gurny et al, 1985). To produce particles of poly(hydroxybutyric acid) (PHB) and poly(lactic acid) (PLA) a solvent evaporation process was employed as described by Beck, Tice et al. (Beck et al, 1980, 1983, 1983a; Tice and Lewis, 1983; Gilley et al, 1984; Tice and Gilley, 1985).

The solvent-evaporation technique was however modified slightly for our purposes (Koosha and Müller, R.H., 1987). The polymer was dissolved in an organic solvent (chloroform, methylene chloride) and dispersed in an aqueous phase using a Silverson homogenizer (pre-emulsification). The aqueous phase contained a surfactant to stabilize the o/w emulsion. To achieve a smaller droplet size, an additional homogenization step using a sonic probe was introduced (Dawe Soniprobe type 7532B, 100 W, or type 7532A, 150 W). The sonication led to a reduction in particle size, but simultaneously some evaporation of the organic solvent took place, due to the partitioning of the solvent from the microdroplets into the continuous phase and its evaporation from the surface. After sonication, most of the remaining solvent was removed by rotary evaporation under vacuum, leading to the formation of polymer particles. A range of production parameters influence the size and size distribution of the resulting particles (Koosha, 1989; Koosha and Müller,R.H., 1989):

- method of emulsification (stirrer, homogenizer, sonic probe)
- type of surfactant present in the aqueous phase
- concentration of the surfactant
- viscosity of the aqueous phase
- ratio of organic to aqueous phase
- type of organic solvent (chloroform, methylene chloride)
- polymer concentration in the organic phase
- type of polymer (PHB, PLA, PLA/GA)
- molecular weight of polymer
- stirring rate during pre-emulsification
- sonication time with sonic probe
- power output of sonic probe

- velocity of solvent evaporation; mainly determined by:
    - temperature during solvent evaporation
    - pressure during solvent evaporation

The effect of each of the parameters on particle size and size distribution is discussed in detail elsewhere (Koosha, 1989). Many different surfactants have been investigated with regard to their ability to lead to the formation of small particles within a narrow size distribution. In order to be suitable for intravenous injection the particles should be << 5 µm. A series of Tagat (polyoxyethylene-glycerol-monooleates), Tegin (partial esters of glycerol, ethylene glycol or 1,2-propylene glycol with natural fatty acids), Tween (polyoxyethylene sorbitan fatty acid ester), Brij (polyoxyethylene fatty alcohol ether) and Myrj (polyoxyethylene fatty alcohol ester) surfactants have been investigated (Table 5.2./1, 2 and 3) (Koosha, 1989; Koosha and Müller, R.H., 1989). The particle size distributions were determined using a laser diffractometer (Malvern Particle Sizer). PHB polymer with a MW 21.500 was used (ICI material).

Table 5.2./1: PHB particle sizes obtained with Tegin 90, Poloxamer 188, Tagat 0 and 02. The emulsification was performed using a sonic probe, the solvent was evaporated at normal pressure in a beaker (*) and under reduced pressure in a rotary evaporator.

surfactant	particle peak = 80% in size range (µm)	percentage of particles in size range (µm)			
		< 1.5	< 5.0	< 10.5	> 23.7
Tagat 02	2.4 - 8.2	0.9	58.0	93.6	--
Tagat 02*	0.5 - 3.9	28.6	98.1	100.0	--
Tagat 0	2.4 - 8.2	3.8	63.9	96.1	--
Tagat 0 + Tegin 90*	---	0	6.4	17.7	50
Tegin 90	2.4 - 8.2	0	47.3	88.0	--
Poloxamer 188	---	25.8	86.7	99.7	--

Table 5.2./2: PHB particle sizes obtained with Tween surfactants. The emulsification was performed using a sonic probe (Dawe), the solvent was evaporated under reduced pressure in a rotary evaporator.

surfactant	particle peak = N% in size range (µm)	percentage of particles in size range (µm)			
		< 1.5	< 5.0	< 10.5	> 23.7
Tween 20	aggregates				
Tween 21	2.4 - 6.4 (N=77%)	11.6	86.6	100.0	--
Tween 40	aggregates				50
Tween 60	1.5 - 5.0 (N=73%)	18.6	91.9	100.0	--
Tween 61	aggregates 100% > 1.8				49
Tween 65	aggregates 100% > 2.4				
Tween 80	2.4 - 6.4 (N=60%)	2.6	56.7	78.4	3
Tween 81	3.0 - 13.6 (N=67%)	4.4	40.8	76.0	--
Tween 85	1.5 - 3.9 (N=63%)	16.1	87.7	99.8	--

Table 5.2./3: Composition of surfactants used in the particle production process (EO (n) - polyoxyethylene, n - no. of units).

trade name	chemical composition	HLB
Tween 20	EO (20) - sorbitan monolaurate	16.7
21	EO (4) - sorbitan monolaurate	13.3
40	EO (20) - sorbitan monopalmitate	15.6
60	EO (20) - sorbitan monostearate	14.9
61	EO (4) - sorbitan monostearate	10.1
65	EO (20) - sorbitan tristearate	10.5
80	EO (20) - monooleate	15.0
81	EO (5) - monooleate	10.1
85	EO (20) - trioleate	11.7

Production of carriers - Emulsification evaporation technique

The parameters used for assessment of the quality of the resulting particles were
a) the percentage below 5 µm,
b) the width of the size distribution (about 80% of the particles should be in a very narrow size range = peak of particles),
c) the absence of aggregates, i.e. particles larger than 23.7 µm.
Tagat 02 (20 units EO per molecule) and Tagat 0 (30 units EO) showed no large differences in the size distribution of the produced particles. Slower evaporation (normal pressure) was seen to lead to the production of smaller particles as seen with Tagat 02.
Surfactants such as Poloxamer 188 produced particle populations with a large percentage below 5 µm. However the size distribution (from 0.5 to 10.5 µm) was too wide to produce particles with acceptable release properties. There were only a small number of particles below 1 µm in batches produced with Poloxamer 338 and 407 due to the width of the size distribution and the formation of aggregates. Combinations of surfactants were studied (Koosha, 1989; Koosha and Müller, R.H., 1989). Some led to improvements by creating narrower size distributions, whereas others, such as the combination of Tagat 0 and Tegin 90 increased the portion of aggregates. The Tween surfactants lead to very different results. Some were not suitable at all, whereas some produced relatively narrow size distributions (e.g. Tween 85). The esters with oleic acid seemed to be most suitable (Tween 80, 81, 85). Using the Dawe sonic probes, however only a small percentage of particles below 1.5 µm could be produced (Table 5.2./2). The chemical composition of the surfactants is given in Table 5.2./3. No direct relationship between the HLB of the Tween surfactants and their suitability for particle production could be found.
The particles produced with Brij 96 and 98 surfactants were relatively small, Brij 35 led to the production of particles which were larger, but which had a relatively narrow size distribution, Brij 58 was least suitable and created a particle population with a trimodal size distribution (Table 5.2./4). No large differences were obtained with the different surfactants of the Myrj series (Table 5.2./4). The chemical composition of Brij and Myrj surfactants is given in Table 5.2./5.
In summary, Brij 96 and Myrj 51 and 52 surfactants led to the production of the smallest particles, suitable for intravenous injection. Other detergents produced larger particles, but with narrow size distributions. They may have alternative applications e.g. for intraarticular drug delivery (e.g. against arthritis). Some detergents were completely unsuitable, creating wide size distributions and/or large numbers of aggregates.
Particles were prepared using polyvinyl alcohol (PVA) and the anionic sodium lauryl sulphate (SDS) as surfactants. In both, 100% of the particles

Table 5.2./4 PHB particle sizes obtained with Brij and Myrj surfactants. The emulsification was performed using a sonic probe (Dawe), the solvent was evaporated under reduced pressure in a rotary evaporator.

surfactant	particle peak = N% in size range (μm)	percentage of particles in size range (μm)			
		< 1.5	< 5.0	< 10.5	> 23.7
Brij 35	2.4 - 8.2 (N=84%)	0.3	63.6	94.8	1
Brij 58	3 peaks !	-	24.1	61.2	3
Brij 56	2.4 - 8.2 (N=51%)	11.7	63.8	86.3	--
Brij 96	0.5 - 1.2 (N=76%)	86.0	100.0		--
Brij 98	0.5 - 1.9 (N=72%)	55.9	99.9	100.0	--
Myrj 49	0.5 - 1.5 (N=54%)	54.2	96.0	100.0	--
Myrj 51	0.5 - 1,9 (N=71%)	55.9	99.6	100.0	--
Myrj 52	0.5 - 1.9 (N=75%)	61.4	99.8	100.0	--
Myrj 59	2.4 - 6.4 (N=52%)	21.0	74.3	90.4	4

obtained were below 1.2 μm. Addition of co-surfactants did not necessarily decrease the particle size (e.g. addition of cetyl alcohol to SDS) but did influence the width of the distribution. By optimization, some reductions in the polydispersity of the particles could be achieved.

The effects of the concentration of the organic phase, the evaporation temperature and the molecular weight of the polymer on the resulting particle size are given in Fig. 5.2./1, 2 and 3. An increased organic phase concentration might be favourable for production of a better yield, but it leads to an increase in particle size. The smallest particles with the least aggregates were produced by evaporation under reduced pressure at room temperature. The molecular weight of the polymer had only a small effect on the particle size.

Table 5.2./5: Composition of surfactants used in the particle production process (EO (n) - polyoxyethylene, n - no. of units).

trade name	chemical composition	HLB
Brij 35	EO (23) - laurylether	16.9
56	EO (10) - cetylether	12.9
58	EO (20) - cetylether	15.7
96	EO (10) - oleylether	12.4
98	EO (20) - oleylether	15.3
Myrj 49	EO - stearate	15.0
51	EO - stearate	16.0
52	EO (40) - stearate	16.9
59	EO (100) - stearate	18.8

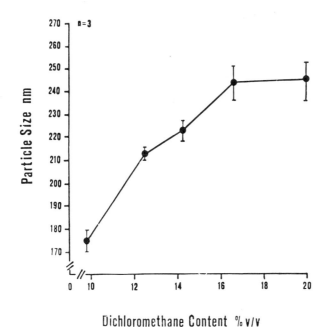

Fig. 5.2./1: Effect of the concentration of the organic phase on the particle size.

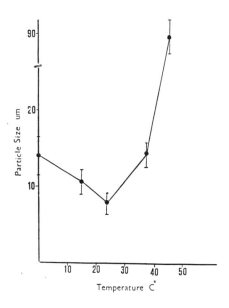

Fig. 5.2./2: Effect of the evaporation temperature on the particle size.

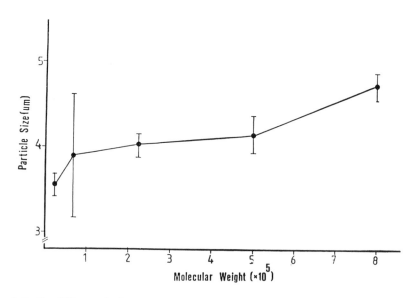

Fig. 5.2./3: Effect of the molecular weight of PHB on the particle size.

166

5.2.2. Particle production by microfluidization

Most of the particles produced using the sonic probe were well above 1 micrometer in size. To reduce the droplet size in the o/w emulsion, a high pressure homogenization was performed. The sonic probe was replaced by a Microfluidizer M110. Microfluidization is a patented method (Cook and Lagace, 1985) whereby the emulsion is formed by the interaction of jet streams of the emulsion-forming liquid mixture. Two fluid streams interact under pressure in microchannels and impinge in a low-pressure turbulent zone of the liquid mixture. The apparatus contains nozzles with elongated orifices to eject the liquid under pressure. The two liquid streams interact along a common liquid jet interaction front. The liquid sheets formed by the streams from the nozzles impinge head-on at an angle of 180° in an interaction chamber. A pressure up to 10,000 psi can be applied leading to a liquid flow velocity of more than 100 m/s. The smallest sample size in the Microfluidizer was 15 ml, the product can be continuously processed or recycled by a closed loop. To produce particles, the emulsions were recycled and passed 5 times through the interaction chamber. The pressure applied was around 7,000 psi.

Microfuidization led to a distinct decrease in the resulting particle size (Koosha et al, 1987, Koosha and Müller, R.H., 1988). Use of the Brij surfactants which were very efficient when used with the sonic probe led to the production of particles in the size range of 100 to 300 nm (PCS diameter), with the total particle population below 1.2 µm (laser diffractometer). The size distribution was relatively narrow as indicated by a polydispersity index of around 0.16 (Table 5.2./6 and 7).

Even lower particle sizes were obtained using other surfactants such as SDS and PVA (Fig. 5.2./4) (Koosha and Müller, R.H., 1988). Smaller particles could be produced using the sonic probe by replacing the Dawe apparatuses by a Labsonic™ 2000 (B. Braun Melsungen, FRG). The latter probe was more efficient and led to a better dispersion of the o/w pre-emulsion.

Table 5.2/6: PHB (mw 21.500) particle sizes obtained after emulsification with a Dawe sonic probe.

emulsifier	peak of distribution in size range	percentage of particles in this size range
Brij 35	2.4 - 8.4 µm	84.2 %
Brij 96	0.5 - 1.2 µm	76.0 %
Brij 98	0.5 - 1.9 µm	71.9 %

Table 5.2/7: PHB (mw 21.500) particle sizes obtained after microfluidization.

emulsifier	mean size (PCS)		polydispersity index
Brij 35	170 nm	+/- 3.3nm	0.146
Brij 96	221 nm	+/- 3.2nm	0.169
Brij 98	210 nm	+/- 2.6nm	0.167

PARTICLE SIZE vs. PVA CONCENTRATION

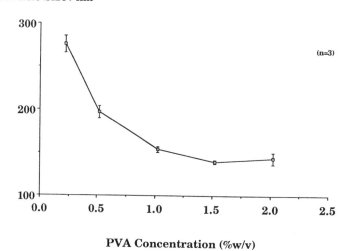

Fig. 5.2/4: Effect of the PVA concentration of the emulsion-forming liquid
mixture on the size of PHB particles produced by microfluidization .

5.2.3. Purification and isolation of particles

Excess surfactants were removed either by dialysis using a high-purity
Spectra/Por tubing or by repeated centrifugation, discarding of the
supernatant and resuspension of the particles in water. Particles produced
with PHB and SDS as surfactant (PHB/SDS) showed some aggregation after

removal of SDS by dialysis. However these aggregates were weak and could be removed by sonication. The particles were freeze dried for storage. Particles produced with PVA and SDS could be redispersed without problems.

5.3. Radiolabelling of particles

5.3.1. Labelling with iodine-131

Non-biodegradable polystyrene particles can be labelled using the method of Huh et al., 1974. The particle suspensions are irradiated (Co-60 source) in the presence of sodium iodide NaI. Radical sites are produced on the particle surface by reaction of OH or other radicals from the water phase. These sites react with iodide leading to a surface bonding:

$$
\begin{array}{ccc}
| & H_2O & | \\
- C-H + I^- & \text{-------->} & -C-I & + & 1/2\ H_2 & + & OH^- \\
| & \text{irradiation} & |
\end{array}
$$

The fraction of iodine bound to the surface depends on the irradiation time, the particle surface (particle diameter) and on the iodine concentration. The relationship is however very complex. Up to a certain level, the fraction bound to the particle surface increases with increasing irradiation time. The maximum is reached when the rates of C-I bond formation and bond breakage are equal (equilibrium). At a given iodine concentration and at a certain particle size only a maximum fraction can be bound irrespective of the irradiation time. For the 60 nm polystyrene latex particles a labelling efficiency of 30 to 40% was achieved (1.25% particle suspension, iodine concentration below 0.001M, 1×10^4 Gy in 24 hours). The fraction of surface-bound iodine decreases with increasing particle size. This explains the poor labelling efficiency obtained with the latex particles larger than 500 nm (c.f. chapter 8.2). For 1 μm latex a 6% labelling efficiency was obtained, this is approximately as reported by Huh (1974) for 481 nm particles.

The exposure to gamma-irradiation leads to a degradation of the polystyrene particles resulting in a decrease in their diameter, but coagulation of the system was not observed. The surface degradation of the particles will with time lead to the removal of surface-bound iodine.

This labelling method is very convenient and therefore labelling of biodegradable PHB and PLA particles was attempted. However larger doses (2.5×10^4 Gy in 3 days) led to coagulation of the particles. Reducing the dose avoided this coagulation but the resulting labelling efficiency was very low (Table 5.3/1). The surface degradation, as observed with the polystyrene particles, might be the cause of the low fraction of bound iodine.

Table 5.3./1: PCS particle size and polydispersity index of <u>unlabelled</u> particles and the efficiency of labelling with iodine.

polymer	particle size	polydispersity index	labelling efficiency
PHB	325 nm	0.176	8.5 %
PLA	340 nm	0.184	5.6 %

5.3.2 Labelling with indium-111

The labelling with I-131 is convenient because of the short half-life of I-131 (8 hours). This reduces problems of disposal and contamination. As it is a surface label, it is released to some extent from the surface, especially after injection of latex (> 300nm). With the larger particles, a substantial amount of the label is quickly released and appears in the bladder during the first 4 hours after injection (up to 10% of the body activity in the bladder region). Such a cleavage from the surface will be even more distinct after the injection of <u>degradable</u> carriers (PHB, PLA). It therefore seemed more appropriate to use a label which is incorporated within the bulk phase of the particle.

Indium-111 was regarded as a suitable label because of its short half-life of 6 hours and the lower energy of its irradiation compared to I-131. It is used for gamma-scintigraphy studies in human and is therefore of interest for future <u>in vivo</u> studies with PHB and PLA particles. The isotope is available as an organic complex with Oxine (8-hydroxy quinoline) which is soluble in organic liquids. Its solubility in chloroform and methylene chloride was used to incorporate the label during the production of the particles. This led to core-labelled carriers (Koosha and Müller, R.H., 1988a). Labelling by this method proved to be very efficient (Table 5.3./2).

The <u>in vitro</u> release of the label was studied in phosphate buffered saline (PBS, pH 7.4), PBS containing 1% w/v bovine serum albumin (BSA), distilled water (W) and distilled water containing 1% w/v serum albumin (W+BSA). The release of radiolabel was determined by gamma-counting at 37° C over a period of 72 hours. The <u>in vitro</u> release profiles show that after 72 hours, only 30 to 40% of the label was released in water and BSA-containing media

Table 5.3./2: PCS particle size and polydispersity index of _labelled_ particles and the efficiency of labelling with In-111-Oxine.

polymer	particle size	polydispersity index	labelling efficiency
PHB	113 nm	0.085	86 %
PLA	250 nm	0.079	83 %

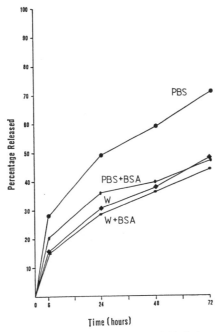

Fig. 5.3./1: Release kinetics of In-111-Oxine complex from labelled particles (Müller, R.H. et al, 1988) in phosphate buffer pH 7.4 (PBS), distilled water (W) and buffer and water with 1% bovine serum albumin (PBS+BSA, W+BSA).

(Fig. 5.3./1) (Müller, R.H. et al, 1988). The fastest release was observed in PBS, but the addition of BSA reduced the release of the radioactive label possibly due to the formation of an adsorption layer of BSA on the particle surface. The slow release indicates that sufficient activity will be retained for the evaluation of the _in vivo_ organ distribution of the particles using gamma-scintigraphy.

171

5.4. Drug incorporation and release profiles

Model drugs were used to study the loading capacity of the particles. Suitable model drugs should be soluble in organic liquids (to be able to be dissolved in the methylene chloride during the production process), easy to analyse (UV spectrometer), and have some water solubility; additionally, radioactively labelled drugs should be available for future gamma-scintigraphy studies. Prednisolone and tetracaine-base fitted these requirements and were incorporated into PHB and PLA particles (Koosha, F. and Müller, R.H., 1988b). Drug loading efficiencies up to around 50 % were achieved (Table 5.4./1). The release profiles were determined using a continuous flow system (Koosha et al, 1988a) based on an Amicon Diaflo ultrafiltration cell fitted with type M2 ultrafilters (mw cut off: 1000). The release medium (phosphate buffer) was pumped from a reservoir under constant pressure through the Amicon cell. The continuous flow created sink conditions.

It was found that the particles with the lowest loading capacity (drug to polymer ratio 1:8) had the fastest drug release rate (Fig. 5.4./1). This was surprising as it was expected that the rate of release of the drug from the polymer matrix would be slower. At low drug content, it was assumed

Table 5.4./1: Drug-loading efficiency of PHB and PLA particles; drug to polymer ratio 1:1 (Koosha et al, 1988a).

type of microsphere	particle size (μm)	percentage of drug content
PHB-Prednisolone	0.45	29.8
	11.14	37.6
	25.20	46.8
PHB-Tetracaine	0.25	14.5
	5.45	19.1
PLA-Prednisolone	4.35	27.4
	26.00	37.2
PLA-Tetracaine	0.36	55.6
	11.72	47.5

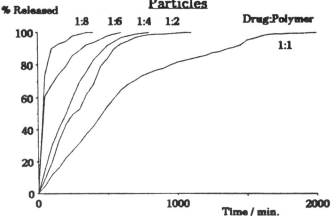

Fig. 5.4./1: Release of prednisolone from PHB particles at different ratios of drug to polymer (Koosha et al, 1988a).

that a homogenous matrix with the drug randomly distributed throughout the polymer particle was formed. However, in the crystallization process (during the solvent evaporation) it is likely that a separation of polymer and drug took place, leading to the accumulation of drug on the particle surface. This would explain the observed fast release rate. The release was slower at higher drug to polymer ratios. This might be due to the formation of a heterogeneous matrix, with the drug being contained within channels in the polymer particles. The drug is released by diffusion through the channels into the surrounding medium. It appeared that only a small amount of drug is located on the particle surface.

In in vitro studies using a continuous flow system, all of the incorporated drug was released within 2 to 3 days. This relatively fast rate is most likely due to the small size of the carriers, the solubility properties of the model drugs, and the short distance for diffusion out of the channels of the polymer matrix. Controlled release over a longer period of time could be achieved by using drugs with lower solubilities and/or larger carriers. A more detailed discussion can be found elsewhere (Koosha, 1989; Koosha and Müller, 1989a).

6. BIODEGRADABLE FAT EMULSION CARRIERS

6.0. Parenteral fat emulsions as drug carriers

Fat emulsions based on soya oil, egg lecithin and water are used for
parenteral nutrition, to provide a sufficient caloric supply for the
patient (Davis, 1976). The mean droplet size employed for such purposes
ranges from 200 to about 400nm. Fat emulsions can also be employed as
carrier vehicles for drugs as sustained release devices, in RES function
tests and radiopaque agents (Davis, 1974 and 1976). Emulsions used for
parenteral drug delivery can be administered intravenously, intramuscularly
or subcutaneously. By choosing different oils and emulsifying agents, the
appropriate system for delivery can be designed (Davis, 1982). Fat
emulsions can be used for drug delivery in a similar way as liposomes.
Liposomes are difficult to prepare reproducibly on a large scale and are
prone to physical stability problems. Fat emulsions can easily be prepared
reproducibly on a large scale and are physically stable for over two years
(Müller, R.H. et al., 1988a).

The main concern with regard to the physical stability of emulsions is the
formation of droplets larger than 5 µm, which can lead to capillary
blockage. Characterization of the emulsion systems can be performed by size
and charge determinations of the droplets using microscopic and laser light
scattering techniques (Müller, R.H. et al., 1987c and 1988c). The stability
of emulsions can also be followed by pH (Ozil and Rochat, 1988), viscosity
and conductivity measurements and the use of stress tests , e.g. increased
temperature or centrifugation of the emulsions (Ondracek et al, 1985).
However, the application of a stress changes the emulsion properties, e.g.
reduction of temperature can increase the rigidity of the emulsifier film,
and questions arise as to how relevant the results of stress test are for
the prediction of the long-term stability of fat emulsions (Müller, R.H.
and Lucks, 1988).

The incorporation of drugs into fat emulsions can also lead to changes in
their stability. Amphiphilic drugs can interact with the emulsifier film
and reduce its stability, added electrolytes lower the zeta potential of
the droplets and reduce the stabilizing effect of the electrostatic
repulsion between them (Lucks et al., 1988). Similar effects are seen in
total parenteral nutrition (TPN emulsion systems). These systems contain
additional amino acids, vitamins and electrolytes which cause changes in
the stability of the TPN emulsion mixtures (Burnham et al., 1983; Thomas,
1987; Müller, R.H. et al., 1988d).

Fat emulsions have been used as carriers for cytotoxics (Parborji et al.,
1988), to increase the vasodilatory effect of prostaglandin E_1 (Mizushima

et al., 1983) and to reduce the toxic side effects of drugs, e.g. amphotericin (Washington et al., 1988). They have also been employed as controlled release formulations, e.g. for physostigmine (Benita et al., 1986) and for passive targeting (Scieszka et al., 1988; Haynes and Cho, 1988). In passive targeting, uptake of the emulsion droplets by the liver can be increased by preparation of gelatinized fat emulsions which are stronger opsonized and therefore taken up by the RES to a larger extent (Tonaki et al., 1976).

For the preparation of fat emulsions, ultrasonication with a sonic probe or high pressure emulsification can be employed, e.g. using a Microfluidizer (Washington and Davis, 1988).

6.1. Materials and methods

Fat emulsions were produced with soya oil (10% w/w), egg lecithin (Lipoid E80), Antarox CO990, Poloxamine 908 and three Poloxamer surfactants as emulsifiers (0.5 to 7.0 %) and double distilled water. The emulsions were made isotonic by the addition of glycerol (2.5%). Addition of NaCl would cause emulsion instability.

The surfactant was either dissolved in the water phase (Poloxamine 908, Poloxamers) or dispersed (Lipoid E80) using a Silverson homogenizer. After addition of the soya oil, a pre-emulsification with the Silverson homogenizer was performed followed by a high-pressure emulsification of 5 passes through the Microfluidizer. The content of large particles in emulsions prepared by microfluidization and without further treatment was measured without filtering the emulsions.

The emulsions were characterized by PCS measurements (mean droplet diameter) and Laser Diffractometry (Malvern Particle Sizer 2600). Measurements were taken directly after production and after standing for 1 day. To assess the stability of the emulsions, stress tests were performed (freeze thaw cycling and addition of calcium chloride).

6.2. Production of emulsion carriers

Fat emulsions were prepared in the presence of surfactant concentrations ranging from 0.5% to 7.0% to study the influence of the nature and concentration of surfactant on the size and stability of the resulting emulsions. The emulsions containing Poloxamine 908 and Poloxamer 188, 338 and 407 as surfactants showed little difference in the mean emulsion droplet size. The droplet size decreased in an almost exponential manner from about 270 nm to around 150 nm with increasing surfactant concentration

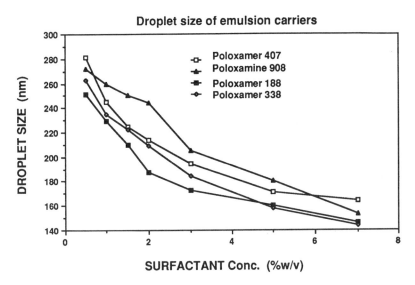

Fig. 6.2./1: Droplet size (PCS diameter) of emulsion carriers prepared with varying concentrations of Poloxamine and Poloxamers as surfactants.

(Fig. 6.2./1). A size of around 150 nm seems to be the lower limit for preparation of the emulsion carriers. The interfacial energy of the system increases with decreasing droplet size limiting the smallest droplet size which can be obtained in macroemulsions. Only microemulsions possess particle sizes between a few nanometers and 200 nm.

However, it is questionable whether microemulsions are in fact emulsion systems with three phases (oil, surfactant layer, water) or if they are swollen micelles or solutions (Müller, R.H., 1983; Franzky, 1986). The lowest measured size of 150 nm is below that typically quoted as the lowest size for macroemulsions, i.e. 200 nm. This observed smaller size might be due to a contribution of light scattered from surfactant micelles in the dispersion medium. The PCS diameter is a mean value calculated on the light scattering from all the material in the sample.

The mean particle sizes of the emulsion carriers prepared with Poloxamer 188, 338 and 407 showed no change after 1 day's storage (Fig. 6.2./2 and 3). A slight increase was found for the emulsion prepared with Poloxamine 908 containing between 1 and 2% surfactant (Fig. 6.2./4). This indication of a slightly lower stability of the Poloxamine 908 emulsion was confirmed by stability tests. The Antarox CO 990 emulsions showed a stronger increase in droplet size on storage than the Poloxamine 908 stabilized systems (Fig. 6.2./5). The increase in droplet size is not due to a shift in the size distribution but rather the formation of larger particles by droplet

177

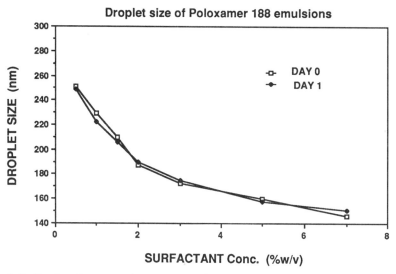

Fig. 6.2./2: Droplet size (PCS diameter) of emulsion carriers prepared with
Poloxamer 188 immediately after preparation (= day 0) and after 1 day's
storage.

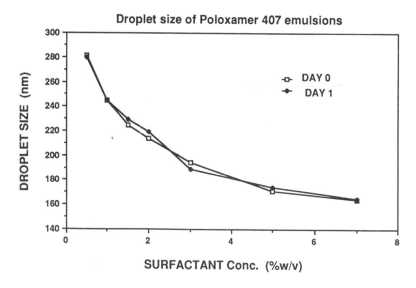

Fig. 6.2./3: Droplet size (PCS diameter) of emulsion carriers prepared with
Poloxamer 407 immediately after preparation (= day 0) and after 1 day's
storage.

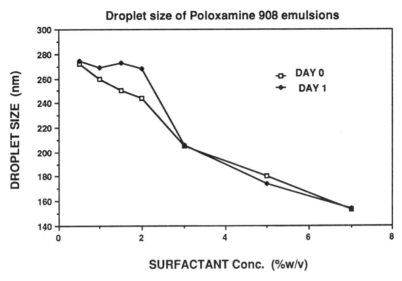

Fig. 6.2./4: Droplet size (PCS diameter) of emulsion carriers prepared with Poloxamine 908 immediately after preparation (= day 0) and after 1 day's storage.

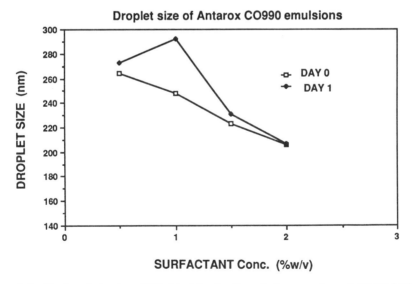

Fig. 6.2./5: Droplet size (PCS diameter) of emulsion carriers prepared with Antarox CO990 immediately after preparation (= day 0) and after 1 day's storage.

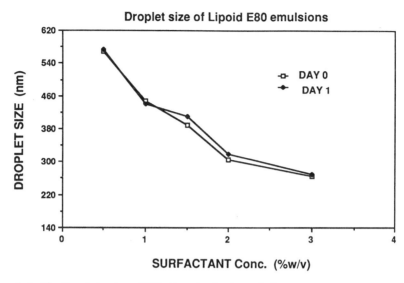

Fig. 6.2./6: Droplet size (PCS diameter) of emulsion carriers prepared with Lipoid E80 immediately after preparation (= day 0) and after 1 day's storage.

coalescence. Consequently, the mean diameter and the polydispersity index increase. After 1 day large droplets were found floating on the surface of the Antarox emulsion. This surfactant was obviously not suitable for stabilization of a soya oil based emulsion carrier and was therefore not investigated further.

The droplet size was much larger in emulsions prepared with Lipoid E80 than in the emulsions stabilized with Poloxamine, Poloxamer or Antarox. The difference was however less distinct at the higher surfactant concentration of 3%. The reduction in particle size in emulsions prepared with low concentrations of Lipoid E80 was related to the number of passes through the Microfluidizer. In the current study the number of passes was kept constant at 5 to enable a better comparison of the emulsifying properties of the different surfactants. The droplet size in commercial fat emulsions based on egg lecithin is between 220 and 400 nm and shows little change during storage over a period of a few years (Müller, R.H. et al., 1988a; Müller, R.H., unpublished data). Therefore no change was expected after 1 day of storage (Fig. 6.2./6).

The conditions of the emulsification process such as pressure, number of cycles and viscosity of the pre-emulsion, play an important role in the nature of the resulting emulsion and need optimization. A detailed study of optimization of these parameters was not performed because it was only

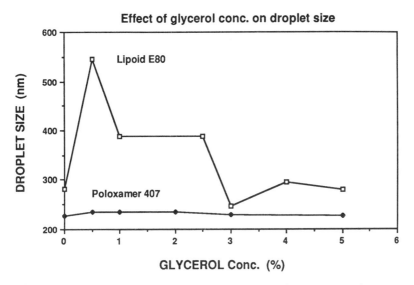

Fig. 6.2./7: Dependence of the mean droplet size (PCS diameter) of Lipoid E80 and Poloxamer 407 emulsion carriers on the glycerol content (glycerol added before microfluidization).

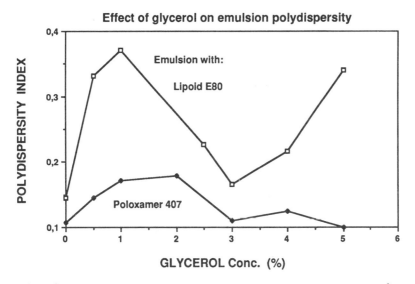

Fig. 6.2./8: Dependence of the polydispersity index of Lipoid E80 and Poloxamer 407 emulsion carriers on the glycerol content (glycerol added before microfluidization).

intended to show that emulsion carriers of good quality and stability could be produced as alternative to polymeric carriers. The influence of homogenization parameters on the resulting product can easily be shown by varying the viscosity of the aqueous phase. For isotonicity requirements the emulsions contain glycerol which can be added before or after the emulsification process. To study the most suitable time of addition, emulsions were prepared with increasing glycerol contents. For the Poloxamer 407 stabilized emulsion increasing the glycerol content produced little effect on the mean droplet size. Large differences were however observed for Lipoid E80 stabilized systems and these were not linearly related to the glycerol content (Fig. 6.2./7). The smallest droplet sizes were obtained without glycerol and at a glycerol concentration of 3%. A more distinct effect of the glycerol content was seen for the Poloxamer 407 emulsion by plotting the polydispersity index versus the glycerol concentration (Fig. 6.2./8). The distributions of the droplet populations are much narrower at low or medium glycerol concentrations, especially so for the Lipoid E80 emulsions. Based on this data, the glycerol was added after the microfluidization process.

6.3. Characterization of Poloxamer 188 emulsion carriers

The characterization by PCS and Laser Diffractometry yielded similar results for all the emulsions, so the emulsions stabilized with Poloxamer 188 are taken as an example to demonstrate the observed effects. As a general tendency, the droplet size decreased with increasing surfactant concentration. However, the decrease in size was accompanied by an increase in the width of the size distribution as indicated by a higher polydispersity index (Fig. 6.3./1). Obviously, the production of an emulsion with a low droplet size but with a narrow size distribution is rather difficult. In the systems containing high surfactant concentrations, no particles larger than 1.2 µm could be detected on the day of preparation (Fig. 6.3./2). However, the systems are on such a high energy level that the least stable droplets coalesce. After standing for 1 day, larger droplets similar to those present in systems with low surfactant concentrations had formed. For all emulsions a similar maximum droplet size was found on day 1 (Fig. 6.3./2).

The increase in the maximum size is correlated with an increase in the diameter 90% from day 0 to day 1 (Fig. 6.3./3). Simultaneously, the percentage of particles between 0.5 µm and 1.2 µm decreases (Fig. 6.3./4). The laser diffractometer used (Malvern Particle Sizer) could only detect particles larger than 0.5 µm. The percentage below 1.2 µm does therefore not include the bulk population of around 200 nm. Furthermore, it should be

182

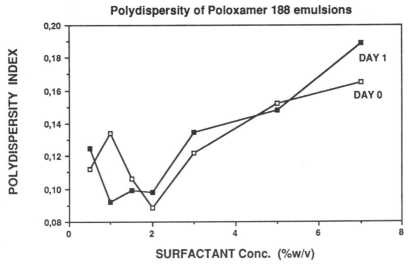

Fig. 6.3./1: Dependence of the polydispersity index of Poloxamer 188 emulsion carriers on the Poloxamer surfactant concentration. Increasing surfactant concentration leads to a decrease in particle size but an increase in the polydispersity index.

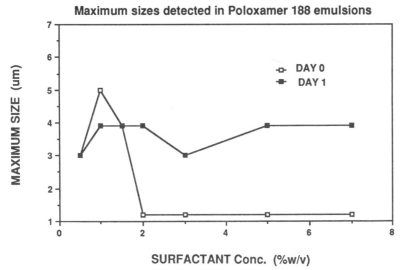

Fig. 6.3./2: Dependence of the maximum droplet sizes detected in Poloxamer 188 emulsion carriers on the Poloxamer surfactant concentration on the day of preparation (day 0) and after 1 day's storage.

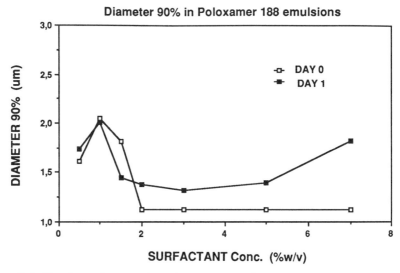

Fig. 6.3./3: Dependence of the diameter 90% measured in Poloxamer 188 emulsion carriers on the Poloxamer surfactant concentration on the day of preparation (day 0) and after 1 day's storage.

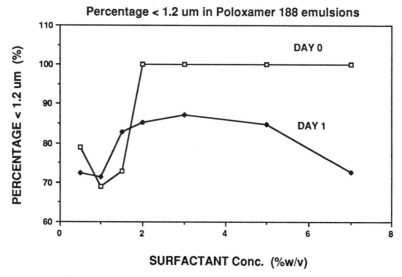

Fig. 6.3./4: Dependence of the percentage of particles below 1.2 μm in Poloxamer 188 emulsion carriers on the Poloxamer surfactant concentration measured on the day of preparation (day 0) and after 1 day's storage.

noted that an identical maximum size and diameter 90% do not necessarily mean that all the emulsions contain the same percentage of larger droplets in the total population. The laser diffractometer gives only relative information of the particle fractions between 0.5 and 118 µm and does not quantify the amount. Two emulsions can therefore possess identical laser characterization data but contain totally different percentages of larger particles in relation to the total droplet population. New laser diffracto-meters, covering the whole size range avoid this problem (Sympatec Helos, Malvern MasterSizer).

From the characterization data, a surfactant concentration of 2 to 3% seems to be the optimum for the production of emulsion carriers. It leads to a relatively small particle size (ca. 180 nm), a narrow size distribution (polydispersity index ca. 0.10), a low diameter 90% (1.1 µm) and a high percentage of particles below 1.2 µm (ca. 85%). Further surfactant addition leads to little improvement.

6.4. Stability testing of emulsion carriers

To estimate the stability of the produced emulsion carriers, stress test were performed. The most accurate investigations are long term tests, but these require long time periods of months or years (Müller, R.H. et al, 1988a). Stress tests are faster (hours, days or weeks) but each stress applied to a system changes its properties and therefore alters its stability. The stability under stress might be very different from that under "normal" storage conditions. Therefore it has to be considered how relevant results obtained from stress tests are for the estimation of the long term stability of emulsion systems (Müller, R.H. and Lucks, 1988). At the very least, stress tests provide information which can be used to make predictions about the long term stability. As accelerated stability tests (stress tests) are used:

1. Shaking test: The emulsion is shaken at room temperature at a certain frequency (e.g. 200 Hz).

2. Shaking or storage test at higher temperature: e.g. 40° or 60°.

3. Multiple autoclaving: Multiple autoclaving of the emulsion.

4. Freeze-thaw cycling: The emulsions are frozen at a certain rate, stored in this condition for some time and then thawed. The cycle is repeated several times.

5. Electrolyte addition: The addition of electrolytes reduces the electrostatic repulsion and determines the rigidity of the emulsifier film.

These tests have a number of disadvantages. Shaking increases the probability of particle collision, thereby imitating the number of collisions which occur during long term storage. This however gives the particles a high kinetic energy which might allow them to overcome electrostatic repulsion and consequently coalesce. This would not happen at a low droplet kinetic energy when movement is due to the Brownian motion of water molecules. Tests at higher temperatures change the properties of the emulsifier film. The increased temperature leads to a less viscous, and therefore less rigid and less stable emulsifier film. Freezing can also have adverse effects on emulsion stability. When the freezing temperature is below the phase transition temperature of the emulsifier film (e.g. composed of lecithin) the rigidity of the emulsifier film is strongly increased. In this gel-like state the film is more rigid than in the liquid crystalline phase. The freezing eliminates the electrostatic repulsion between droplets and presses them together. Stability then depends solely on the rigidity and stabilizing qualities of the emulsifier film. The result of freeze-thaw cycling depends very much on factors such as the rate of freezing, the freezing temperature, the time of storage in the frozen state, the vial used for the test and the number of freeze-thaw cycles. For characterization of the stability of the produced emulsion carriers, freeze-thaw cycling and the addition of electrolytes (calcium chloride) were employed as stress tests.

6.4.1 Freeze-thaw cycling

Samples of emulsion (1.0 ml) containing 1.0% surfactant were placed in conical Eppendorf vials (volume 1.5 ml) and frozen to -20° in a freezer. They were stored for 15 hours overnight, thawed and kept at room temperature for 9 hours. Laser diffractometer measurements (Malvern Particle Sizer 2600) were performed 3 hours after thawing of the emulsion. Before sampling, the emulsions were shaken to distribute floated oil droplets evenly. If phase separation had occurred, the emulsions were shaken to redisperse the top oil phase. Creaming of the top layer does not necessarily mean that the particles have coalesced to larger droplets or totally separated into an oil phase. Although the weak manual shaking can redisperse formed droplet aggregates, it will not re-emulsify coalesced oil droplets.

The maximum droplet size present in the emulsions was measured. The upper size limit of the highest size class in which particles were still detected was taken as maximum size (e.g. if the largest particles were detected in the size class 3.9 µm - 5.0 µm, the maximum size was 5.0 µm). The percentage of particles below 1.2 µm, (i.e. the percentage of particles between 0.5 µm and 1.2 µm) in the particle population ranging in droplet size from 0.5 to 118 µm was also determined. The main droplet population of about 200 to 300 nm is not included in this percentage. The third characterization parameter determined was the diameter 90%, i.e. the size below which 90% of the particles are. This parameter is very sensitive to the presence of even a few large droplets, especially when considering that the diameter is not a number but a weight diameter. The size distributions measured with the Malvern Particle Sizer are weight distributions.

The emulsions investigated were prepared with the surfactants Poloxamer 188, 338 and 407, Poloxamine 908 and Lipoid E80. Two Lipoid E80 emulsions were tested; the emulsion described in chapter 6.2 will be referred to as Lipoid E80(2). A first batch of Lipoid emulsion (Lipoid E80 (1)) was less efficiently homogenized but was included in the test to determine the effect of the homogenization process on the emulsion stability. It may be that emulsions which are identical in their chemical composition have different stabilities due to different production (homogenization) techniques. Most commercial fat emulsions for parenteral nutrition are of identical composition (soya oil, egg lecithin, water) but show differences in stability due to variations in the composition of the egg lecithin (minor components) and the emulsification process used.

Nine freeze thaw cycles were performed. The maximum size showed little change for the Poloxamer 188 and 407 stabilized emulsion carriers, but after 5 cycles, a slight increase was found in the Poloxamer 338 containing system (Fig. 6.4./1). The Poloxamine 908 emulsion had a maximum size between 6 and 20 μm after each of the first 5 cycles, but after the 7th cycle the system contained particles up to 120 μm in diameter and was much less stable than the Poloxamer emulsion carriers.

The Lipoid emulsions were relatively stable over the first 5 cycles, but in the following cycles the Lipoid E80 (1) emulsion broke, resulting in droplets over 100 μm (Fig. 6.4./2). After nine cycles both Lipoid emulsion showed phase separation.

Correspondingly, the percentage of particles below 1,2 μm did not alter very much for the Poloxamer 188 and 407 emulsions but decreased after 5 cycles for the slightly less stable Poloxamer 338 system (Fig. 6.4./3).

The less efficiently homogenized Lipoid E80 (1) emulsion exhibited a sharp drop in the percentage of droplets below 1.2 μm during the first 2 cycles (Fig. 6.4./4). The drop is much less steep for the well homogenized Lipoid E80 (2) emulsion. This demonstrates the importance of the emulsification technology on the physical stability of the resulting emulsion.

After the first freeze-thaw cycles, the percentage of particles below 1.2 μm reduced for the Poloxamine 908 emulsion; the value drops very close to zero after 7 cycles, indicating the destruction of the emulsion. Surprisingly, after 8 cycles the percentage again increases and reaches 84% after the ninth cycle. This phenomenon is not due to a re-emulsification of the coalesced droplets, but rather to further coalescence of the unstable droplets to form particles of a size outside the measuring range of the instrument (droplets larger 120 μm). The more stable droplets which remain form a population which is still in the measuring range, thereby giving a false reading of 84% below 1.2 μm. This indicates that the emulsion consists of unstable droplets which coalesce to form a population of larger droplets. The more stable droplets show no coalescence and this population remains unchanged. Breaking of a unimodal emulsion therefore leads to the formation of a bimodal size distribution. A similar behaviour has been found for other emulsion systems (Müller, R.H and Lucks, unpublished data). The laser diffractometer used could not quantify the number of droplets larger than 0.5 μm in relation to the mean droplet population at 200 to 300 nm. Therefore, visual inspection of the samples was an important additional criterion. After 3 cycles, all the Poloxamer emulsions showed large visible droplets floating on the surface. These few large droplets were outside the measuring range of the instrument and/or were too few to be detected in the presence of the large number of small particles. The measured maximum sizes of 8 or 5 μm are therefore to some extent misleading. Both Lipoid E80 emulsions also had large droplets floating on their surfaces but the less stable emulsion Lipoid E80 (1) had distinctly more larger droplets than

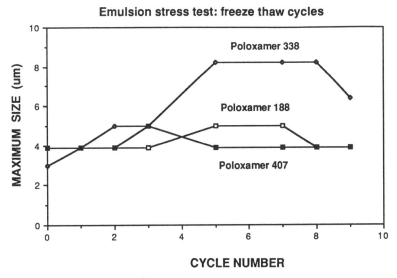

Fig. 6.4./1: Maximum size detected in Poloxamer 188, 338 and 407 stabilized fat emulsions during nine freeze-thaw cycles.

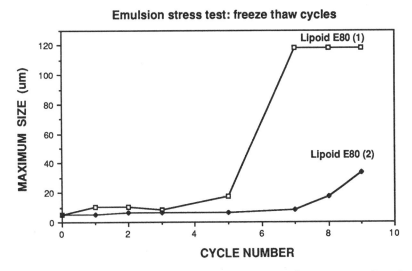

Fig. 6.4./2: Maximum size detected in two Lipoid E80 emulsions (batch (1) and (2)) during nine freeze-thaw cycles.

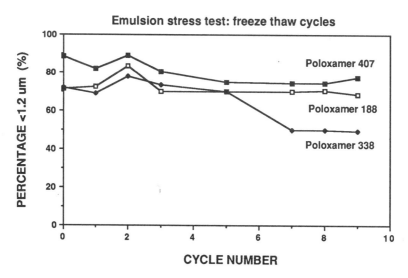

Fig. 6.4./3: Percentage of particles < 1.2 μm in Poloxamer 188, 338 and 407 stabilized fat emulsions during nine freeze-thaw cycles.

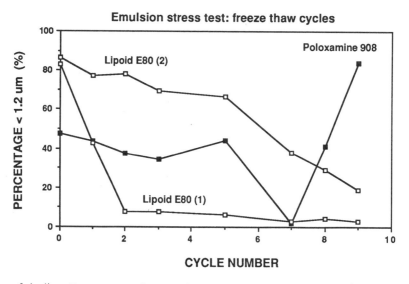

Fig. 6.4./4: Percentage of particles < 1.2 μm in two Lipoid E80 emulsions (batch (1) and (2)) during nine freeze thaw-cycles.

batch (2). The Poloxamine 908 system had the largest number of floating oil droplets.

After nine freeze-thaw cycles, the Lipoid emulsions showed separation into water and oil/emulsifier phases. All of the Poloxamer and Poloxamine 908 emulsions were still intact although there was an increased number of larger droplets floating on their surfaces. This indicates that the less stable droplets had coalesced, and that the ones which were of higher stability had not coalesced at all, even over a large number of cycles. The droplets which "survive" the first cycles can be considered as being stable.

The diameter 90% (D90%) measurements confirm that of those tested, the Poloxamer 188 and 407 emulsions are the most stable. Increases in the diameter 90% show that the Poloxamer 338 emulsion carrier is slightly less stable (Fig. 6.4./5). The decrease in the diameter after 9 cycles is due to the formation of larger droplets outside the measuring range of the instrument. The difference in stability between the 2 Lipoid E80 emulsions can clearly be seen by the strong increase in the D90% of E80 (1) after 5 cycles (Fig. 6.4./6).

The appearance of the population of larger droplets in the Poloxamine 908 emulsion and the remaining stable population is shown by the distinct increase in D90% after 5 cycles and the subsequent drop after 8 cycles (Fig. 6.4./7).

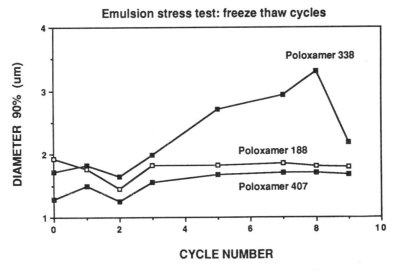

Fig. 6.4./5: Diameters 90% detected in Poloxamer 188, 338 and 407 stabilized fat emulsions during nine freeze-thaw cycles.

191

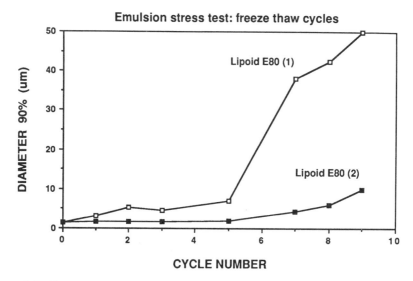

Fig. 6.4./6: Diameters 90% detected in two Lipoid E80 emulsions (batch (1) and (2)) during nine freeze-thaw cycles.

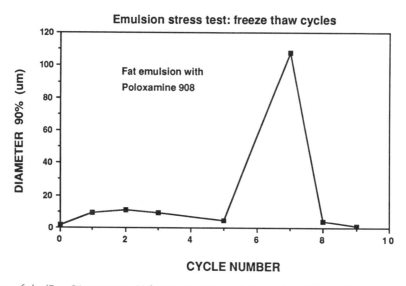

Fig. 6.4./7: Diameters 90% detected in a Poloxamine 908 emulsion during nine freeze-thaw cycles.

From the freeze thaw cycling results, it can be concluded that the
Poloxamer 188 and 407 emulsion are the most stable; the Poloxamer 338 and
Poloxamine 908 are less stable. All of the systems were more stable than
the egg lecithin (Lipoid E80) emulsions and did not undergo phase
separation. The instabilities observed with the Poloxamer and Poloxamine
emulsions are obviously due to the presence of a fraction of less stable
droplets which coalesce to form larger droplets. The vast majority of the
droplets however stay stable over the whole test period. This is reflected
by the increase and subsequent decrease in the maximum size detected and
the diameter 90%.

6.4.2. Constant freeze test

The result of a freeze-thaw test depends very much on the conditions
chosen. To study the effect of long-term freezing compared to freeze-thaw
cycling on the emulsion stability, samples from the same emulsion batches
were kept frozen for two periods of 7 days. The emulsions were thawed and
characterized after 7 and 14 days of freezing.
The superior stability of the Poloxamer emulsions compared to the
Poloxamine 908 and Lipoid E80 emulsions was confirmed. However, in contrast
to the freeze thaw cycles, the emulsion containing Poloxamer 188 was
slightly less stable than the emulsion containing Poloxamer 338, as
indicated by the maximum size detected after 14 days (Fig. 6.4./8). The
Lipoid E80 (1) emulsion proved to be the least stable and particles up to
118 µm in diameter were observed after 14 days freezing (= 2 x 7 days)(Fig.
6.4./9). The Poloxamine 908 emulsion contained larger particles than the
Lipoid E80 (2).
In general, the constant freezing of 14 days had a less damaging effect
than 9 days of freeze thaw cycling as indicated by the smaller increases in
the maximum particle size. No phase separation was observed with the
lecithin emulsion Lipoid E80 (2). However, freezing over a period of 7 days
is more damaging for the unstable systems than a freezing time of 15 hours
(1 freeze thaw-cycle). There is a distinct drop in the percentage of
droplets below 1.2 µm for the less stable Poloxamer 188 emulsion (Fig.
6.4./10), and a steeper drop for the Poloxamine 908 and Lipoid E80
emulsions (Fig. 6.4./11).
Obviously the emulsions are not "conserved" and fixed in a certain
condition after being frozen. The stress continues and more and more oil
droplets coalesce under the constant pressure of the ice crystals. However,
repeated freezing and thawing over a certain time (e.g. 7 x 1 day) seems to
be more damaging than constant freezing over the same period of time (7
days). Plotting the diameter 90% versus the storage time in the frozen

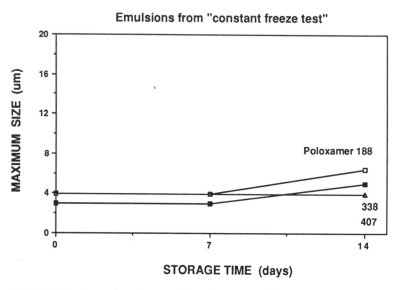

Fig. 6.4./8: Maximum size detected in Poloxamer 188, 338 and 407 emulsions after 7 and 14 days of constant freezing.

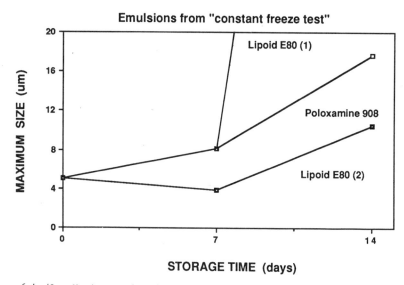

Fig. 6.4./9: Maximum size detected in Poloxamine 908 and two batches of Lipoid E80 emulsions (batch (1) and (2)) after 7 and 14 days of constant freezing.

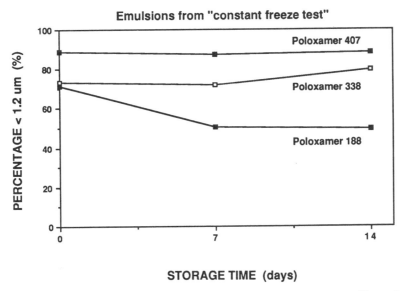

Fig. 6.4./10: Percentage of droplets below 1.2 μm in Poloxamer 188, 338 and 407 emulsions after 7 and 14 days of constant freezing.

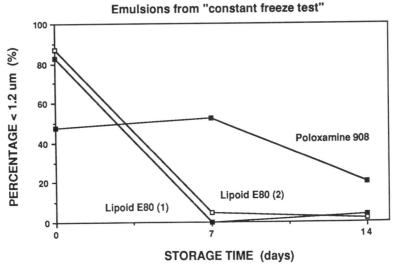

Fig. 6.4./11: Percentage of droplets below 1.2 μm in Poloxamine 908 and two batches of Lipoid E80 emulsions (batch (1) and (2)) after 7 and 14 days of constant freezing.

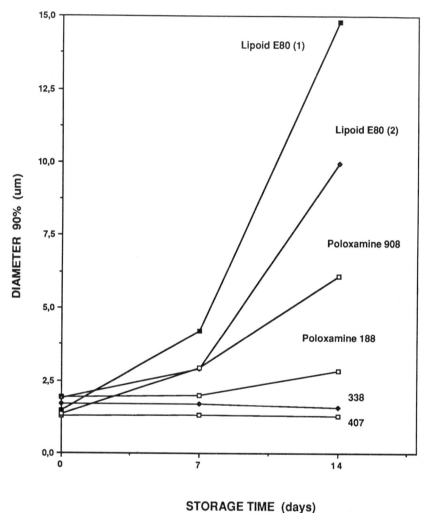

Fig. 6.4./12: Diameter 90% in emulsions stabilized with Poloxamer 188, 338 and 407, Poloxamine 908 and Lipoid E80 (batch (1) and (2)) after 7 and 14 days of constant freezing.

state distinguishes very well between the stability of the different emulsions (Fig. 6.4./12). The Poloxamer stabilized systems are most, Poloxamine 908 and Lipoid E80 (2) less and Lipoid E80 (1) least stable.

196

6.4.3. Stability following electrolyte addition

The addition of electrolytes to emulsions reduces the droplet zeta potential and the electrostatic repulsion between droplets. This causes instability in the emulsions because of the missing stabilizing repulsion between the droplets. The emulsion stability is mainly determined by the properties of the emulsifier film (e.g. rigidity). The addition of electrolytes can therefore be used to eliminate the stabilizing repulsive forces in emulsions and to look at the stabilizing effects of added emulsifier.

The addition of calcium salts to emulsions reduces the zeta potential from about -50 mv to zero at salt concentrations between 3 and 5 mmol/l. A further increase in salt concentration leads to a charge reversal and a positive zeta potential of about +10 mV. Addition of a concentration of about 100 mmol again causes a reduction in zeta potential to approximately zero (Müller, R.H. and Heinemann, 1987). To observe a distinct effect, 100 mmol calcium ions were added to the fat emulsions in the stress tests. The emulsions were characterized immediately after the addition of calcium chloride and after storage for 24 and 48 hours. In the Poloxamer and Poloxamine containing-emulsions, stabilization is mainly steric rather than electrostatic. Therefore indeed little change was expected in the Poloxamer systems and this was the case in practise. The maximum size showed little change over a period of 48 hours (Fig. 6.4./13). Similar results were found for the Poloxamine 908 and Lipoid E80 (2) emulsions, Lipoid E80 (1) again proved to be the least stable emulsion (Fig. 6.4./14). The percentage of droplets below 1.2 µm in diameter shows little change for the Poloxamer (Fig. 6.4./15) and Poloxamine emulsions (Fig. 6.4./16). A slight drop was however observed for the Lipoid E80 (2) emulsion, a very distinct drop for Lipoid E80 (1) (Fig. 6.4./16).

These results correlated well with the diameters 90% which were constant for the Poloxamers (Fig. 6.4./17) and increased slightly for the Poloxamine 908 and Lipoid E80 (2) emulsion. A strong increase in D90% was found for Lipoid E80 (1) (Fig. 6.4./18).

The electrolyte stress tests yielded similar results as the freeze-thaw cycle and constant freeze tests. From the data obtained in all the tests, the emulsions could be placed in order of decreasing stability. The Poloxamer emulsions are the most stable systems. The Poloxamine 908 and the Lipoid E80 (2) are less stable but behaved very similar in the electrolyte stress test. In the freeze-thaw cycle test, the Poloxamine 908 carriers proved to be more stable. Large surface droplets were present in this emulsion, but total phase separation which occurred with both Lipoid emulsions did not take place. The Lipoid E80 (1) emulsion was found to be the least stable against added electrolytes.

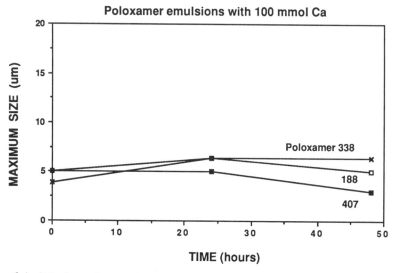

Fig. 6.4./13: Dependence of the maximum droplet size detected in Poloxamer 188, 338 and 407 stabilized emulsions on the standing time after addition of 100 mmol calcium chloride.

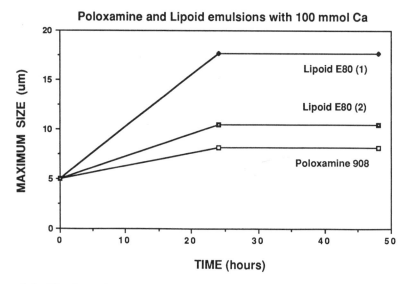

Fig. 6.4./14: Dependence of the maximum droplet size detected in Poloxamer 908 and Lipoid E80 (1) and (2) emulsions on the standing time after addition of 100 mmol calcium chloride.

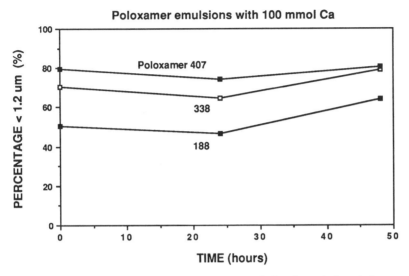

Fig. 6.4./15: Dependence of the percentage of droplets below 1.2 μm in diameter in Poloxamer 188, 338 and 407 stabilized emulsions on the standing time after addition of 100 mmol calcium chloride.

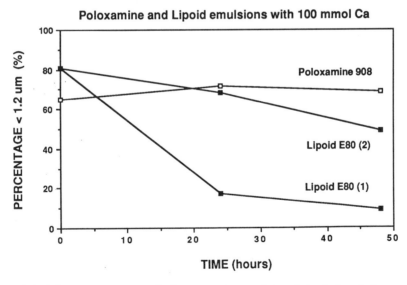

Fig. 6.4./16: Dependence of the percentage of droplets below 1.2 μm in diameter in Poloxamer 908 and Lipoid E80 (1) and (2) emulsions on the standing time after addition of 100 mmol calcium chloride.

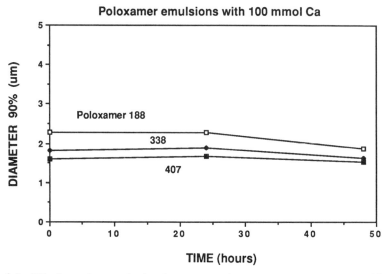

Fig. 6.4./17: Dependence of the diameter 90% measured in Poloxamer 188, 338 and 407 stabilized emulsions on the standing time after addition of 100 mmol calcium chloride.

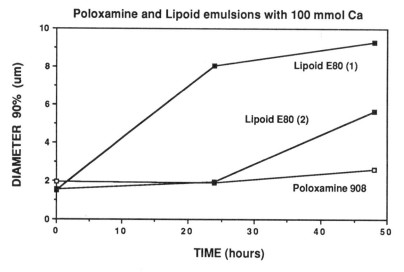

Fig. 6.4./18: Dependence of the diameter 90% measured in Poloxamer 908 and Lipoid E80 (1) and (2) emulsions on the standing time after addition of 100 mmol calcium chloride.

6.5. Summary

Biodegradable soya oil-based emulsion carriers of potential use for site-specific drug delivery and drug targeting could be prepared using coating polymers as surfactants. The emulsification was performed by a micro-fluidization technique. At low surfactant content (0.5%) the resultant emulsions contained droplets in the size range 250 to 290 nm. By increasing the surfactant concentration to 7%, a decrease in droplet size to about 150 nm could be achieved. The optimum surfactant concentration was considered to be in the range of about 2% to 3%. The emulsions produced at this surfactant concentration had a small particle size (180 nm to 240 nm), a narrow size distribution (polydispersity index ca. 0.10) and a small content of particles larger than 5 μm.

The microfluidization technique was found to be most effective when the viscosity of the water/oil/surfactant pre-emulsion was low. It was found that in order to produce emulsions in a low size and narrow size distribution, the addition of glycerol to obtain isotonicity should be performed after the microfluidization step.

Of the emulsions examined, the Poloxamer 188, 338 and 407 emulsions proved to be most stable. They showed no or little change in their characterization parameters within the first 24 hours after preparation and were least effected by the stress tests.

The Poloxamine 908 emulsion carriers are slightly less stable as seen by changes in the PCS diameter during the first 24 hours after preparation and the extent of coalescence observed in the stress tests.

The instabilities observed in the stress tests suggest the formation of a second droplet population within the emulsion, where less stable particles coalesce to form a population of larger particles in the presence of the stable mean population. The normally distributed droplet population transforms to a bimodal size distribution.

Antarox CO990 was found not to be suitable for use as a stabilizer for soya oil-based emulsion carriers.

Two batches of conventional egg lecithin (Lipoid E80) emulsions were prepared as a comparison to the emulsion carriers. Batch (1) was of the same composition as batch (2), but was less efficiently homogenized. In the stress tests, batch (2) showed similar (electrolyte test) and slightly reduced (freeze thaw cycles and constant freeze test) stability when compared to the Poloxamine 908 emulsion.

The less effectively homogenized Lipoid E80 (1) emulsion was distinctly less stable than the emulsion (2). This demonstrates the influence of emulsification "technology" on the resulting stability of fat emulsions and emulsion carriers.

```
┌─────────────────────────────────────────────────────────────────┐
│  7. CELL CULTURES AS IN VITRO TEST SYSTEM FOR DRUG CARRIERS       │
│                                                                   │
└─────────────────────────────────────────────────────────────────┘
```

7.0. Applications of cell culture test systems

Cell cultures are useful in vitro test system for obtaining basic
information about particulate carriers. They have been used to study

1 - the affinity of carriers to cell populations, e.g. investigations on
the influence of the composition of liposomes on their interaction with
hepatocytes (Burkhanov et al., 1988)

2 - the receptor-mediated uptake of particulates using asialfetuin-labelled
liposomes in hepatocyte cultures (Hara et al., 1988)

3 - the uptake and toxicity of polymerised liposomal carriers in macrophages (Juliano et al., 1985)

4 - the toxicity of polymeric microspheres in macrophages (Edman et al.,
1984)

5 - the influence of the surface properties (emulsifying agents) of
emulsion carriers on their phagocytosis (Davis and Hansrani, 1985)

6 - the effectiveness of antibody-mediated targeting of carriers to tumour
cells (Illum et al., 1983)

7 - the phagocytosis/endocytosis ability of cells, e.g. phagocytosis of
microspheres by tumour cells (Kramer and Burnstein,1976)

8 - the toxicity of polymer particles in relation to their physico-chemical
characteristics (Müller. R.H. et al., 1988b).

Cell cultures can be used in addition to physico-chemical characterization
as a test system for the characterization and in vitro selection of
colloidal carriers. Apart from information about the affinity to cell
populations, they are useful tools for obtaining basic information about
the cell-toxicity of carriers. Although PLA polymers have been proved to be
biocompatible and non-toxic as implants, they also possess some cellular
toxicity (Smith and Hunneyball, 1986).

7.1. Phagocytosis studies with peritoneal mouse macrophages

Mouse peritoneal macrophages can be collected and cultured relatively
easily. Assuming that the process of non-specific phagocytosis does not
differ between macrophage populations, they can be used to study phagocytosis and the effect of surface modification of particulates on the
uptake by the cells. The properties of Poloxamer and Poloxamine coating
films on latex model carriers have been characterized with regard to their
thickness, charge reducing effect and their interaction with charged serum
components (c.f. 2., 3.3. and 3.4.). These coating polymers have been used

to coat 5.25 µm latex particles in order to study the protective effect of the coating materials against phagocytosis by macrophages (Illum et al, 1987). The cell culture results discussed in chapter 7.1. were obtained by L.O. Jacobsen (Illum et al., 1987).

7.1.1. Method

5.25 µm latex particles were coated as described previously (c.f. 2.). A mouse macrophages cell suspension was plated into culture dishes whereby the cell number was adjusted that each plate contained 1.25×10^6 cells. After 24 hour incubation the coated and uncoated particles were added (5 particles per cell) and incubated with the cells up to 90 minutes. The dishes were then washed and the cells stained with Giemsa. The number of phagocytosed particles was determined microscopically (Illum et al, 1987).

7.1.2. Phagocytosis of Poloxamer and Poloxamine coated latex particles

The number of phagocytosed particles was expressed as the phagocytic uptake relative to the control of uncoated latex particles (Table 7.1./1). A reduction in phagocytic uptake of 5.25 µm latex was observed whereby high molecular weight polymers creating a thick coating layer were most effective. The phagocytic uptake decreased with increasing coating layer thickness. This effect was attributed to steric stabilization of the particles by the coating layer which reduces both the aggregative propensity (Buscall and Ottewill, 1986) and their interaction with macrophages. In vitro, Poloxamer 338 and 407 were most effective to prevent phagocytosis by macrophages. A distinct reduction was also found for Poloxamine 908.

This results seemed to correspond to the reduced uptake of Poloxamer coated 60 nm polystyrene particles by liver and spleen macrophages observed in vivo (Illum et al., 1986). After intravenous injection, Poloxamine 908 coated 60 nm latex particles avoided RES recognition and phagocytosis by the liver and spleen macrophages. The particles remained in blood circulation (Illum et al., 1987a).

Such circulating particles can be employed as devices for the controlled release of drugs. However, it would be desirable to increase the size of the particles from 60 nm to 500 nm or 1 µm. A larger size would provide a higher absolute drug loading capacity per particle and give more flexibility in the design of the particle matrix for a long-term drug release. As seen by the reduction in phagocytic uptake, the Poloxamers coated the larger latex particles but the thickness of the coating layer was not

Phagocytosis of Poloxamer and Poloxamine coated latex particles

Table 7.1./1: Relative phagocytic uptake of 5.25 μm latex particles coated with Poloxamers and Poloxamine 908 (in order of decreasing phagocytic uptake, after Illum et al, 1987). The coating layer thickness given was determined on 60 nm latex particles.

coating agent	coating layer thickness (Å)	relative phagocytic uptake (%)
none	0	100
Poloxamer 108	58	100.4
Poloxamer 188	76	95.4
Poloxamer 217	58	87.6
Poloxamer 235	35	86.5
Poloxamer 237	80	83.5
Poloxamer 335	53	66.7
Poloxamer 288	130	56.5
Poloxamer 238	132	47.0
Poloxamer 338	158	36.7
Poloxamer 407	154	21.6
Poloxamine 908	134	69.5

determined. It was assumed that the coating thickness measured on 60 nm latex is also applicable to 5.25 μm latex particles because the coating layer thickness at the plateau level is not influenced by particle size (Law and Kayes, 1983). This assumption, together with the observed effects using coated 5μm particles, led to the conclusion that steric stabilization protects the particles against macrophage uptake. For large particles, a layer of 230 Å and for 60 nm particles, a layer of 100 Å should be sufficient to afford this protection (Illum et al., 1987a).

The Poloxamer 407 and Poloxamine 908 coatings proved to be effective in reducing phagocytosis of large particles in vitro (cell cultures). Studies were therefore undertaken to investigate the ability of Poloxamer 407 and Poloxamine 908 coated larger carriers to avoid RES uptake in vivo (c.f. chapter 8). These studies should provide the information required to determine the maximum size of particles which can still avoid RES clearance.

The in vivo organ distribution could not confirm the protective effects of the polymers on larger particles observed in vitro. The coated larger latex were cleared by the RES (c.f. 8.). This demonstrates the problems of validity and interpretation encountered when using in vitro cell culture results to predict in vivo behaviour.

The results obtained from the in vivo studies and the physico-chemical characterizations prove that

1. the coating layer is thinner on 5 µm latex than on 60 nm particles (e.g. only 55 Å for Poloxamine instead 130-150 Å).

2. The protective effect of coating layers in vivo does not depend on the coating layer thickness and steric stabilization.

The reduced coating layer thickness on large particles is due to a less hydrophobic surface. Although all of the different sized polystyrene particles were made using the same materials, they exhibit differences in surface hydrophobicity (e.g. number of charged, hydrated groups). The difference in coating-polymer adsorption is therefore not a size, but a surface hydrophobicity effect. Different sized particles composed of the same material do not necessarily possess the surface properties required for identical adsorption.

With regard to the thin coating layers measured on larger latex particles, the interpretation of the results obtained with the mouse peritoneal macrophages needs to be reconsidered. The polymers which coat thickly onto 60 nm latex, produce a coating layer of about 50 to 60 Å on larger latex particles. This layer thickness is sufficient to reduce phagocytosis. The calculations of the minimum coating layer thickness for steric stabilization in vitro which are based on a larger thickness need to be re-calculated.

The thin coating layers explain why negligible particle phagocytosis was seen ($< 5\%$) with 60 nm latex particles coated with most polymers (Illum et al., 1987). Even polymers such as Poloxamer 108 and 188 produce a coating layer of 50 - 75 Å on 60 nm latex and therefore sufficient protection against phagocytosis in vitro. The coating layer properties of 108 on 60 nm latex (thickness, hydrophobicity) are estimated to be similar to the coating layer properties of Poloxamer 407 on 5 µm latex.

Studies with 60 nm latex will therefore not be suitable for screening potentially protective coating materials. To obtain a better differentiation in the phagocytic uptake, it will be necessary to employ model carriers with a lower surface hydrophobicity than 60 nm latex (e.g. 5 µm latex).

7.2. Toxicity studies in hepatocyte cultures

7.2.1. Method

Liver cells were obtained by perfusion of the liver of Sprague Dawley rats with collagenase after removal of Ca^{++} by preperfusion with a chelator (Şeglen, 1976). The hepatocytes were separated by centrifugation, and the cell number and viability were determined (trypan blue exclusion test), and the cells divided into 35 mm culture dishes to give 1.25×10^6 cells per dish. Waymouth medium containing 10% foetal calf serum (FCS) with additional insulin and penicillin/streptomycin was used as the culture medium. The cells were cultured for 24 hours prior to the experiments (for details see Bräuer, 1990).

The toxicity of Poloxamer and other ethoxylated surfactants was determined by the measurement of the intracellular enzyme, lactate dehydrogenase (LDH) which is released following cell-membrane damage. The LDH released into the cell culture medium was determined using the reaction:

$$\text{pyruvate} + \text{NADH} + \text{H}^+ \xrightarrow{\text{LDH}} \text{lactate} + \text{NAD}^+$$

The rate of change in the NADH concentration (absorbance at 334 nm) is determined and compared to the total activity achieved after lysis of cells with Triton X-100.

7.2.2. Interaction of ethoxylated surfactants with hepatocytes

To obtain more information about the interaction of coating polymers with cells, hepatocytes were incubated with Poloxamers and Poloxamine 908 (Bräuer, 1990; Müller, R.H. et al., 1989) as a cell culture model to test the toxicity and cell-interaction of the polymers. The Poloxamer and Poloxamine data will be used to make comparisons with novel synthesized coating polymers.

The hepatocytes were incubated with increasing polymer concentrations and the LDH release measured as a percentage of the reference (=100% release). Polymers were examined differing in their coating properties and effects in vivo:

Poloxamer 184: forms a thin, relatively hydrophobic coating layer which does not protect against phagocytosis.

Poloxamer 188: creates a less hydrophobic coating layer of medium thickness and does produce some reduction in liver/spleen uptake.

Poloxamer 338 and 407, and Poloxamine 908: form thick coating layers with the lowest hydrophobicity observed, and lead to a distinct reduction in or total avoidance of RES clearance.

The LDH release caused by Poloxamer 184 after 1 hour was found to be small over the concentration range investigated (up to 0.15%). However, measurement after 24 hours revealed a distinct toxic effect, which led to cell death at the higher concentrations used (Fig. 7.2./1). The polymer seemed to interact with the hepatocytes leading to membrane damage and LDH release. The interaction with the membrane might take place via the hydrophobic regions of the coating polymer (hydrophobic interaction) or the micelles formed by the coating polymer which might provide a similar hydrophobic surface as the coating films of Poloxamer 184.

Incubation with Poloxamers 188, 338 and 407 and Poloxamine 908 which reduce RES uptake in vivo, did not lead to a significant toxic effect even at concentrations 100 fold greater than that which caused cell death with Poloxamer 184 (Fig. 7.2./2). An increase in the test concentration above 10% polymer was not possible because of the increased viscosity of the solutions. Diffusion of the coating polymers into the cell is not likely because of their high molecular weights (ranging from 8,000 to 27,000). In contrast to Poloxamer 184, the above polymers did not seem to interact with the cell membranes to an extent which caused measurable LDH release.

Incubation of hepatocytes with Tagat surfactants containing short EO chains and forming similar coating layers to Poloxamer 184, led also to a LDH

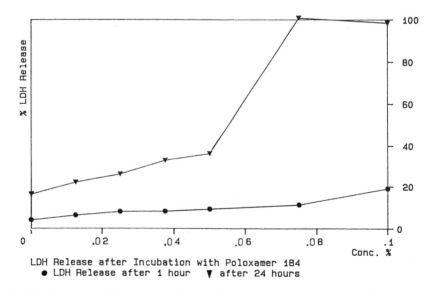

LDH Release after Incubation with Poloxamer 184
● LDH Release after 1 hour   ▼ after 24 hours

Fig. 7.2./1: LDH release after incubation of hepatocytes with Poloxamer 184 (after 1 and 24 hours)(Müller, R.H. et al. 1989).

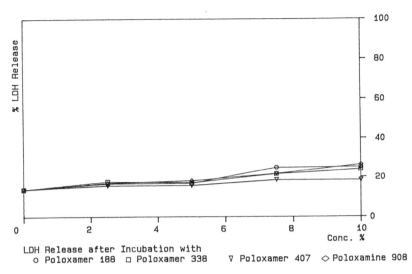

Fig. 7.2./2: LDH release after 24 hours incubation of hepatocytes with Poloxamers 188, 338 and 407 and Poloxamine 908 (Müller, R.H. et al., 1989).

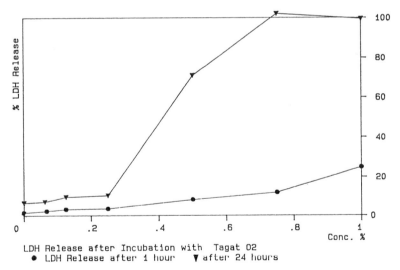

Fig. 7.2./3: LDH release after incubation of hepatocytes with Tagat 02 (after 1 and 24 hours)(Müller, R.H. et al. 1989).

releases (Fig. 7.2./3). In vivo, the Tagat surfactants did not protect against RES clearance (c.f. 8.4.).

The observed low toxicity of those coating polymers which protect against

RES clearance seems to be due to a lack of interaction with cell membranes. This lack of interaction can be seen as:

1. A primary effect essential for polymers which avoid phagocytosis.

The protection of the coating layer formed by these polymers is due to their lack of interaction with membranes reducing the adhesion to macrophages.

2. A secondary effect of the low hydrophobicity of the polymers.

The polymers produce low hydrophobicity surface coatings which resist the adsorption of opsonins via hydrophobic interaction. Their micelles possess a similarly low hydrophobicity and will not (hydrophobically) interact with membranes to cause toxicity.

No matter whether the lack of membrane damage by coating polymers avoiding RES clearance is a primary or secondary effect, the LDH measurements in hepatocytes could be used as a screening test for new polymers. It cannot lead to a positive selection but, in combination with other characterization methods, can be used to exclude unsuitable surfactants. To avoid RES clearance, the polymers need to create uncharged particles with low surface hydrophobicity and a lack of membrane interaction (as measured by LDH release).

Measuring the LDH release caused by polymer solutions will mainly determine the effect of the polymer micelles on the cell membrane. The surface properties of the polymer micelles might differ from the properties of the polymer coating layers on drug carriers. Therefore, at the present, the interaction of coated carriers without free surfactant or micelles present is investigated (Bräuer, 1990).

The LDH release does not differ significantly for the coating polymers, Poloxamers 188, 338 and 407 and Poloxamine 908. There are however marked differences in their protective effects against RES uptake in vivo; Poloxamer 188 is the least effective. These differences are not reflected in differences in membrane damage, as measured by LDH release. This could be due to the low sensitivity of the LDH assay, in comparison to other measures of membrane damage such as the determination of K^+ loss by the cells (Malik et al., 1983). At present, the interaction of polymers with hepatocytes is being studied by determination of potassium release using atom absorption spectrometry (AAS) (Bräuer, 1990).

A final assessment of the relevance of the membrane interactions of polymers on their ability to facilitate avoidance of macrophage uptake cannot be made at present. Measures of membrane interaction in cell cultures might possibly provide an additional method for screening new coating polymers. The hepatocyte studies described above will at least provide information useful for assessment of the toxicity of newly synthesized polymers.

8. IN VIVO DISTRIBUTION OF CARRIERS

8.0 Gamma-scintigraphy for the determination of the organ distribution of particles after i.v. administration

Gamma scintigraphy is a non-invasive technique which can be used to follow the distribution within the body of gamma-emitting pharmaceutical formulations. The technique has been widely used in studies of the GI transit of oral dosage forms (Davis 1983), the evaluation of oral controlled release formulations (Wilson et al., 1982) and investigations of parenteral dosage forms (Mills et al., 1980), inhalation aerosols (Malton et al., 1982) and ophthalmic preparations (Wilson et al, 1983; Hilditch et al, 1983) as well as many other pharmaceutical formulations.

To allow its study by gamma-scintigraphy, the dosage form needs to be labelled with a suitable radioactive isotope. It is important that the radioactive label is tightly bound to the carrier. Otherwise one will follow the distribution of the label instead of the particles or emulsion droplets. Dual isotope techniques can be used to monitor two parameters, e.g. in the case of parenteral fat emulsions, the metabolism of the emulsifier (labelled with I-131) and the soya oil (labelled with indium-111) can be followed simultaneously. One of the great advantages of gamma scintigraphy is that it enables the study in vivo of very fast dynamic processes such as the phagocytosis of colloidal particles or fat emulsions by the reticuloendothelial system (Davis and Hansrani, 1980).

Gamma-scintigraphy was used to investigate the ability of polymer coatings to protect carriers against phagocytosis by RES macrophages. To determine the velocity of clearance by the RES, dynamic views consisting of one frame (scintigram) every 20 or 30 seconds were taken during the first 10 or 15 minutes after injection of the labelled carriers.

Clearance of the injected carriers by RES macrophages occurs very rapidly. When the immune system recognizes particles as foreign, the uptake of most of the particles occurs within the first 5 minutes. Fig 8.0./1 shows the uptake of antimony trisulfide (Sb_2S_3, Technescan™) colloid after i.v. injection. The antimony trisulfide colloid was prepared by the addition of Tc-99m solution to the precolloid, heating of the mixture in boiling water for 30 minutes and addition of citrate buffer. The first 4 scintigrams (Fig. 8.0./1) show the body distribution of the colloid during the first 80 seconds (one scintigram taken over a period of 20 s). During the first 40 seconds most of the activity is located in the lungs (LU), head region (H) and the liver (LI) due to circulation of the colloid in the blood and rapid uptake by the liver. After 60 s and 80 s a more distinct image of the

211

skeleton can be seen, due to the uptake of the colloid by the RES cells of the bone marrow. Clearance by the macrophages of the liver and spleen occurred so rapidly that after 80 s around 50% of the injected activity was located in these regions (Table 8.0./1). Throughout this time the activity in the hind leg region showed little change.

After 3 minutes, the skeleton image is more distinct although the activity in the skeleton is low compared to the high activity in the liver/spleen region. To obtain a more dominant image of the skeleton compared to the liver, the saturation level of the scintigram colour scale would need to be decreased. High activities were found in the liver and lungs, the latter due to colloid still circulating in the blood and not yet phagocytosed (Fig. 8.0./2). The image obtained after 7 minutes shows that the clearance has been completed. The activity in the lung is lower than before due to the clearance of the colloid from the blood stream. Some activity in the lung region is left due to the accumulation of colloid in the bones of the rib cage. Clear liver and skeleton images are visible. The image of the skeleton appears less visible than before, but this is simply due to the automatic scaling of the scintigram relative to the highest activity present, i.e. the liver. The activities calculated in the liver and hind leg regions remained constant after 7 minutes (Table 8.0./1). The decrease in activity in the hind leg is less distinct than the increase in liver activity. The activity remains in the hind leg area because colloid circulating in the blood is localized in the bones of the hind leg region. Only a fraction of the circulating colloid accumulates in the liver and therefore removing some activity from the hind leg region.

Table 8.0./1: Time-dependent uptake of antimony trisulfide colloid in liver region and reduction of activity in hind leg region (n=1).

time	% total activity	
	liver	hind leg
40 s	37.2 %	14.3 %
60 s	42.4 %	14.1 %
80 s	50.3 %	14.3 %
2 min	56.5 %	13.1 %
3 min	60.4 %	12.4 %
7 min	68.8 %	12.5 %
15 min	68.9 %	12.5 %

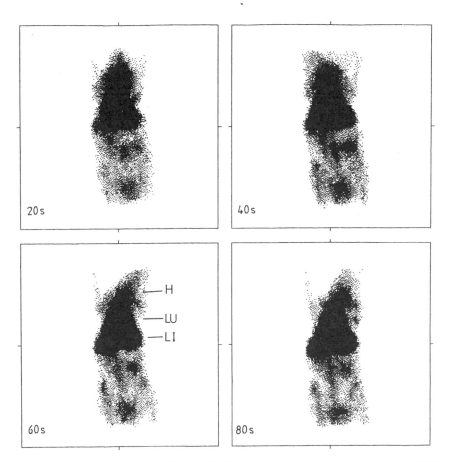

Fig. 8.0./1: Scintigrams obtained after injection of antimony trisulfide colloid (right marginal ear vein, NZW rabbits). The scintigrams are taken 20, 40, 60 and 80 seconds after injection (each scintigram is taken over a frame time of 20 s). High activities are found in the head region (H), lung (LU) and liver (LI). The scintigram after 80 s shows already some accumulation in the skeleton.

The scintigrams demonstrate the need for site-specific targeting of imaging formulations. Technescan is used as a diagnostic product for liver, spleen, bone marrow and lymph node scintigraphy. However, it is less suitable for bone marrow scintigraphy because around 70% accumulates in the liver and spleen. Targeting of colloid to the bone marrow, which may be achieved by surface modification with a coating polymer such as Poloxamer 407 would be a distinct improvement.

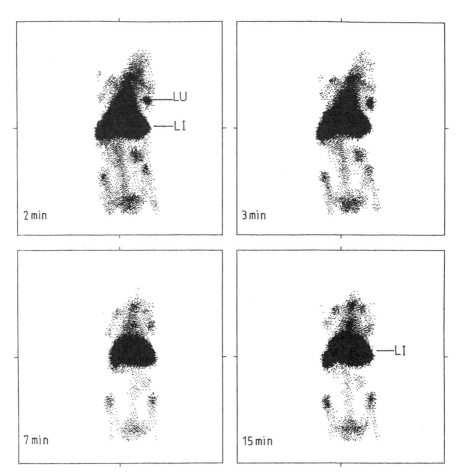

Fig. 8.0./2: Scintigrams obtained after injection of antimony trisulfide colloid (right marginal ear vein, NZW rabbits). The scintigrams are taken 2, 3, 7 and 15 minutes after injection (each scintigram is taken over a frame time of 20 s). The activity is much reduced in the head region, high activities are found in the lung (LU) and liver (LI). The scintigrams show a more distinct skeleton image. After 7 mins the colloid clearance is finished and no differences can be seen in scintigrams taken at later times.

As seen on the scintigrams after injection of the antimony trisulfide colloid, the RES clearance is very rapid. For studies on the ability of coating polymers to reduce the RES clearance of particles, the organ distribution within the first 10 or 15 minutes yields the most important

information. If particles are recognized as foreign to the host, the
clearance will take place very fast and very effectively. If particles are
protected from recognition, for example by coating with Poloxamine 908,
little change in the body distribution occurs during the first few days
after administration. Polystyrene microparticles are non-biodegradable, so
there will be no change in the particle surface properties because of
biodegradation. A re-distribution is more likely to be seen after i.v.
administration of surface modified biodegradable carriers.

8.1 Experimental

The latex particles (2.5% w/v) were labelled with iodine-131 using the
method of Huh et al., 1974. NaI-131 was added to the particles and the
suspension was irradiated over 1 to 2 days with a total radiation dose of
1.25×10^4 to 2.5×10^4 Gy (Co 60 source). The labelling efficiency was
found to be 30-40% for small latex particles (60 to 140 nm), but lower for
larger particles (10% for 910 nm). After labelling, the particles were
dialysed over 2-3 days to remove the free iodine. Dialysis was performed
until less than 1% free iodine was left in the sample. The radioactive
particles were coated by overnight incubation with an equal volume of 2%
coating polymer solution.
PHB particles were labelled by incorporation of an In-111-oxine (8-hydroxy
quinoline) complex during the production process. After evaporation of the
organic solvent, the particles were dialysed to remove free In-oxine. A
high purity dialysis tubing (Spectrapor™) was used in order to avoid
particle aggregation due to leakage of substances from the dialysis tube.
Coating of the particles was performed in the manner described above.
The injection volume was between 0.5 and 1.2 ml for each animal, and was
administered into the right marginal ear vein. The total activity injected
was approximately 2-4 MBq for the iodinated latex particles and 2-6 MBq for
the indium labelled PHB particles. Female NZW rabbits were used weighing
between 2.0 and 3.5 kg for the latex particle studies and 2.0 and 2.5 kg
in weight for the PHB particle studies. Scintigrams were obtained using a
Maxi Camera II (General electronics, USA). Imaging of the rabbits on the
gamma camera was performed by taking dynamic views over the first 10 or 15
minutes and static views at later times (1-6 hours, 1-6 days). At the end
of the experiment the rabbits were dispatched. The organs were removed and
their activities determined in a well counter. Activity was measured in the
liver, spleen, kidneys, heart, bone marrow (hind leg) and carcass.
The figures 8.1./1-4 show the types of scintigrams obtained after location
of particles in different organs. Intravenous injected unmodified particles
are taken up by the liver and spleen and lead to an accumulation of

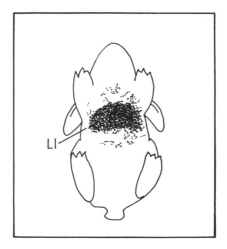

Fig. 8.1./1: Scintigram obtained after injection of unmodified particles. Up to 90% of the particles accumulate in the liver and spleen creating a clear liver (LI) image. Only in large rabbits, separated images of liver and spleen can be seen on the scintigram. In smaller rabbits, liver and spleen form one region (modified after Illum et al., 1987a).

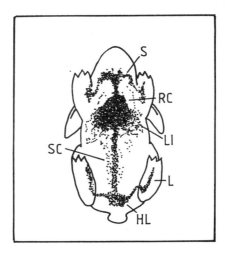

Fig. 8.1./2: Injection of colloid for liver and bone marrow scintigraphy leads to accumulation of activity in the liver and the skeleton. Images of the spinal column (SC), the hind leg (HL) region with the legs (L), the rib cage (RC) and the shoulder girdle (S) appear on the scintigram (modified after Illum et al., 1987a).

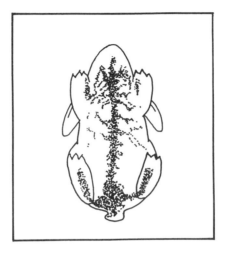

Fig. 8.1./3: Selective delivery to the bone marrow creates only an image of the skeleton. No activity is found in the liver and spleen region (modified after Illum et al., 1987a).

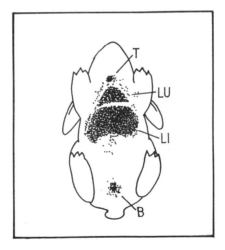

Fig. 8.1./4: After injection of labelled fat emulsion with a low uptake by the RES, an image of the liver (LI) and the lungs (LU) will appear on the scintigram (high blood flow in these organs). Release of label excreted with the urine leads to the accumulation of activity in the bladder (B), and for iodine also in the thyroid (T) (modified after Illum et al., 1987a).

217

radioactivity in the liver region (Fig. 8.1./1). After Injection of colloids for liver and bone marrow scintigraphy (Technescan), a liver image and the shape of the skeleton appear on the scintigram (Fig. 8.1./2). Site-specific delivery of particles to the bone marrow creates only an image of the skeleton, no liver can be seen on the scintigram (Fig. 8.1./3). After administration of fat emulsions, a high radioactivity will be found in the liver and the lung region. The fast metabolism of the fat emulsions leads to the release of radioactive label. In the case of excretion with the urine, a higher activity will be found in the kidneys and the bladder (Fig. 8.1./4). Radioactive iodine released from the surface of labelled polystyrene particles can also be found in the thyroid within 24 hours after injection of the particles (Fig. 8.1./4). The extent of accumulation of radioactive marker in kidneys, bladder and thyroid indicate how tightly the label is bound.

8.2. Organ distribution of Poloxamer/Poloxamine coated carriers

8.2.1 Organ distribution of 142 nm model carriers

A polystyrene latex with a mean particle size of 142 nm was used as model
system to investigate the ability of Poloxamer/Poloxamine coatings to
protect carriers larger than 60 nm against RES uptake. After radioactive
labelling with 131-I, the particles were coated with Poloxamine 908 and
Poloxamer 407 and characterized by PCS measurements (Table 8.2.1./1).

Table 8.2.1./1: PCS size, polydispersity index and coating layer thickness
of uncoated and coated latex particles (radioactive labelled).

latex particles	particle diameter (nm)	standard deviation (nm)	polydispersity index	coating layer (Å)
uncoated	142	2	0.096	-
Poloxamine 908 coated	167	1	0.038	> 126
Poloxamer 407 coated	168	1	0.053	> 131

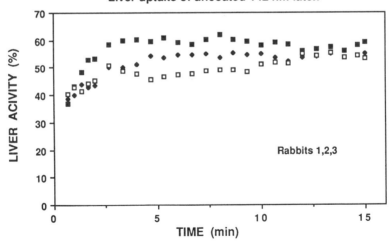

Fig. 8.2.1./1: Uptake of uncoated 142 nm latex particles by the
liver/spleen (% of total injected activity) within the first 15 minutes
after i.v. injection.

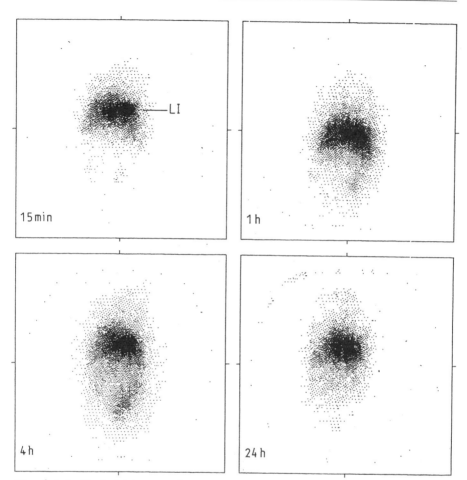

Fig. 8.2.1./2: Scintigrams of i.v. injected uncoated 142 nm latex particles after 15 min., 1 hour, 4 hours and 24 hours. The particles accumulate in the liver. After 1 and 4 hours, a higher total activity in the rest of the body can be seen due to the release of label from particles localised in the liver.

Coating with the two sterically stabilizing polymers removed aggregates from the latex suspension as shown by the reduction in the polydispersity index of the coated compared to the uncoated particles. The coating layer thickness can be calculated from the increase in particle size after coating, but this value might be higher than measured because of a decrease in the mean size due to the removal of aggregates. The coating layers are therefore thicker than 126 and 131 Å. These coating layer thicknesses were

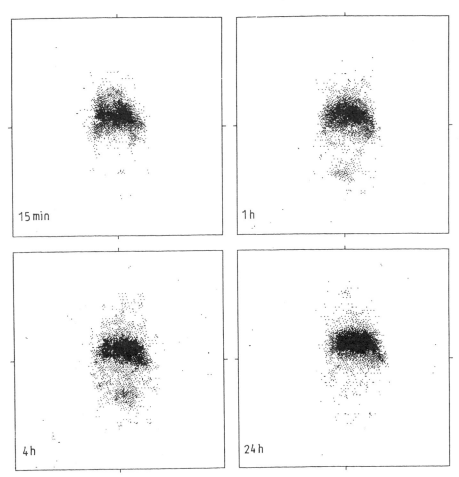

Fig. 8.2.1./3: Scintigrams of i.v. injected uncoated 76 nm latex particles after 15 min., 1 hour, 4 hours and 24 hours. The particles accumulate in the liver. After 4 hours, the activity in the rest of the body had increased only slightly indicating very little release of label form particles localised in the liver.

similar to those observed after adsorption onto 60 nm latex particles. Injection of uncoated latex particles led to their rapid clearance from the blood stream by the RES. Within the first 5 minutes after i.v. injection, up to 60% of the particles were taken up by liver and spleen (Fig. 8.2.1./1). In the corresponding scintigrams, a clear liver image is obtained (Fig. 8.2.1./2); little activity is found in the rest of the rabbit's body. After 1 and 4 hours, the activity in the rest of the body increased slightly due to release of the radioactive label from the particle surface. After 4 hours, a higher activity was present in the bladder, due to excretion of I-131 in the urine. After 24 hours, all of the free iodine had been excreted and the total body activity was reduced; the scintigram obtained at this time is similar to that obtained 15 minutes after injection.

The amount of free label released from the particle surface depends on the stability of the bond between the label and the particle. As mentioned above, a more stable iodine labelling was achieved when small particles were used. In the scintigrams of i.v. injected 76 nm polystyrene latex, a clear liver image was seen. The activity in the rest of the body, due to iodine released from the particle surface was markedly reduced (Fig. 8.2.2./3).

Coating of the larger particles seems to be less effective at reducing RES uptake than using coated 60 nm latex. With the coated small particles an activity of only 25 to 30% was found in the liver spleen region. This is almost identical with the blood pool, that means the activity found in the liver region after radioactive labelling of erythrocytes. The labelled erythrocytes are not cleared by the RES and the liver activity found with these particles represents the percentage which will be measured when particulates circulate in the blood stream.

Coating of 142 nm latex particles with Poloxamine 908 reduced the liver uptake only to 30 to 35% (Fig. 8.2.1./4). Considering a blood pool in the liver of 25% of the injected activity, a very small number of the particles are actually taken up by the macrophages of the liver/spleen (about 5-10%). From HIC studies it is known that latex particles are not homogenous in their surface hydrophobicity. A more hydrophilic subpopulation of the 142 nm latex particles might be coated less effectively (thinner and more hydrophobic coating layer) resulting in RES recognition and uptake of 5-10% of the coated particles by the liver. The majority of the Poloxamine 908 coated 142 nm latex seems to be protected against RES uptake similar to the coated smaller 60 nm latex.

Injection of the latex coated with Poloxamer 407 led to an activity in the liver/spleen region of 25 to 34% (Fig. 8.2.1./5). There is a slight variation in the uptake within the group of 3 rabbits. In one rabbit almost no liver uptake takes place (taking into account a liver blood pool of 25%), whereas in 2 rabbits about 5% to 10% are taken up. These results seem to be slightly less consistent than those obtained after the injection of coated 60 nm particles.

Poloxamine 908 and Poloxamer 407 coatings seem to protect the 142 nm polystyrene particles to a similar extent against uptake by liver and spleen macrophages. No differences in the organ distribution of particles coated with both polymers were found as observed with 60 nm latex

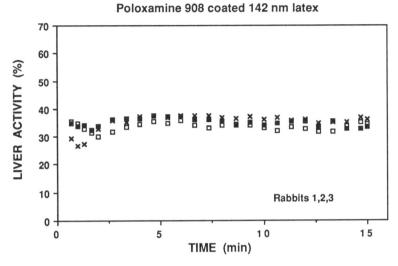

Fig. 8.2.1./4: Uptake of Poloxamine 908 coated 142 nm latex particles by the liver/spleen during the first 15 minutes after i.v. injection (% of total injected activity).

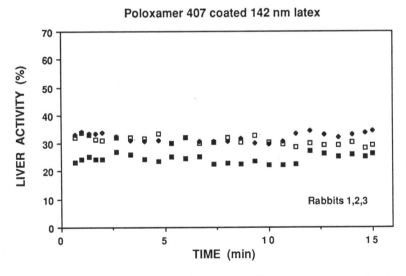

Fig. 8.2.1./5: Uptake of Poloxamer 407 coated 142 nm latex particles by the liver/spleen during the first 15 minutes after i.v. injection (% of total injected activity).

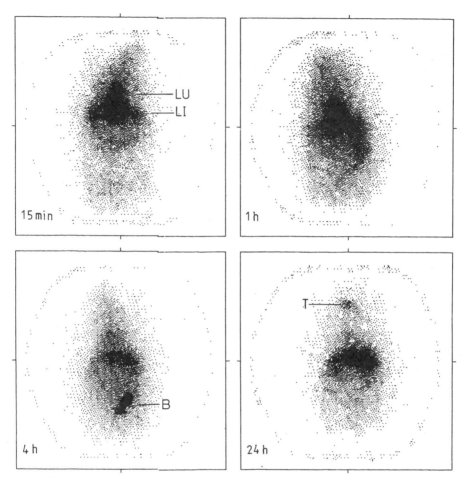

Fig. 8.2.1./6: Scintigrams of i.v. injected 142 nm latex particles coated with Poloxamine 908 (15min., 1 hour, 4 hours and 24 hours). Due to particles circulating in the blood, a high body activity and a lung image were found. (LI - Liver, LU - lung, B - bladder, T - Thyroid).

particles. The Poloxamer 407 coated 142 nm particles showed no accumulation in the bone marrow.

The scintigrams obtained with the Poloxamine and Poloxamer coated particles show a high activity in the liver but also in the lung (LU) and the rest of the body (Fig. 8.2.1./6 and 7). The majority of the injected particles circulate in the blood. The lung and liver images obtained are due to the high blood flow through these organs. After 4 hours, the lung activity decreased and in the scintigram of the Poloxamine coated latex a bladder

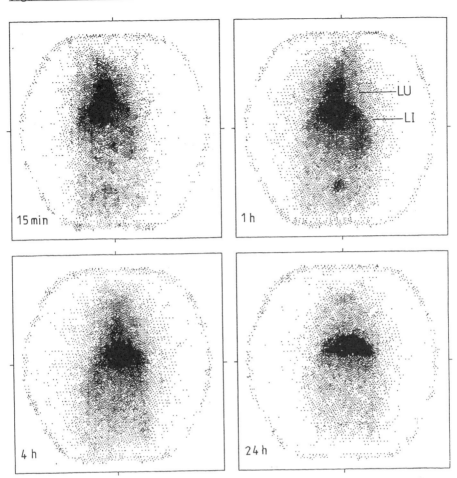

Fig. 8.2.1./7: Scintigrams of i.v. injected 142 nm latex particles coated with Poloxamer 407 (15min., 1 hour, 4 hours and 24 hours). Due to particles circulating in the blood, a high body activity and a lung image were found. (LI - Liver, LU - lung).

image can be seen (due to released label) (Fig. 8.2.1./6). After 24 hours, the lung image has disappeared due to increased uptake of particles by the RES. On dissection day 6, more than 40% of the activity were found in the liver compared to 25-35% on the injection day. However, there is still activity in the rest of the body due to circulating particles. The thyroid (T) could be seen in some of scintigrams due to the accumulation of released radioactive iodine.

The organ distribution of the carriers was monitored over a period of 6

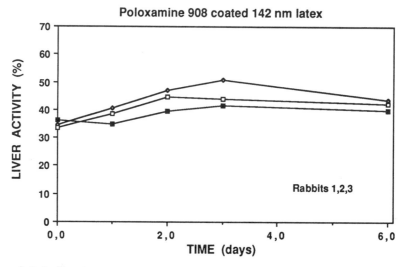

Fig. 8.2.1./8: Activity in liver/spleen region for Poloxamine 908 coated 142 nm latex particles over a period of 6 days (activity 15 min. after injection = day 0).

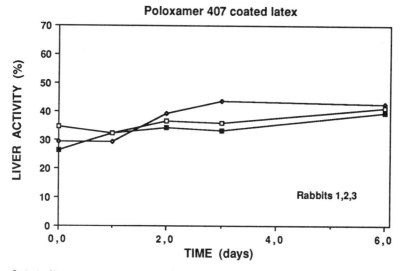

Fig. 8.2.1./9: Activity in liver/spleen region for Poloxamer 407 coated 142 nm latex particles over a period of 6 days (activity 15 min. after injection = day 0).

Organn distribution of Poloxamer/Poloxamine coated 142 nm model carriers

Table 8.2.1./2: Activity in the liver/spleen region of latex 6 days after
injection (% of total body activity).

rabbit number	percentage in liver/spleen region		
	uncoated 142 nm latex	Poloxamine 908 coated latex	Poloxamer 407 coated latex
1	66.3	43.6	42.7
2	54.1	40.1	39.8
3	60.0	42.2	41.3

days. Poloxamine 908 coated <u>60 nm</u> carriers remained in circulation without
an increase in liver uptake with time. For the larger <u>142 nm</u> coated
carriers, a slight increase in activity in the liver/spleen region was
found (Fig. 8.2.1./8 and 9, Table 8.2.1./2) but the activity is much lower
than that obtained with the uncoated latex.

Free radioactive label released from the particles can interfere with the
gamma-scintigraphic assessment of their organ distribution. Within the
first few hours after injection, some iodine is released from the particle
surface and excreted via the bladder. For small latex particles (< 200 nm),
the labelling proved to be stable and only a small amount of label was
released within the first 4 hours. The interference caused would therefore
be negligible.

The stability of the label also needs to be considered when monitoring the
organ distribution over a few days. The <u>rate of release of the label</u> from
the surface might depend on the compartment in which the particles are
located (e.g. liver, serum). The compartmental location may also effect the
<u>rate of excretion</u> of the released label. Iodine released in the serum will
be eliminated via the kidneys more rapidly whereas Iodine released in the
liver will have some affinity for the liver tissue and will therefore be
excreted more slowly. This will contribute to an increase in activity in
the liver/spleen area as observed with the coated 142 nm latex.

It is considered, therefore, that the organ distribution observed within
the first 15 minutes after i.v. injection gives most reliable information
as to the fate of the labelled carriers. The amount of free label in the
injected samples was below 1%. When one considers the time it takes for
free label to appear in the bladder, one can assume that the amount of
iodine released from the particle surface within the first few minutes is
very small. A correction of the data for free label is therefore not
necessary.

After 6 days, the rabbits were dispatched and the radioactivity was

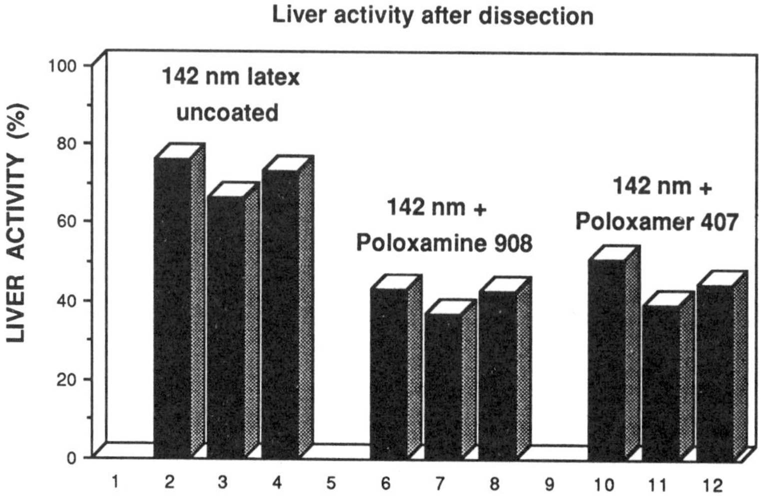

Liver activity after dissection

Fig. 8.2.1./10: Activity in the liver of rabbits 6 days after injection with uncoated and Poloxamine 908 and Poloxamer 407 coated latices.

determined in the organs and the carcass (Fig. 8.2.1./10). Only very low activities were found in the lungs, heart and kidneys. The activity in the liver was much lower for the rabbits injected with coated latex than in those injected with uncoated (control) latex. Little difference was found in uptake by the spleen (142 nm latex: 3.3%; Poloxamine 908 coated latex: 2.2%; Poloxamer 407 coated latex: 2.8%; mean of 3 rabbits).

8.2.2 Organ distribution of 383 nm model carriers

For further investigations on the uptake of larger coated carriers, 383 nm latex particles were coated and injected. Prior to injection the particles were characterized by PCS (Table 8.2.2./1). The coating layers were found to be much thinner on the 383 nm latex than on the 60 nm latex. Also, the affinity of Poloxamer 407 for the particle surface seems to be lower than that of Poloxamine 908. In the Rose Bengal adsorption studies (c.f. chapter 3.4.1) a slightly lower surface hydrophobicity was found for latex particles larger than 100 nm. This difference in particle surface hydrophobicity diminishes the hydrophobic interaction between the polystyrene surface and the Poloxamer and Poloxamine coating polymers resulting in a thinner coating layer.

According to the 'theory of steric stabilization' particles coated with

Table 8.2.2./1: PCS size, polydispersity index and coating layer thickness of uncoated and coated latex particles after radioactive labelling.

latex particles	particle diameter (nm)	standard deviation (nm)	polydispersity index	coating layer (Å)
uncoated	383	3	0.036	-
Poloxamine 908 coated	398	5	0.033	75
Poloxamer 407 coated	393	2	0.049	50

layers of a thickness below 100 Å are not sufficiently sterically stabilized to protect them against macrophage uptake (Davis and Illum, 1988). After i.v. administration they should therefore be cleared from the bloodstream by the RES. However, if one considers the theory of steric stabilization to be invalid, if the particles had correct surface properties they should also remain in circulation (non-charged, hydrophilic). The question was, whether the thinner coating layer imparted the particles with the same surface properties as the thicker coating layers achieved on 60 nm latex.

Injected 383 nm latex particles, coated with Poloxamine 908 were rapidly uptaken by the liver and spleen. After 5 minutes, more than 50% of the injected particle dose was found in the liver/spleen region (Fig. 8.2.2./1), and after 15 minutes 70 to 80% was taken up.

With a slow, but steady increase in liver/spleen activity, however, the clearance of the coated particles was much slower than that of the uncoated particles (Fig. 8.2.1./1).

The coating layer therefore seems to provide some protection against macrophage uptake resulting in a reduced uptake velocity, but insufficient to totally protect against RES clearance. A similar behaviour was found for the Poloxamer 407 coated 383 nm polystyrene particles (Fig. 8.2.2./2). Despite the measured thinner coating layer (50 Å), the clearance velocity seemed to be slightly lower than for Poloxamine 908 coated latex (layer thickness 75 Å).

There are two possible explanations for this behaviour. Firstly the accuracy of the determination of adsorbed layer thicknesses on larger particles by PCS is much lower than on small ones. The standard deviation of PCS is about 1% which is 40 Å for the investigated latex particles. There might therefore be less difference in the coating layer thicknesses (Table 8.2.2./1) than first thought. Another possibility is that the thickness of the coating layer is not as important as the surface

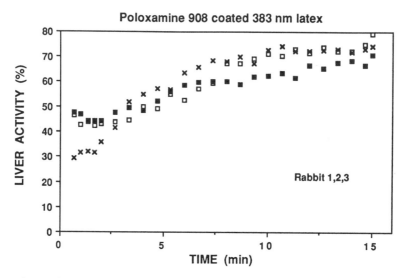

Fig. 8.2.2./1: Uptake of Poloxamine 908 coated 383 nm latex particles by the liver/spleen (% of total injected activity) within the first 15 minutes after i.v. injection.

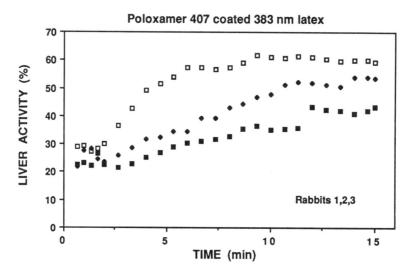

Fig. 8.2.2./2: Uptake of Poloxamer 407 coated 383 nm latex particles by the liver/spleen (% of total injected activity) within the first 15 minutes after i.v. injection).

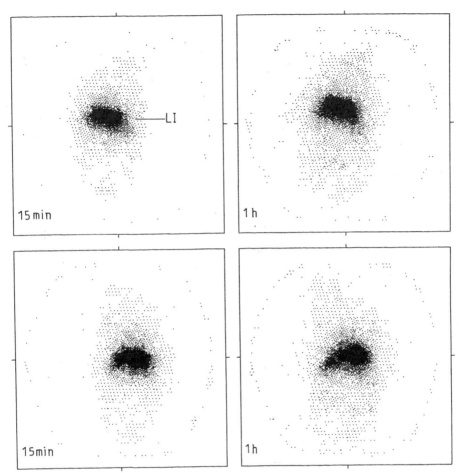

Fig. 8.2.2./3: Scintigrams of i.v. injected 383 nm latex particles coated with Poloxamine 908 (upper) and Poloxamer 407 (lower scintigrams) (left - after 15min., right - after 1 hour). The particles are mainly taken up by the liver (LI).

hydrophilicity. Despite a possibly thinner coating layer, the adsorbed Poloxamer 407 might provide a more hydrophilic surface than the Poloxamine 908 coating.

The scintigrams were similar to the ones obtained with uncoated latex (Fig. 8.2.2./3). A distinct liver image and very little activity in the rest of the body was found. The organ distribution was monitored over a period of 6 days (Fig. 8.2.2./4 and 5). The liver/spleen activities found on day 6 are given in Table 8.2.2./2 (gamma camera data).

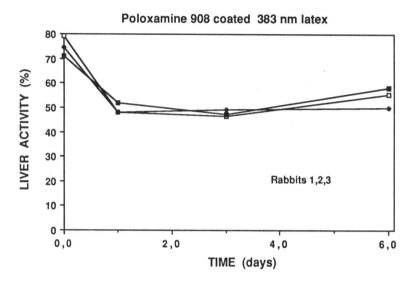

Fig. 8.2.2./4: Activity in liver/spleen region for Poloxamine 908 coated 383 nm latex particles over a period of 6 days.

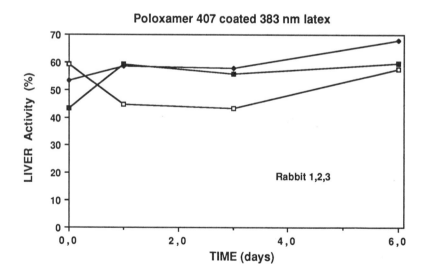

Fig. 8.2.2./5: Activity in liver/spleen region for Poloxamer 407 coated 383 nm latex particles over a period of 6 days.

Table 8.2.2./2: Activity in the liver/spleen region of latex 6 days after
injection (% of total body activity, gamma camera data).

rabbit number	percentage in liver/spleen region		
	uncoated 142 nm latex	383 nm latex coated with	
		Poloxamine 908	Poloxamer 407
1	66.3	55.4	57.4
2	54.1	49.8	68.0
3	60.0	58.2	59.7

After the gamma-camera imaging the rabbits were dispatched and the activity
was counted in the organs and the carcass. There was again little activity
in lung, heart and kidneys. A liver activity of 70 to 80% was found which
is in accordance with literature data for the liver uptake of uncoated
latex particles (Fig. 8.2.2./6). The percentages in the spleen were in the
range found for uncoated latex (3.7% for Poloxamine 908 and 4.0% for
Poloxamer 407 coated latex; mean of 3 rabbits).

To determine the kinetics of liver/spleen uptake, an e-function can be
fitted using the organ counts obtained from the dynamic frames. From the e-

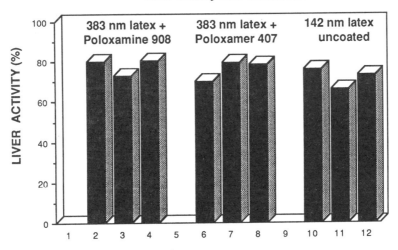

Fig. 8.2.2./6: Activity in liver of rabbits injected with 383 nm latex
coated with Poloxamine 908 and Poloxamer 407, and uncoated 142 nm latex
(dissection on day 6 after injection).

Table 8.2.2./3: Rate constant (s) and time 50 percent (s) cal~culated from the fit of an e-function to the liver/spleen counts obtained from their dynamic frames (1 data point every 20s).

| rabbit no. | 383 nm latex particles coated with | | | |
| | Poloxamine 908 | | Poloxamer 407 | |
	rate const.	t50% (s)	rate const.	t50% (s)
1	3.05 E-3	227	7.28 E-3	95
2	5.58 E-3	124	1.79 E-3	387
3	2.01 E-3	345	2.41 E-3	288

function fit the rate constant can be obtained and the time after which 50% of the total particle dose were taken up by the liver can be calculated (Table 8.2.2./3).

For uncoated latex particles, a proper fit cannot be performed because the uptake is very fast (< 2 min) and there are therefore insufficient data points for a fit (Fig. 8.2.2./7). A similar situation is found with

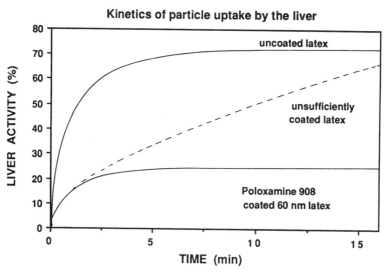

Fig. 8.2.2./7: Liver/spleen uptake of uncoated latex, latex protected against phagocytosis by Poloxamine 908 coating, and latex insufficiently coated (e.g. 383 nm particles). The insufficient coating can not avoid RES recognition and phagocytosis of the particles by the liver and spleen, but it reduces the uptake velocity.

particles protected against liver uptake (e.g. Poloxamine 908 coated 60 nm latex). The blood pool of 25% of the total injected activity is reached in a time shorter than 2 minutes. Only for particles coated less effectively and therefore taken up by the liver much slower, a rate constant and time 50% can be calculated (Fig. 8.2.2./7). The calculation is based on the counts measured during the first 7 minutes after injection.

8.2.3. Organ distribution of 496 nm model carriers

To investigate the fate of coated carriers larger than 383 nm after i.v. injection, 496 nm polystyrene latex particles were coated with Poloxamine 908 and Poloxamer 407. After labelling, and prior to injection the particles were characterized by PCS (Table 8.2.3./1).

Table 8.2.3./1: PCS size, polydispersity index and coating layer thickness of uncoated and coated latex particles after radioactive labelling and prior to injection.

latex particles	particle diameter (nm)	standard deviation (nm)	polydis-persity index	coating layer
uncoated	496	6	0.066	-
Poloxamine 908 coated	469	5	0.027	YES
Poloxamer 407 coated	491	7	0.049	YES

The size of the latex after coating was below that of the uncoated particles. This is due to the removal of aggregates from the latex by the sterically stabilizing coating polymers, resulting in a decrease in the polydispersity index. The decrease in the polydispersity index proves that coating took place. However, a coating layer thickness cannot be calculated in the usual way. The size decrease due to de-aggregation in the latex suspension is much larger than the expected size increase due to polymer adsorption. The coating with Poloxamine 908 might be greater than that with Poloxamer 407 as indicated by a stronger decrease in the polydispersity index.

Particles not used for injection were stored for 3 days and again characterized by PCS measurements. As was seen for biodegradable particles (cyanoacrylates, PHB), irradiation treatment led to particle flocculation. Although this was not observed for small latex (60 nm), the 496 nm

Table 8.2.3./2: PCS size, polydispersity index and coating layer thickness
of uncoated and coated latex particles after radioactive labelling and 3
days of storage.

latex particles	particle diameter (nm)	size increase (nm)	polydis- persity index	polydisp. index increase
uncoated	540	44	0.133	+0.077
Poloxamine 908 coated	489	20	0.082	+0.055
Poloxamer 407 coated	506	15	0.095	+0.046

particles showed an increase in size due to particle aggregation (Table
8.2.3./2) as indicated by the higher polydispersity index. However, the
increase in size and polydispersity index for the coated latices was
minimal, again indicating the presence of coating layers. Determination of
the coating layer thickness could be performed by zeta potential measurements (c.f. chapter 9).

Injection of the Poloxamine 908-coated particles led to a liver/spleen
uptake of 40 to 50% within the first 15 minutes (Fig. 8.2.3./1). No
increases in uptake were found within 6 days after injection (Fig.
8.2.3./2). Similar results were obtained with the Poloxamer .407 coated
latex (Fig. 8.2.3./3 and 4).

The scintigrams obtained with the coated particles show a distinct liver
image and little activity in the rest of the body (Fig. 8.2.3./5).

The calculated liver uptake of 50% of the particles appeared to be too low.
After counting the activity in the organs on day 6, a total liver and
spleen activity of up to 80% were found. This is similar to the value
obtained for uncoated latex particles which are rapidly cleared by the RES
(Fig. 8.2.3./6). For the spleen an activity of 5.2% for the Poloxamine 908,
and of 3.4% for the Poloxamer 407 coated carriers was found in organ
counting (mean of 3 rabbits).

The labelling efficiency of these latex particles was relatively poor (17%)
and the injected activity was lower than used in other studies. This lower
activity necessitated longer imaging times and the relatively high background counts led to distortions. This could account for the fact that
uptake as determined by gamma-scintigraphy was only around 50%. From the
organ counts, it was clear that the coated 496 nm latex had been cleared by
the RES in a similar way to the coated 383 nm particles. In both cases,
polymer coating took place but was insufficient to effectively protect
against RES clearance.

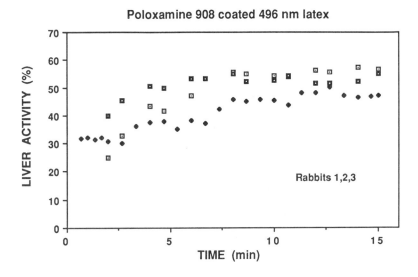

Fig. 8.2.3./1: Uptake of Poloxamine 908 coated 496 nm latex particles by the liver/spleen (% of total injected activity) within the first 15 minutes after i.v. injection.

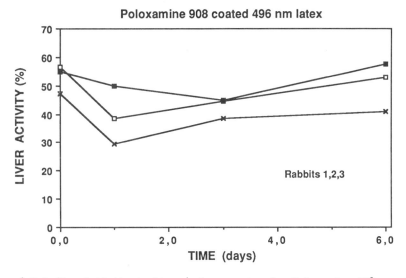

Fig. 8.2.3./2: Activity in liver/spleen region for Poloxamine 908 coated 496 nm latex particles over a period of 6 days.

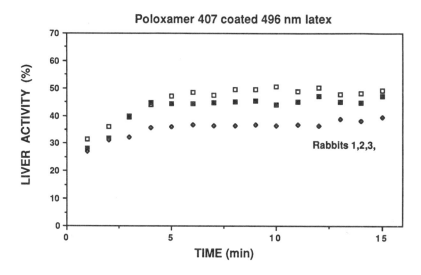

Fig. 8.2.3./3: Uptake of Poloxamer 407 coated 496 nm latex particles by the liver/spleen (% of total injected activity) within the first 15 minutes after i.v. injection.

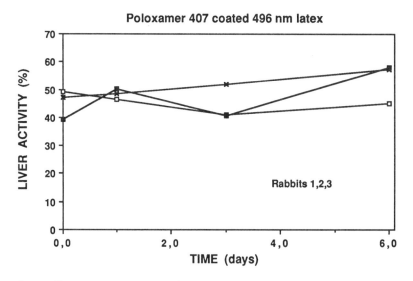

Fig. 8.2.3./4: Activity in liver/spleen region for Poloxamer 407 coated 496 nm latex particles over a period of 6 days.

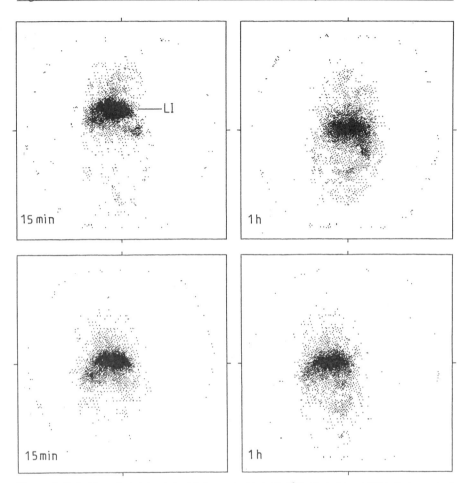

Fig. 8.2.3./5: Scintigrams of i.v. injected 383 nm latex particles coated with Poloxamine 908 (upper) and Poloxamer 407 (lower scintigrams) (left - after 15min., right - after 1 hour). The particles are mainly taken up by the liver (LI).

Calculations of the rate constants and the time 50% should be less affected by the low activity used than measures of the total liver uptake. For the 496 nm coated latex larger rate constants and shorter times 50% were obtained (Table 8.2.3./3).

Considering the results from the organ counts, the total uptake by the RES (liver/spleen) seems to be similar for 383 nm and 496 nm coated latex, whereas the uptake velocity might be increased for the larger coated particles. To determine whether the observed effects are due to the larger

Liver activity after dissection

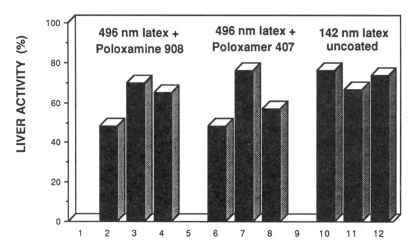

Fig. 8.2.3./6 Activity in the liver of rabbits injected with 496 nm latex coated with Poloxamine 908 and Poloxamer 407, and uncoated 142 nm latex (dissection on day 6 after injection).

Table 8.2.3./3: Rate constant (s) and time 50% (s) percent calculated from the fit of an e-function to the liver/spleen counts obtained from their dynamic frames (1 data point every 20s).

| rabbit no. | 496 nm latex particles coated with | | | |
| | Poloxamine 908 | | Poloxamer 407 | |
	rate const.	t50% (s)	rate const.	t50% (s)
1	3.63 E-3	190	9.07 E-3	76
2	9.51 E-3	72	16.00 E-3	43
3	5.01 E-3	138	7.42 E-3	93

size of the coated carriers, the thinner coating layer (and consequently reduced steric stabilization) and/or differences in surface properties of the coating layer, the carriers were investigated using HIC and charge measurements (c.f. chapter 9).

8.2.4. Organ distribution of 910 nm model carriers

After the high liver/spleen uptake of coated latex particles in the size range 400 to 500 nm it seemed that it would be impossible to obtain a protective coating on even larger 910 nm latex particles. Radioactive labelling using NaI-131 and gamma-irradiation was inefficient (about 5% labelling efficiency). Loss of latex due to labelling problems meant that only one rabbit was injected with each type of particle. Characterization of the irradiated latex particles by PCS proved that coating took place (Table 8.2.4./1). Coating of the particles removed aggregates and resulted in a size decrease compared to the uncoated latex. The Poloxamine 908 coating seemed to be more efficient than the one with Poloxamer 407 as indicated by a stronger decrease in size. In general however, the particle populations were very polydisperse. Again, a coating layer thickness could not be calculated due to the size decrease.

Table 8.2.4./1: PCS size, polydispersity index and coating layer thickness of uncoated and coated latex particles after radioactive labelling.

latex particles	particle diameter (nm)	standard deviation (nm)	polydispersity index	coating layer
uncoated	910	25	0.140	-
Poloxamine 908 coated	734	17	0.182	YES
Poloxamer 407 coated	881	11	0.155	YES

The scintigrams could not be analysed because of the low activity injected and the high background counts. The rabbits were dispatched after 6 days as before and the activity in the organs was determined. A similar liver uptake was found for uncoated and Poloxamer 407 coated latex (53,7% and 53.4% respectively) and the liver activity for the Poloxamine 908 coated latex was slightly lower (40.6%). The spleen uptakes were 2.2%, 0.7% and 1.2%, respectively. Despite the small sample number, these and previously obtained results indicated that effective coating of particles larger than 150 nm was not possible.

8.2.5. The organ distribution of different size model carriers

The coating of particles with surfactants can protect them against phagocytosis by different macrophage populations. Coating of 60 nm poly-styrene latex with Poloxamine 908 protects them against uptake by liver/spleen macrophages and by phagocytic cells in the bone marrow (Illum et al, 1987). 60 nm particles coated with Poloxamer 407 are not phagocy-tosed by liver/spleen macrophages, but are taken up by the bone marrow (80%) (Illum and Davis, 1987). Increasing the size of the Poloxamer 407 coated latex (e.g. 142 nm particles) restricts the access of the particles to the bone marrow across the sinusoid-fenestrations (fenestration size appr. 90 nm, c.f. 8.3.). Because they are protected from liver/spleen uptake the particles circulate in the blood stream in a similar manner to Poloxamine 908 coated particles. The organ distribution of Poloxamer 407 coated particles therefore depends on their size limiting physically the access to a tissue (bone marrow).

To determine whether coating of different size latex particles with

Table 8.2.5./1: Ratio of the activity in different organs calculated on the basis of the total activity per organ or the activity per gram organ (n = 3 rabbits, * n = 2).

latex particle size (nm)	coating	ratio of organ counts liver/spleen	counts per gram organ liver/spleen	liver/bone	spleen/bone
142	none	23	0.17	8.7	35.8*
	908	20	0.17	6.2	23.0*
	407	16	0.23	3.2	13.8
383	908	21	0.24	16.6	71.5
	407	20	0.24*	13.3	48.4
496	908	14	0.18	7.5	41.8
	407	15*	0.27*	9.9*	36.4

The organ distribution of different size model carriers

Poloxamine 908 or Poloxamer 407 altered their affinity for different organs, the ratios of the activities in the liver, spleen and bone marrow were calculated (Table 8.2.5./1). The ratio of the organ counts can however be misleading if one of the organs is much smaller or larger than average. An average spleen of NZW rabbits (2 - 3 kg) is around 1.5 g, but spleens of 0.5 and 2.8 g have been found. To correct for the organ size, the activity per gram tissue was also calculated. If the organ anomalies were too large, a mean of only 2 rabbits (*n=2) is calculated.

The activity ratios of the liver to spleen showed little difference between particles coated with the two polymers. However, for the 142 nm latex, the ratios of liver to bone marrow and spleen to bone marrow were lower for Poloxamer 407 than for Poloxamine 908 coated latex, or uncoated latex indicating a higher affinity for the bone marrow. This could possibly be explained by the presence of latex particles which are much smaller than the mean size of 142 nm. These particles would still have access to the bone marrow via the fenestrations of the sinusoids.

In the larger size latex (383 and 496 nm), only a few very small particles with access to the bone marrow were present and similar liver/bone and spleen/bone ratios were obtained for particles coated with the two polymers.

8.3. Organ distribution of ethoxylated nonylphenol coated latex

Ethoxylated phenols such as Antarox CO and Gafac RE surfactants are
possible replacements for Poloxamer and Poloxamine polymers. They provide a
hydrophobic anchor group (nonyl-phenol) and EO chains of a length of up to
100 units. It has been shown that Antarox CO990 and Gafac RE960 form
coating layers on 60 nm latex particles of a thickness of 70 to 80 Å (c.f.
2.2.). For Gafac RE 960 such a thick coating could only be achieved in the
presence of physiological salt concentrations. These thicknesses are
similar to those obtained with Poloxamer 188 which led to a reduction in
the liver uptake of coated particles (appr. 20%) (Illum et al., 1986). If
steric stabilization works, Antarox and Gafac coating layers should lead to
a similar reduction in the liver uptake as observed with Poloxamine 908.
Latex particles (67 and 142 nm) were coated with Antarox CO 990 and 76 nm
latex with Gafac RE960, the latter in physiological NaCl solution. It was
hoped that the Antarox CO990 particles would show reduced liver uptake
similar to that found with Poloxamer 188 coated latex (Illum and Davis,
1983). Gafac RE960 has a similar structure to Antarox CO990 but has a
charged group at the end of the EO chain. Comparison of the distribution of
latex particles coated with the negatively charged Gafac RE960 and the
uncharged Antarox CO990 should give some indication as to the importance of
the charge in determining their biofate. Both coatings should provide a
similar steric protection against macrophage uptake.

8.3.1. Organ distribution of Gafac RE960 coated 76 nm latex

Injection of the 76 nm latex coated with Gafac RE960 led to a rapid uptake
by the liver and spleen (Fig. 8.3./1). The uptake profile is identical to
that obtained for uncoated latex. Within the first 2 minutes, more than 50%
of the injected particles were found in the liver/spleen region. This rapid
uptake indicates no protection was afforded by the sterically stabilizing,
but charged coating polymer Gafac RE960.
These results demonstrate that steric stabilization cannot protect against
macrophage uptake when the particles are immunologically recognizable due
to the presence of charged groups on the coating layer. The organ
distribution of the Gafac RE960 coated particles was monitored over a
period of six days, after which the rabbits were dispatched. The activity
in the organs was determined. Mean liver and spleen activities of 68% and
1.5% respectively were found (control of uncoated latex 72% and 3.9%).

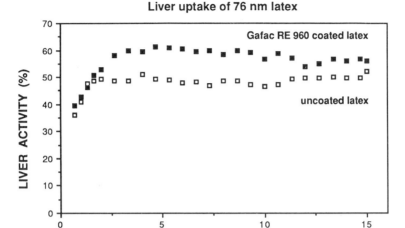

Fig. 8.3./1: Uptake of uncoated and Gafac RE960 coated 76 nm latex particles in the liver/spleen within the first 15 min. after injection (n=3).

8.3.2. Organ distribution of Antarox CO990 coated 142 nm latex

Injection of 142 nm latex coated with Antarox CO990 led to a reduction in the velocity of uptake by the liver/spleen (Fig. 8.3./2) similar to that found with Poloxamine 908 and Poloxamer 407 coated 383nm latex particles. The total activity in the liver and spleen after 15 minutes was distinctly below that found for uncoated 142 nm latex. In a similar way to the coated 383 nm latex, the liver/spleen activity increased further with time (Fig. 8.3./3). After 6 days the rabbits were dispatched and the organ activity determined. Low activities were found in the lungs, heart and kidneys. The liver and spleen activities were similar to those found for uncoated 142 nm latex (Fig. 8.3./4).

A total protection against liver/spleen uptake was not expected because of the thinner coating layer provided by Antarox CO990 (70 - 80 Å) compared with Poloxamine 908 and Poloxamer 407 (130 to 150 Å, as measured on 60 nm latex!). However, the reduction in uptake (during the first 15 minutes) is similar to the one reported with Poloxamer 188 (Illum et al., 1986) and demonstrates that the Poloxamers and Poloxamines can be replaced by molecules providing a hydrophobic anchor group and a hydrophilic chain which creates a hydrophilic surface. Attachment of charged groups to such chains leads to recognition by the body (Gafac RE960) indicating that

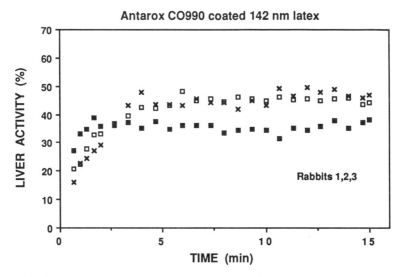

Fig. 8.3./2: Uptake of Antarox C0990 coated 142 nm latex particles by the liver/spleen (% of total injected activity) within the first 15 minutes after i.v. injection.

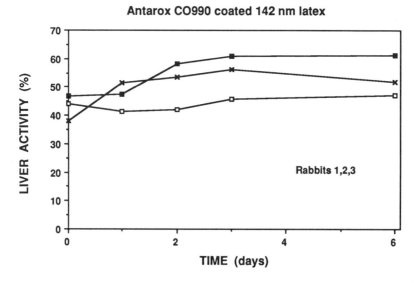

Fig. 8.3./3: Activity in liver/spleen region for Antarox C0990 coated 142 nm latex particles over a period of 6 days.

246

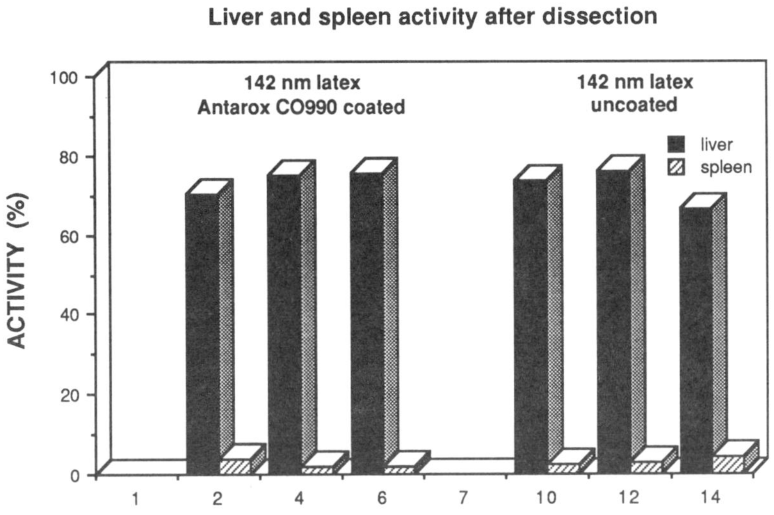

Liver and spleen activity after dissection

142 nm latex
Antarox CO990 coated

142 nm latex
uncoated

■ liver
▨ spleen

ACTIVITY (%)

100
80
60
40
20
0

1 2 4 6 7 10 12 14

Fig. 8.3./4: Activity in the liver and the spleen of rabbits injected with 142 nm latex uncoated and coated with Antarox CO990 (dissection on day 6 after injection).

surface properties (uncharged and hydrophilic) rather than steric stabilization are the determining factors.
To provide complete protection against liver/spleen uptake, the structure of the Antarox CO990 molecule needs to be modified (e.g. elongation of the EO chain to 150 to 200 units). Chemical modification and synthesis of new coating materials is currently underway.

8.3.3. Organ distribution of Antarox CO990 coated 76 nm latex

As shown with the Poloxamine/Poloxamer coated 142 nm latex, the coating layers are thinner compared to 60 nm particles. Therefore, smaller latex particles (76.3 nm) were coated with Antarox CO990 and injected. The coating layer of >70 Å increased the size of the coated particles to around 90 nm. The size of the fenestrations in the liver sinusoids is around 100nm, but varies slightly between individuals and is affected by physical conditions (e.g. ethanol leads to a dilation of fenestrations). The coated 76nm latex was therefore close to the threshold size which restricts access to the bone marrow.
In two rabbits (nos. 1 and 2, c.f. figures) a slightly increasing liver uptake was observed during the first 15 minutes after the injection (Fig.

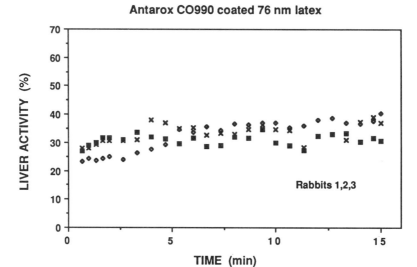

Antarox CO990 coated 76 nm latex

Fig. 8.3./5: Uptake of Antarox CO990 coated 76 nm latex particles by the liver/spleen (% of total injected activity) within the first 15 minutes after i.v. injection.

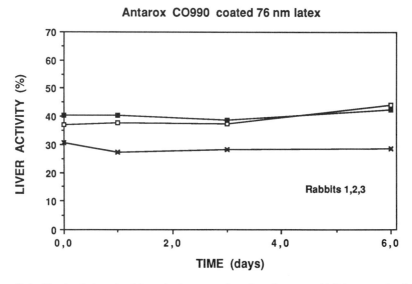

Antarox CO990 coated 76 nm latex

Fig. 8.3./6: Activity in liver/spleen region for Antarox CO990 coated 76 nm latex particles over a period of 6 days. The liver activity for rabbit 3 is lower due to some uptake by the bone marrow.

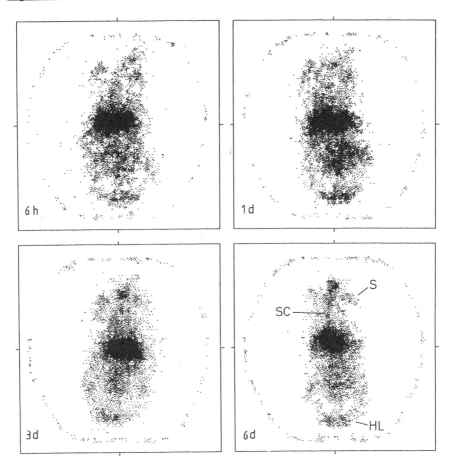

Fig. 8.3./7: Scintigrams obtained with Antarox CO990 coated 76 nm latex in rabbit no. 3 (after 4 hours, 1, 3 and 6 days). Especially the scintigram on day 6 shows activity in the bones such as spinal column, hind leg and shoulder girdle region similar to Poloxamer 407 particles taken up by the bone marrow. The liver activity is due to the particles in the blood pool of the liver and particles taken up by Kupffer cells.

8.3./5). The total uptake was reduced to 35 to 40% and showed little change over a period of 6 days (Fig. 8.3./6).
As the coating layer of Antarox CO990 is thinner and less hydrophilic (as shown by PCS and HIC) than that of Poloxamer/Poloxamine, this reduced protection against RES clearance was expected. In these two rabbits the sinusoidal fenestrations seemed to be smaller than the bulk of the particles restricting their access to the bone marrow.

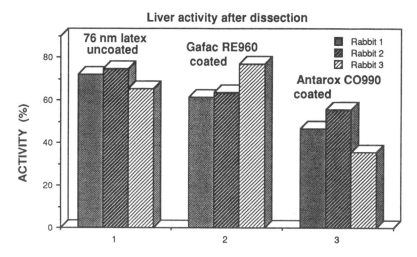

Fig. 8.3./8: Liver uptake of rabbits injected with uncoated, Gafac RE960 and Antarox CO990 coated 76 nm latex. One rabbit injected with Antarox coated latex shows a relatively low liver uptake due to some accumulation of particles in the bone marrow.

In one rabbit (no. 3) the fenestration size seemed to be larger allowing access of a larger number of particles to the bone marrow. The liver uptake showed no increase with time (Fig. 8.3./5 and 6) similar to Poloxamine 908 coated 60 nm latex. The total uptake at about 30% was however slightly higher than that measured with the Poloxamine 908 coated latex (25%) and Poloxamer 407 coated latex which had no access to the bone marrow (size of coated carrier > 125 nm). The scintigrams obtained with the Antarox coated 76 nm particles in this rabbit show some similarity to the scintigrams obtained with Poloxamer 407 coated 60 nm latex (Illum and Davis, 1987). However, a liver image due to particles circulating in the blood or taken up by the liver/spleen could be seen (Fig. 8.3./7).

On day 6 the rabbits were dispatched and the radioactivity in the organs was determined. Again, low activities were found for the lungs, heart and kidneys. For the two rabbits with smaller sinusoidal fenestrations (nos. 1 and 2) which prevented access of the injected coated particles to the bone marrow, liver uptakes of 46% and 56% were found. This is below the uptake measured with uncoated latex particles of this size (around 70%) (Fig. 8.3./8). For the third rabbit (no. 3) a liver activity of only 36% was found.

The Gafac RE 960 coated 76 nm latex accumulated to a similar extent in the liver as the uncoated control (60 to 80%, Fig. 8.3./8) indicating no

protection by the sterically stabilizing but charged coating. The mean
spleen activities were 3.5% and 2.5% for uncoated and Gafac RE960 coated
latex respectively, and 1.6% for the Antarox C0990 coated particles.

8.3.4. Organ affinity of ethoxylated nonylphenol coated latex

To assess changes in the affinities for the different organs, the ratio of
activities in the liver, spleen and bone were calculated (c.f. 8.2.5.)
(Table 8.3./1).
For uncoated 142 nm latex particles and those coated with Poloxamine 908
and Poloxamer 407 little difference was found in the liver/spleen ratio of
the total counts. However, for the 142 nm latex coated with Antarox C0990
an increased ratio of 34 was found indicating a slight shift in the uptake
from the spleen to the liver. The same trend was seen for the liver/spleen
ratio calculated as counts per gram tissue.
As for Poloxamer 407 coated 142 nm latex, the liver/bone and spleen/bone
ratios decreased indicating some affinity to the bone marrow (6.8 and 26.1

Table 8.3./1: Ratio of the activity in different organs calculated on the
basis of the total activity per organ or the activity per gram tissue (n =
3 rabbits, * n = 2). Coating materials: 908 = Poloxamine 908; 407 =
Poloxamer 407; C0990 = Antarox C0990; RE960 = Gafac RE960 (C0990** - n=1).

latex particle size (nm)	coating	ratio of organ counts liver/spleen	counts per gram organ liver/spleen	liver/bone	spleen/bone
142	none	23	0.17	8.7	35.8*
	C0990	34	0.27	6.8	26.1
	908	20	0.17	6.2	23.0*
	407	16	0.23	3.2	13.8
76	none	21	0.30	9.9	35.4
	RE960	52	1.06	12.1	15.3
	C0990	42	0.44	2.6	8.4
	C0990**	33	0.66	2.0	3.3

respectively). The decrease in these ratios was less distinct for the Antarox CO990 coated latex because of the competitive uptake by liver/spleen macrophages and phagocytosing cells in the bone marrow. The Poloxamer 407 coated latex particles are only taken up by phagocytosing bone marrow cells and not by liver and spleen macrophages, leading to much lower ratios (3.2 and 13.8 respectively, control 8.7 and 35.8).

The smaller 76 nm Antarox CO990 coated latex particles showed a similar shift in the organ affinity as the 142 nm coated ones. The liver/spleen ratio increased to 42 (control 23) and the liver/bone and spleen/bone ratio decreased to 2.6 and 8.4 respectively (control 9.9 and 35.4, Table 8.3./1). In one rabbit (no. 3) a very different distribution was found (CO990** in Table 8.3./1), possibly due to the presence of larger sinusoid-fenestrations allowing the particles more access to the bone marrow. This led to a further decrease in the ratio of liver and spleen to the bone. However, the shift from spleen to liver observed with the other coated Antarox CO990 particles was also found.

Although a decrease in liver uptake was expected for the Gafac RE960 coated particles, they were cleared by the RES. This was most likely due to the charge of the coating and the general opsonization due to a surface which was found to be more hydrophobic than a Poloxamine 908 coating layer (c.f. HIC results, chapter 9). The Gafac RE960 coated particles showed an even more distinct shift in their organ affinity. The liver/spleen ratio increased from 21 (control) to 52 (total counts per organ) and from 0.30 (control) to 1.06 (counts per gram tissue). This indicates that it might be possible to alter the organ uptake by chemical modification of the coating polymers. It is unlikely that macrophage subpopulations are able to recognize the differences in the chemical structure of the polymer. Possibly differences in surface hydrophobicity change the affinity for different opsonic factors. The variation in the composition of the adsorbed opsonins might lead to a preferential uptake by one macrophage population. Compared with the control, the uptake ratio liver/bone increased for Gafac RE960 coated particles. This is not caused by a reduction in the bone marrow uptake but by the preferential uptake of the particles by the liver rather than the spleen. Consequently, the spleen/bone ratio decreased.

The behaviour of the Gafac RE960 coated particles does not support the theory that steric stabilization protects against phagocytosis by the RES. After their recognition as foreign (due to charge of phosphoric acid group, adsorption of opsonins on hydrophobic surface), the Gafac RE960 coated particles are taken up. Compared to uncoated latex, the affinity for Kupffer cells was increased and reduced for spleen macrophages. Coating materials with such properties can be employed to increase the target specifity to macrophage subpopulations of the RES or to improve the organ specifity.

8.4. Organ distribution of carriers and fat emulsions surface-modified with ethoxylated glycerides

Coating of 60 nm polystyrene latex particles was performed using ethoxy-lated monoglycerides (Tagat series, c.f. chapter 2.4.). Most of the Tagat surfactants led to a coating layer of around 25 Å (e.g. Tagat I). However, for Tagat R60 (an ethoxylated castor oil) a layer thickness of 74 Å (similar to that seen with Poloxamer 188) was found.

For preliminary studies about the effect of coating with these compounds, 60 nm latex particles coated with Tagat R60 and Tagat I respectively were injected into rabbits (n=1 because of the preliminary nature of the study). Tagat R60 was selected because of the relatively thick coating layer. Tagat I led to the most efficient charge reduction of the coated particles as measured in distilled water (by 17.3 mV).

Injection of the Tagat I coated latex led to a rapid liver/spleen uptake similar to the control of uncoated particles (Fig. 8.4./1). Within about two minutes, 60% of the injected particles were taken up. Parallel to the liver/spleen uptake, the activity in the hind leg region dropped from 17% to 14% (Fig. 8.4./1). The coating afforded no protection against RES uptake.

Injection of Tagat R60 coated latex particles reduced the uptake velocity of the particles to a level similar to 383nm latex coated with Poloxamine

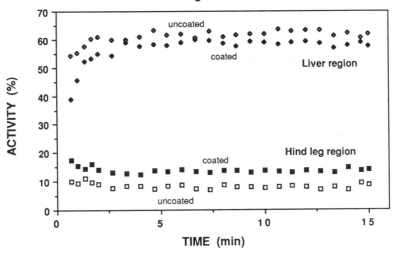

Fig. 8.4./1: Liver and hind leg uptake of uncoated (control) and Tagat I coated 60 nm latex particles within the first 15 minutes after injection (n=1).

Uncoated and Tagat R60 coated 60 nm latex

Fig. 8.4./2: Liver and hind leg uptake of uncoated (control) and Tagat R60 coated 60 nm latex particles within the first 15 minutes after injection (n=1).

908 and Poloxamer 407 (c.f. 8.2.2.). This indicates some (although insufficient) protection against phagocytosis. Although the uptake velocity is slower, after 15 minutes 50% of the particles are located in the liver/spleen region (Fig. 8.4./2). The scintigrams of both types of coated-particle show a clear liver image after 15 minutes (Fig. 8.4./3).

No change in the body distribution was found over a period of 8 days (Fig. 8.4./4 and 5). The spleen activity in the rabbit injected with Tagat R60 coated particles was relatively low (only 1.0%, control 4.0%).

Calculation of the ratios of organ activity showed that the Tagat I coated latex behaved similarly to uncoated particles. Coating with Tagat R60 lead to a shift in uptake from the spleen to the liver (higher liver/spleen ratios), as previously seen with the Antarox C0990 coated latex (Table 8.4./1). The liver/bone and spleen/bone ratios were reduced by similar extents for Tagat R60 and Antarox C0990 coatings. Antarox surfactants are composed of a small hydrophobic region which anchors them to the particle surface and one hydrophilic EO chain which forms the hydrophilic surface of the coating layer. Tagat surfactants are monoglycerides with a small content of diglycerides (hydrophobic part) and one or two attached EO chains. Poloxamers are composed of a hydrophobic propylene oxide centre region with two EO chains, one attached at either end.

In contrast Poloxamine 908 has a large hydrophobic centre region (4

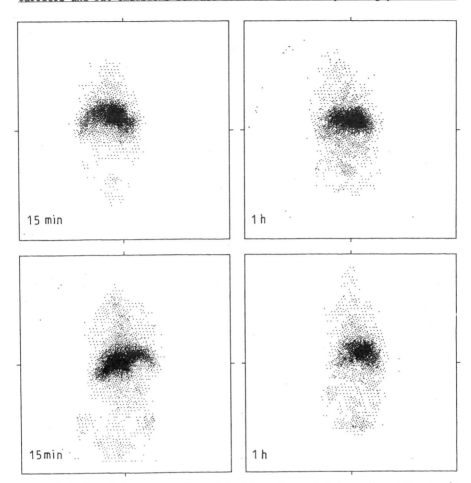

Fig. 8.4./3: Scintigrams after injection of Tagat I (upper) and Tagat R60 coated latex particles (lower scintigrams, left = after 15 min., right = after 1 hour).

propylene oxide blocks) which contains 2 nitrogen atoms (whose pH-dependent protonation might influence the coating layer thickness) with <u>four</u> EO chains attached.

It is possible that the structural similarities between Antarox/Tagat and Poloxamer surfactants could lead to a similar affinity to the bone marrow for coated particles. The Antarox CO990 and Tagat R60 coatings are however thin and too hydrophobic to provide protection against liver/spleen uptake. The liver/spleen uptake is faster than the uptake by the phagocytic cells in the bone marrow leading to much less accumulation in the bone marrow

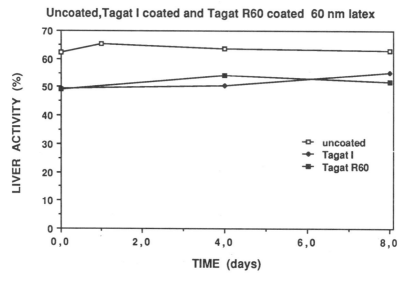

Fig. 8.4./4: Liver activity in rabbits injected with uncoated, Tagat I and Tagat R60 coated 60 nm latex particles over a period of 8 days.

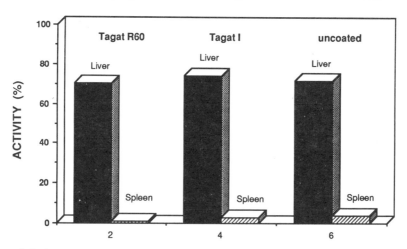

Fig. 8.4./5: Activity in Liver and spleen after injection of uncoated, Tagat I and Tagat R60 coated 60 nm latex particles, organ counting data (on day 8 (n=1)).

Table 8.4./1: Ratio of the activity in different organs calculated on the basis of the total activity per organ or the activity per gram tissue (n = 3 rabbits, * n = 2). Coating materials: CO990 = Antarox CO990 (n=2, CO990** - n=1); RE960 = Gafac RE960; Tagat I and R60 (n=1).

latex particle size (nm)	coating	ratio of organ counts liver spleen	counts per gram organ liver spleen	liver bone	spleen bone
142	none	23	0.17	8.7	35.8*
76	none	21	0.30	9.9	35.4
	CO990	42	0.44	2.6	8.4
	CO990**	33	0.66	2.0	3.3
60	Tagat I	24	0.33	16.2	48.5
	Tagat R60	74	0.62	3.4	5.5

than Poloxamer 407 coated particles. Scintigrams showing a clear skeletal but no liver image present are obtained approximately one hour after injection. The injected particles circulate in the blood stream and are slowly taken up by the bone marrow. In contrast to bone marrow uptake, liver clearance (when it occurs), occurs very rapidly leading to a particle uptake of 60 to 80% within 2 to 5 minutes.

In contrast to the Poloxamer 407 coatings, Antarox, Gafac and Tagat coatings led to a shift in the organ affinity from the spleen to the liver. To target to the liver and to reduce the simultaneous spleen uptake, passive targeting using uncoated particles could be replaced by carriers coated with Gafac RE960 or structurally similar molecules. An overview of the effects observed with carriers differing in size and coating polymers is given in Table 8.4./2.

As mentioned above, the 90 nm Antarox CO990-coated carriers are close to the size for exclusion from the bone marrow. Injection of carriers smaller than the fenestration diameter (e.g. 80nm) could conceivably lead to an accumulation in the bone marrow without liver uptake (investigations are in progress). Modification of the Tagat R60 molecule by elongation of the EO chain and removal of lipophilic components might lead to either increased

Table 8.4./2: Summary of the organ distribution of carriers differing in size and polymer coating. The carrier size is recorded as the size after coating (- size of uncoated latex particle plus twice the coating layer thickness). Particles larger than 100 nm do not have access to the bone marrow because of the restrictive size of the sinusoidal fenestrations.

coating polymer	carrier size	bone marrow uptake	blood circulation	liver uptake	shift spleen to liver
Poloxamine 908	> 100 nm	no	yes	no	no
Poloxamer 407		no	yes	no	no
Antarox C0990		no	no	yes	+
Poloxamine 908	< 90 nm	no	yes	no	no
Poloxamer 407		yes	no	no	no
Antarox C0990	90 nm	yes	no	yes	++
Gafac RE960		no	no	yes	+++
Tagat R60	85 nm	little	no	yes	++++

bone marrow and/or reduced liver uptake and/or changes in the affinity for different macrophage populations.

Tagat R60 is poorly chemically characterized. Its production by the ethoxylation of castor oil will not lead to a uniform product and it is very likely that it contains lipophilic contaminants, due to little or no ethoxylation. These lipophilic contaminants will adsorb onto the particle surface during coating with Tagat R60. The resulting surface will be more hydrophobic than that obtained with purified surfactant. The increased hydrophobicity will lead to increased liver/spleen uptake after i.v. administration.

It may be possible to purify Tagat R60 by the use of Hydrophobic Interaction Chromatography (HIC). A much simpler way of employing Tagat R60 is to use it as an emulsifier in the production of a soya oil parenteral fat emulsions. Ethoxylated products will localize in the interface between the dispersed oil droplets and the water. The lipophilic part of the molecule will partition into the oil phase and the hydrophilic EO chains will protrude into the water to produce a Tagat R60-coated carrier with a

SOYA OIL EMULSION   COATED POLYMERIC CARRIER

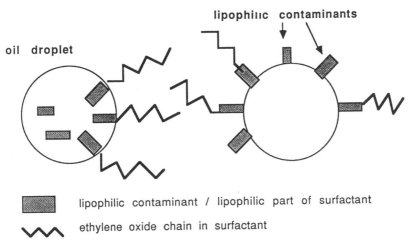

lipophilic contaminant / lipophilic part of surfactant

ethylene oxide chain in surfactant

Fig. 8.4./6: Surface modification of carriers by Tagat R60 adsorption on a polymeric carrier and by production of a soya oil fat emulsion with Tagat R60 as emulsifier. In the oil droplet lipophilic contaminants in Tagat are removed from the interface by partitioning into the lipophilic oil core of the droplet leading to a more hydrophilic carrier surface.

hydrophilic surface. Lipophilic contaminants will partition into the oil core of the droplets (Fig. 8.4./6) and therefore not contaminate the hydrophilic surface.

A fat emulsion containing 10% soya oil and 1.2 % Tagat R60 was produced by pre-emulsification with a Silverson homogenizer and subsequent sonication with a Dawe sonic probe for 5 minutes at 100 Watt. The oil was labelled with lasolocid containing In-111 as radioactive marker. The emulsion was characterized by PCS and found to have a mean diameter of 379 nm and a polydispersity index of 0.279. The polydispersity index is in the upper range found for commercial fat emulsions used in parenteral nutrition (0.100 to 0.250). No particles larger 5 µm could be detected by laser diffractometry.

Intravenous injection of the Tagat emulsion led to a liver uptake of around 25%, much lower than that found for the polymeric particles coated with Tagat R60 (Fig. 8.4./7). The scintigrams obtained within the first 15 minutes showed a distribution of activity throughout the body. Liver and lung images were obtained due to the high blood flow through these organs (Fig. 8.4./9). The images are similar to those obtained for egg lecithin-based fat emulsions.

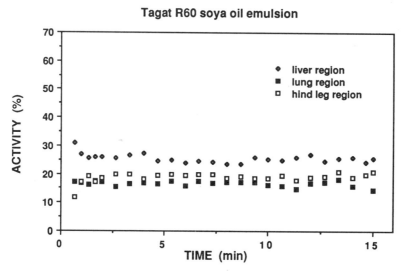

Fig. 8.4./7: Organ distribution of a Tagat R60 soya oil emulsion within the first 15 minutes after injection (activity in liver, lung and hind leg region)

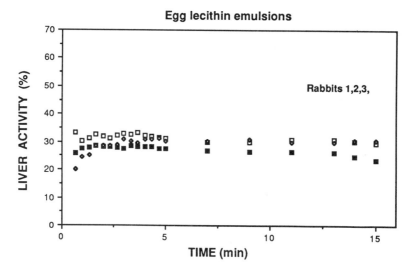

Fig. 8.4./8: Liver uptake of an egg lecithin soya oil emulsion within the first 15 minutes after injection (re-analysed data, by courtesy of P.E. West, Pharmacy Department, Nottingham University)

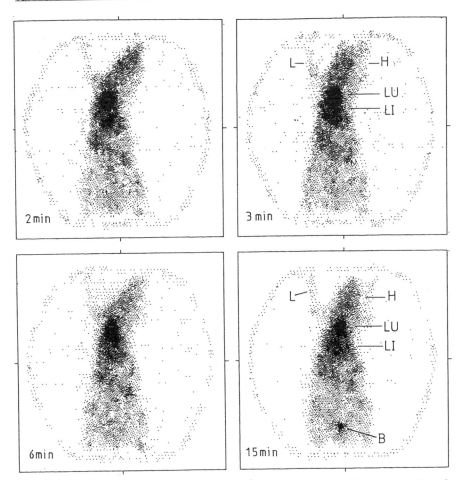

Fig. 8.4./9: Scintigrams obtained 2, 3, 6 and 15 minutes after injection of Tagat R60 fat emulsion. Activity is distributed over the whole body due to emulsion droplets circulating in the blood stream.

For comparison gamma-camera data of the distribution of egg lecithin fat emulsions were re-analysed using the same parameters as for the Tagat emulsion (by courtesy of P.E. West, Pharmacy Department, Nottingham University). A liver uptake of around 25% to 30% was obtained for the egg lecithin emulsions (Fig. 8.4./8).

A major problem associated with the use of fat emulsions, is their rapid metabolism in the body which leads to release of the radioactive marker. The accuracy of gamma-scintigraphy measurements of organ distribution therefore decreases with time. Release of the label and its elimination in

261

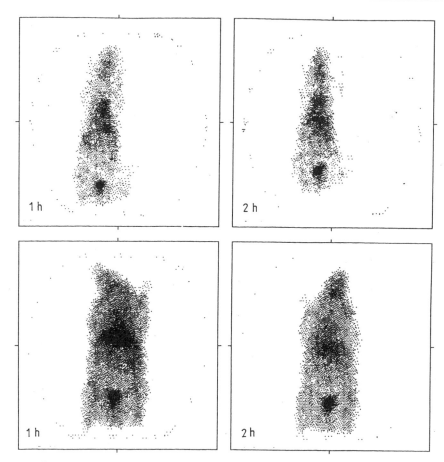

Fig. 8.4./10: Scintigrams obtained after injection of Tagat R60 fat emulsion (upper) and egg lecithin fat emulsion (lower), (left - 1 hour, right - 2 hours after injection).

the urine leads to a decrease in the liver activity after about 1 to 2 hours (Davis et al, 1987). The organ distributions over a period of 2 hours are given in Table 8.4./3 and are similar for both emulsions. The scintigrams obtained show a similar body distribution for both emulsions (Fig. 8.4./10).

The scintigrams show decreasing activity in the liver and lung regions due to metabolism of the fat emulsion. Simultaneously the released radioactive label leads to an increasing activity in the bladder region. For the Tagat R60 emulsion, 4.0%, 8.7% and 10.9% of the total activity was found in the bladder region 5 minutes, 1 and 2 hours after injection.

Table 8.4./3: Organ distribution of Tagat R60 (n=1) and egg lecithin
emulsions (n=3).

| time (hours) | organ distribution (% of injected activity) | | | | | |
| | Tagat R60 emulsion | | | egg lecithin emulsion | | |
	liver	lung	hind leg	liver	lung	hind leg
0.25	25.9	14.4	20.9	28.3	15.6	21.5
1	25.3	12.5	21.4	25.3	14.3	24.7
2	27.6	15.3	18.7	24.4	13.0	24.2

The preliminary in vivo studies described in this chapter highlight the
potential of new molecular structures for use as coating materials to
influence the organ distribution of carriers.
The synthesis of molecules which have a higher affinity for the surface of
biodegradable carriers than Poloxamines and Poloxamers and either protect
against RES uptake or possess a higher affinity for specific macrophage
subpopulations is of particular interest. The changes in organ distribution
obtained with Poloxamine and Poloxamer coated particles were achieved with
non-biodegradable polystyrene latex. The adsorption of these polymers onto
biodegradable polymeric particles was found to be either very poor or non-
existent. The problems encountered do not allow the practical application
of these systems. Alternative approaches are:
- the surface modification of biodegradable polymeric carriers to increase
  Poloxamine and Poloxamer adsorption, or
- the synthesis of new coating materials with larger hydrophobic regions
  and a corresponding higher affinity for the surface of biodegradable
  carriers.
Both alternatives are currently under investigation.

8.5. Body distribution of biodegradable PHB carriers

To investigate the organ distribution of poly(hydroxybutyrate) carriers, nanoparticles were produced and radioactively labelled with In-oxine as described previously (c.f. chapter 5). Uncoated and surface modified PHB particles were injected into NZW rabbits and the organ distribution monitored over a period of 6 days (Koosha et al., 1988; Koosha, 1989).

8.5.1. Body distribution of the free label

In order to distinguish between the distribution of the particles and that of released radioactive label, free In-oxine was injected (n=1). The label distribution between the organs was determined by its partitioning coefficient and the blood flow through the organs. After i.v. injection into the marginal ear vein and on passage through the heart, the free label reached the extensive capillary network of the lungs. The In-oxine is lipophilic and will partition into membranes and surrounding tissue. Because of the high blood flow and large surface area, a large proportion of the injected In-oxine was bound by the lungs within the first 60 seconds. Most of the remaining free label was taken up by the liver which also possesses a high blood flow and large capillary network. After 60 seconds, a clear lung and liver image could be seen on the scintigram (Fig.

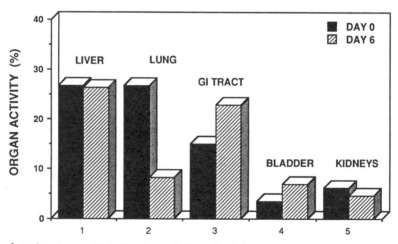

Fig. 8.5./1: Organ distribution of free In-Oxine on injection day and after redistribution on day 6 (gamma-scintigraphy data).

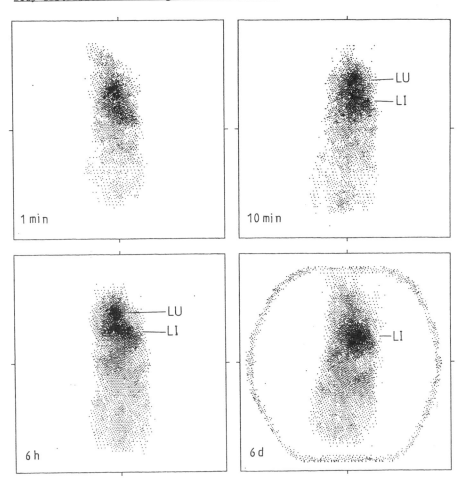

Fig. 8.5./2: Scintigrams obtained after the injection of free In-oxine (1 min., 10 min., 6 hours and 6 days after injection). After injection, the In-oxine accumulates in the lungs and liver. After 6 days a redistribution was found. The label was released from the lungs, and an increased activity in the rest of the body (esp. intestinal region) was seen. A high activity remained in the liver throughout.

8.5./2). No major redistribution of the label was observed in the first 6 hours after injection. However, during the following days the activity in the lungs decreased and the label redistributed to the liver and the rest of the body (Fig. 8.5./1). By day 6, the lung image had disappeared and only a liver and body image were visible (Fig. 8.5./2).

8.5.2. Organ distribution of uncoated PHB nanoparticles

Intravenously administered uncoated PHB nanoparticles (128 nm) were rapidly cleared by the liver and the spleen. In a similar manner to data obtained with polystyrene latex, more than 50 % of the particles were taken up within the first 2 minutes after injection. The scintigrams taken between two and 10 minutes are identical (Fig. 8.5./3).

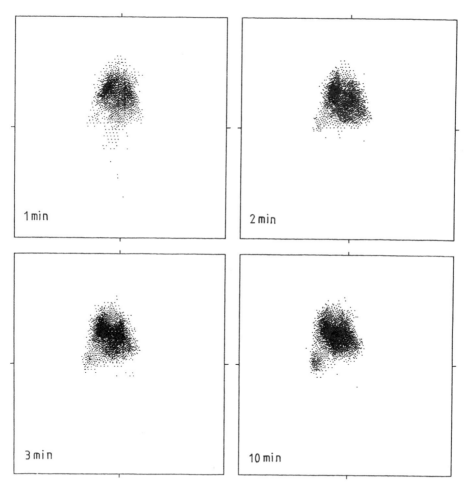

Fig. 8.5./3: Scintigrams obtained after 1, 2, 3 and 10 minutes after i.v. injection of uncoated PHB nanoparticles. The particles are rapidly taken up by the liver and the spleen within the first 2 minutes and a clear liver image can be seen.

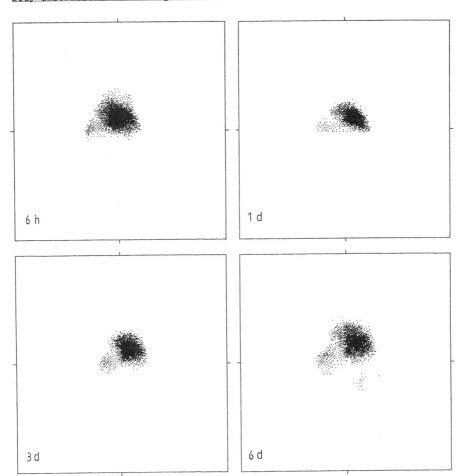

Fig. 8.5./4: Scintigrams of the body distribution of injected uncoated PHB particles (taken after 6 hours, 1, 3 and 6 days). The radioactivity remains localized in the liver indicating the stability of the label.

To investigate the stability of the label, the distribution of activity in the rabbits was monitored over a period of 6 days. Polystyrene latex particles surface labelled with I-131 tended to release some label within the first few hours after injection. However as the In-oxine label was encased inside the nanoparticles during the production process, little loss of the label was expected (c.f. in vitro release studies, chapter 5.3.).

The scintigrams obtained 6 hours after injection were identical to those taken within the first 10 minutes. During the following 6 days, little

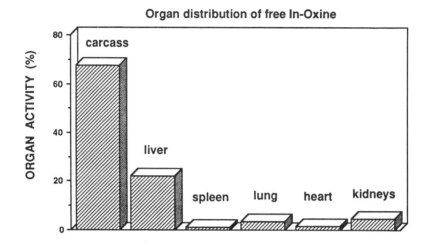

Fig. 8.5./5: Organ distribution of the free label (upper) and the labelled particles cleared by liver and spleen (organ counting, day 6). The distinct difference in the organ distributions indicates only minimal release of label from the particles.

redistribution of radioactivity from the liver region to other tissues was found (Fig. 8.5./4). This indicates minimal release of the In-Oxine label from the particles proving that this method of labelling is more suitable for following the organ distribution of polymeric nanoparticles (Müller, R.H. et al, 1988). The organ distribution determined on day 6 by organ counting shows a marked difference between the distribution of the free label and the labelled particles (Fig. 8.5./5) also indicating minimal release of label. However, it cannot be assumed that no label was released. The high affinity of the In-oxine for membranes and the affinity of the free label for the liver makes it likely, that smaller amounts of released label remain in the liver. A major release of label would have been detected as activity in other parts of the body.

8.5.3. Organ distribution of Poloxamine 908 coated PHB nanoparticles

In order to protect the PHB nanoparticles against RES uptake, attempts were made to coat them with Poloxamine 908. The coating on PHB particles produced using polyvinyl alcohol as surfactant (PHB/PVA particles) was very poor. Either no coating at all or a very thin coating layer was found. A reduction in the time of sonication during the production of PHB/PVA particles resulted in a more efficient coating.

Previous SSIMS analysis of PHB-SDS particles revealed that the SDS surfactant was incorporated into the particle surface (c.f. chapter 3.5), so it is likely that longer sonication times during the production of PHB/PVA particles increased the incorporation of PVA into the particle surface, resulting in an increased surface hydrophilicity. The affinity of Poloxamine 908 to hydrophilic surfaces is low, resulting in a thin or absent coating layer.

A thicker coating layer, > 100 Å, could be obtained on PHB particles produced using SDS as the surfactant (prior to the coating the excess SDS was removed by dialysis). The PHB/SDS particles were characterized by PCS (Table 8.5./1).

It was expected that the PHB-SDS particles coated with the Poloxamine 908 would be able to avoid RES uptake and remain in circulation in the blood. They were coated with the polymer which was able to protect polystyrene particles against liver/spleen uptake and the thickness of the coating

Table 8.5./1: PCS data of uncoated and Poloxamine 908 coated PHB particles.

PHB particles	size (nm)	standard deviation (nm)	polydispersity index	coating layer thickness
uncoated	113	2	0.085	-
Poloxamine 908 coated	135	3	0.087	110 Å

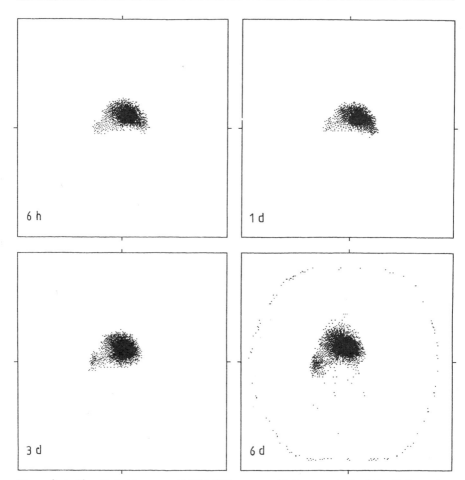

Fig. 8.5./6: Scintigrams of PHB-SDS nanoparticles coated with Poloxamine 908 (taken after 6 hours, 1 , 3 and 6 days). Despite the sterically stabilizing thick coating layer of 110 Å, the particles are rapidly taken up by the liver/spleen. The radioactivity remains localized to the liver after 6 days, indicating the stability of the radioactive label.

layer was above the minimum of 100 Å required for steric stabilization of colloidal dispersions (Davis and Illum, 1988). The size of the PHB particles and the coating layer thickness produced a system similar to 142 nm coated polystyrene latex particles. Protection against RES uptake was achieved for most of these Poloxamine 908 coated latex particles (c.f. 8.2.1.) which possessed a coating layer similar to that found on the PHB-SDS nanoparticles.

Body distribution of biodegradable PHB carriers

Surprisingly, after i.v. administration, the Poloxamine 908 coated PHB-SDS particles were taken up by the liver/spleen as rapidly as the uncoated polystyrene particles. The Poloxamine coating afforded no protection against RES recognition and uptake (Fig. 8.5./6).

In previous in vivo studies using Poloxamine 908 coated latex no desorption of the polymer or displacement by serum components occurred, so a desorption of Poloxamine in the blood is unlikely. There appear to be no components present in the serum which can displace Poloxamine 908 from a polymer surface. By now, dialysis experiments with Poloxamine 908 coated PHB-SDS particles in which the particles were dialysed against volumes which were considered to reflect in vivo conditions, showed no desorption of the polymer (Müller, R.H. and Wallis, 1988; Wallis and Müller, 1990).

The RES clearance of the Poloxamine 908 coated PHB-SDS particles is most likely due to the recognition as foreign by the RES. The subsequent RES clearance demonstrates that steric stabilization has no protective effect when the particles are recognized as foreign by the immune system.

The recognition is possibly due to the contamination of the Poloxamine coating layer by charged SDS residues. As shown with Gafac RE 960 (c.f. 8.3.), charged groups on the surface of a sterically stabilizing coating layer lead to liver/spleen uptake. A second possibility is a difference in the surface hydrophobicity of the Poloxamine coating layer on PHB-SDS and polystyrene latex particles. Although the coating polymer is identical and the coating layer thicknesses similar, the surface hydrophobicity of the coated particles might be different. A more hydrophobic coating layer on PHB-SDS particles would lead to opsonization and RES uptake. The cause of the RES clearance was investigated by surface characterization of the particles (c.f. 9.4). Whatever the reason for recognition and uptake of the coated particles, the data puts into question, the validity of the "theory of steric stabilization".

8.5.4. Organ distribution of PHB nanoparticles surface-modified with PVA

As mentioned in chapter 8.5.3, the coating of PHB/PVA nanoparticles was very poor or non-existent. This was attributed to hydrophilisation of the PHB particle surface due to the incorporation of PVA. To test this theory, the surface hydrophobicity of uncoated PHB-PVA nanoparticles was determined by Hydrophobic Interaction Chromatography (HIC). The particles were found to be similar or even less hydrophobic than Poloxamine 908 coated 60 nm latex particles (c.f. 9.4.).

Furthermore, the PHB/PVA nanoparticles were uncharged in distilled water as shown by electrophoretic mobility measurements, their uptake of charged serum components was as low as found with Poloxamine 908 coated 60 nm latex

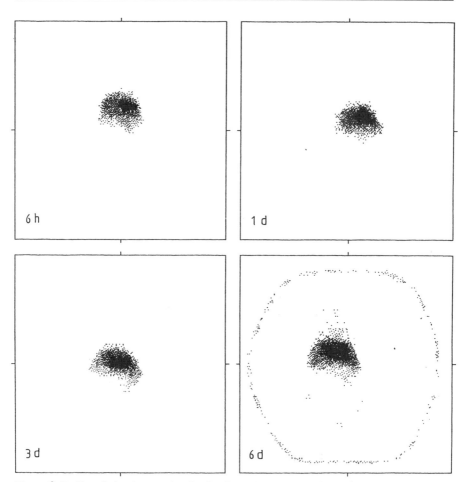

Fig. 8.5./7: Scintigram obtained after injection of PHB/PVA nanoparticles (after 6 hours, 1, 3 and 6 days). The particles were cleared rapidly by the liver/spleen despite their "ideal properties for reduction of RES clearance". Over a period of 6 days, no release of radioactive label from the particles could be detected.

(c.f. 9.6) and their size was relatively small (180 nm). Considering these results the PHB/PVA carriers fulfilled all the criteria which previous work had stated as being necessary for reduction in RES uptake, i.e.:
1. small size, 2. no charge and 3. hydrophilic surface.
The PHB/PVA particles therefore seemed to be an ideal carrier.
However like uncoated polystyrene latex particles, after i.v. injection, the PHB/PVA particles were rapidly taken up by the liver and spleen. A

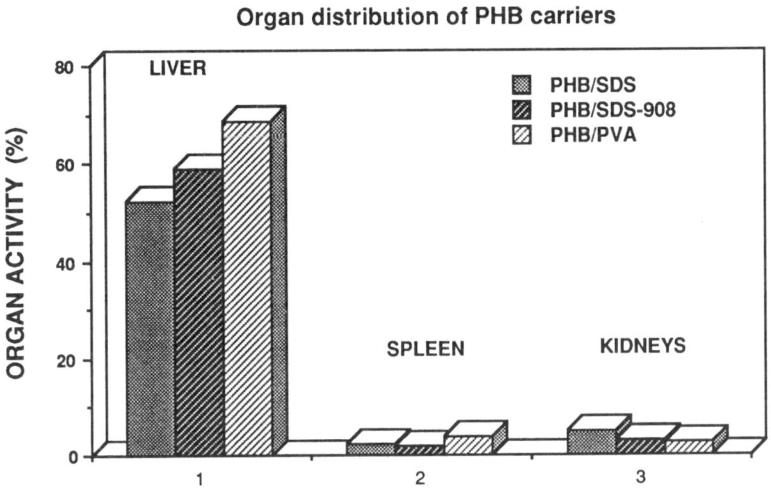

Organ distribution of PHB carriers

Fig. 8.5./8: Organ distribution of uncoated PHB particles produced with SDS as surfactant (PHB/SDS), PHB/SDS particles coated with Poloxamine 908 (PHB/SDS-908) and PHB particles produced using PVA as surfactant (PHB/PVA) (activities determined by organ counting on day 6).

distinct liver image was obtained. Over a period of 6 days, no change in the scintigrams was seen (Fig. 8.5./7). Again, no release of label from the particles could be detected. Clearance of the PHB-PVA particles by the liver indicates that the particle properties which were previously thought as being important, were not the only factors of importance.

The organ distribution determined by organ counting for uncoated and PHB particles surface modified with Poloamine 908 and PVA is given in Fig. 8.5./8. The surface modifications did not reduce the uptake by the liver and spleen.

It is likely, that the PVA chains incorporated into the PHB/PVA particle surface did not provide any steric stabilization. It could be argued, that the sterically stabilizing polymer layer was not present resulting in the observed liver clearance. However, although phospholipids contained in the surface of chylomicrons provide no steric stabilization, the chylomicrons circulate in the blood and are not cleared by the RES. In the absence of steric stabilization, the chylomicrons seem to possess the surface properties required to avoid RES uptake. Possibly the hydroxyl groups of the PVA led to activation of the complement system as observed for hydroxyl groups on Cuprophane membranes (Wegmuller et al., 1986). A sterically stabilizing but complement-activating PVA coating layer will result in the RES clearance of PVA surface modified particles.

8.6. Summary

The organ distribution of Poloxamine 908 and Poloxamer 407 coated latex particles of various size (142 to 910 nm) was determined in NZW rabbits after intravenous injection.

The coating layers obtained on 142 nm latex were slightly less protective against RES uptake than those obtained on 60 nm latex, as indicated by a slightly increased liver/spleen activity (around 30% compared to 25%). However in both cases, the majority of the particles remained in circulation in the blood. The Poloxamer 407 coating seemed to be less protective than the Poloxamine 908 coating. However, in contrast to Poloxamer 407 coated 60 nm latex, no accumulation in the bone marrow was observed with these larger particles. Their access was restricted because of the size of the sinusoidal fenestrations.

The coating produced on the larger 383 nm latex particles proved to be ineffective. A slow but steady increase in the liver/spleen activity was observed within the first 15 minutes after injection. The activity time profile was quite different to that seen for very rapidly cleared uncoated latex. The clearance velocity was much reduced and rate constants and the uptake time 50% (t50%) could be calculated. A much faster clearance was observed for larger particles (496 and 910 nm) where the coating seemed to have almost no effect. The results were in contradiction to *in vitro* investigations in cell cultures in which the two coating polymers proved to be effective at protecting even larger particles (5.25 µm) against phagocytosis by mouse peritoneal macrophages. In knowledge of these *in vitro* results the *in vivo* study was undertaken.

Alternative coating materials (ethoxylated nonylphenols, Antarox CO990 and Gafac RE960) were investigated. Coating with Antarox CO 990 led to some reduction in the liver/spleen uptake of 74 nm latex particles. Similar to Poloxamer 407 coated 60 nm latex, an increased affinity for the bone marrow was found. The number of particles with access to the bone marrow varied between animals. After coating, the closeness of size of the particles to the mean diameter of the sinusoidal fenestrations restricted their access to the bone marrow. Variations in the size of the sinusoidal fenestrations further increased the observed differences between animals in organ distributions.

Larger particles coated with Antarox CO990 were rapidly cleared by liver and spleen.

Gafac RE960 is similar in structure to the non-ionic Antarox CO990 but carries a charged phosphoric acid group at the end of the sterically stabilizing ethylene oxide chain. *In vitro* characterization data showed that the coating of Gafac RE960 of 60 nm latex particles was similar to that of Poloxamer 188. Considering the "theory of steric stabilization" it was expected to find at least some reduction in liver uptake similar to that observed with Poloxamer 188 or Antarox CO990. However, the negatively charged particles were cleared as rapidly as uncoated particles by the liver and spleen.

Coating of 60 nm latex particles with ethoxylated glycerides proved - as expected - to be ineffective because of the thin coating layers obtained. Tagat I and Tagat R60 coated particles were cleared rapidly. The coating layer produced by Tagat R60 was distinctly thicker than that produced by Tagat I. The adsorption of lipophilic compounds in Tagat R60 onto the particle surface might have caused the high liver/spleen uptake. A fat emulsion produced with Tagat R60 showed a reduced liver/spleen clearance. A possible explanation for this is the diffusion of lipophilic contaminants of Tagat R60 in the oil droplets and consequently the formation of an emulsifier layer consisting only of ethoxylated surfactant.

PHB particles produced with SDS as surfactant were cleared rapidly by the liver and spleen. Coating of the PHB/SDS particles with a thick layer - 135 Å of the sterically stabilizing Poloxamine 908 did not provide any protection against phagocytosis. The coated PHB particles were taken up by the liver/spleen as rapidly as uncoated latex particles. Steric stabilization alone did not protect the Poloxamine 908 coated PHB/SDS and the Gafac RE960 coated latex particles against phagocytosis by macrophants in vivo. From these results the theory of steric stabilization cannot be regarded as valid.

PHB particles modified by replacing SDS with PVA in the production process were cleared rapidly by the liver and spleen.

9. RELATION OF THE IN VIVO DISTRIBUTION TO THE SURFACE CHARACTERISTICS OF THE CARRIERS

9.1. Surface hydrophobicity of Poloxamine 908 and Poloxamer 407 coated polystyrene model carriers

Coating of hydrophobic 60 nm polystyrene model carriers with Poloxamine 908 and Poloxamer 407 resulted in uncharged particles with a hydrophilic surface.

After i.v. injection 100 to 150 nm particles coated with these polymers were able to avoid RES recognition and remain in circulation in the blood. Particles smaller than 100 nm, coated with Poloxamine 908 also remained in circulation but those coated with Poloxamer 407 accumulated in the bone marrow. The Poloxamine 908 coating therefore protects against phagocytosis by liver and spleen macrophages and by phagocytosing cells in the bone marrow. Poloxamer 407 however only protects against liver and spleen, but not against bone marrow uptake. Particles between 300 and 1000 nm, coated with Poloxamines and Poloxamers are not protected against RES phagocytosis and are rapidly taken up by the liver and spleen.

Surface characterization of these particles was performed in order to explain these differences in the organ distribution of different sized particles coated with the two chemically similar polymers Poloxamine 908 and Poloxamer 407.

The investigation of coated 60 nm polystyrene latex particles led to the conclusions that both polymers create

- coating layers similar in thickness (120 to 150 Å)
- coated particles which are uncharged at physiological salt concentrations
- a similar reduction in the adsorption of charged serum components
- coating layers which are (at least) very similar in surface hydrophobicity.

To determine the surface hydrophobicity of the various sized coated particles HIC was employed. A range of matrices with increasing hydrophobicity (ethyl-, propyl-, pentyl-, hexyl- and octyl-agarose) were used. The column materials with higher hydrophobicity (hexyl- and octyl-agarose) should be able to resolve the differences in the surface hydrophobicity of particles which appear to be similar after elution from a less hydrophobic matrix (e.g. ethyl-agarose).

9.1.1. Characterization of coated 60 nm latex particles

The 60 nm latex particles coated with the two polymers passed down propyl-agarose columns without interaction. With Triton X-100 solution, no wash

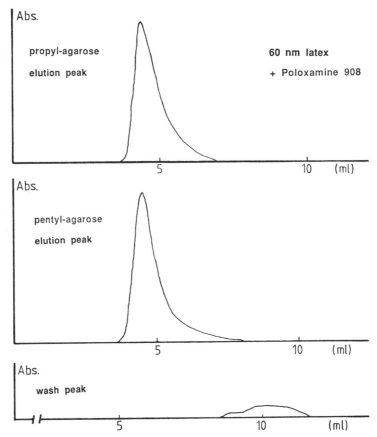

Fig. 9.1./1: Chromatograms of Poloxamine 908 coated 60 nm particles on propyl- and pentyl-agarose gel. On the propyl-gel all the particles could be eluted, none remained on the column (no wash peak). On the pentyl-gel most of the particles were eluted but some with more hydrophobic surfaces remained on the column and could only be removed by washing with 0.1% Triton X-100 solution (wash peak).

peak was obtained, indicating that no particles remained on the column during the elution process. On the more hydrophobic _pentyl_-gel, again most of the particles passed the column with little or no interaction, but some were retained as indicated by the wash peak obtained with Triton X-100 solution (Fig. 9.1/1 and 2).

A large proportion of particles coated with both polymers was retained on the _hexyl_-agarose column (Fig. 9.1./3 and 4), but more of the Poloxamer 407 coated particles were retained and a large wash peak was obtained. This

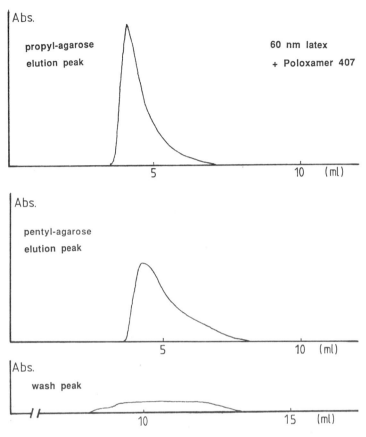

Fig. 9.1./2: Chromatograms of Poloxamer 407 coated 60 nm particles on propyl- and pentyl-agarose gel. On the propyl-gel all the particles could be eluted, none remained on the column (no wash peak). On the pentyl-gel most of the particles were eluted but some with more hydrophobic surfaces remained on the column. The wash peak was slightly larger than the one obtained with Poloxamine 908 coated 60 nm latex particles.

proves that the Poloxamer 407 coating is more hydrophobic than the Poloxamine 908 one.

Neither type of coated particles could pass down the octyl-column nor could the particles retained by this column be washed off using 0-2% Triton X-100 solution. The hydrophobic interaction between this matrix and the coated particles was too strong.

The HIC characterization demonstrated differences in the surface hydrophobicity of the two polymer coatings which might be responsible for the

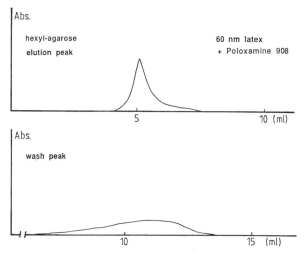

Fig. 9.1./3: Chromatogram of Poloxamine 908 coated 60 nm latex on hexyl-agarose gel. Approximately half the particles could be eluted, the other half possessing more hydrophobic surfaces remained on the column (large wash peak).

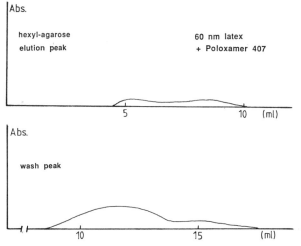

Fig. 9.1./4: Chromatogram of Poloxamer 407 coated latex on hexyl-agarose gel. Only a small fraction of the particles could be eluted, most of them possessed more hydrophobic surfaces and remained on the column. A much larger wash peak was obtained than for Poloxamine 908-coated particles. This demonstrates that the Poloxamer 407 coating layer on 60 nm latex is more hydrophobic than the Poloxamine 908 coating layer.

observed differences in their in vivo behaviour. It is suggested that the more hydrophobic coating of Poloxamer 407 leads to the adsorption of a specific opsonin which is not adsorbed by the less hydrophobic Poloxamine 908 coatings. This opsonin is not recognized by the macrophage sub-populations located in the liver and the spleen but is recognized by phagocytosing cells in the bone marrow (therefore it is called BM opsonin).

The 60 nm latex particles coated with Poloxamer 407 are taken up by the bone marrow whereas Poloxamine 908 coated particles which do not adsorb the BM opsonin escape recognition and circulate in the blood. Particles larger than 100 nm coated with Poloxamer 407 carry the BM opsonin but do not have access to the bone marrow because of the size exclusion of the sinusoidal fenestrations. Consequently, these particles can avoid bone marrow uptake. The BM opsonin is not recognized by the liver and spleen macrophages and as a result the particles circulate in the blood in a similar way to Poloxamine 908 coated carriers. The suggested differences in interaction with serum opsonins need to be proved by investigating the composition of serum components adsorbed to both coatings, but it is however important that with HIC a difference in the properties of the two coatings could be detected. This provides a possible explanation for the observed in vivo behaviour and confirms the suitability of the applied characterization methods.

9.1.2. Characterization of coated 142 nm latex particles

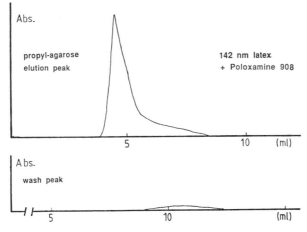

Fig. 9.1./5: Chromatograms obtained for Poloxamine 908 coated 142 nm latex particles on propyl-gel. Only a few particles remained on the column as indicated by the small wash peak.

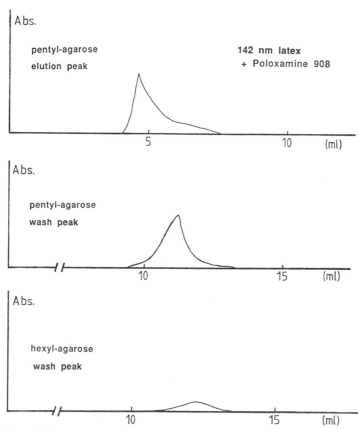

Fig. 9.1./6: Chromatograms obtained for Poloxamine 908 coated 142 nm latex particles on pentyl- (upper two) and hexyl-gel (lower). The particles could only be eluted from the hexyl-gel by washing with buffered 0.1% Triton X-100 solution (wash peak).

The vast majority of the 142 nm Latex particles coated with Poloxamine 908 and Poloxamer 407 passed the propyl column without interaction. Only small wash peaks were obtained (Fig. 9.1./5 and 7). The chromatograms obtained on the _propyl_-columns could not be used to differentiate between the two coating layers in terms of surface hydrophobicity. The difference was however evident in the chromatograms on the _pentyl_-agarose columns. Half of the particles coated with Poloxamine 908 could be eluted with the buffer but only one third of those coated with Poloxamer 407 could be eluted in the same way (Fig. 9.1./6 and 7). As a result, a much larger wash peak was obtained for the Poloxamer 407 coated particles.

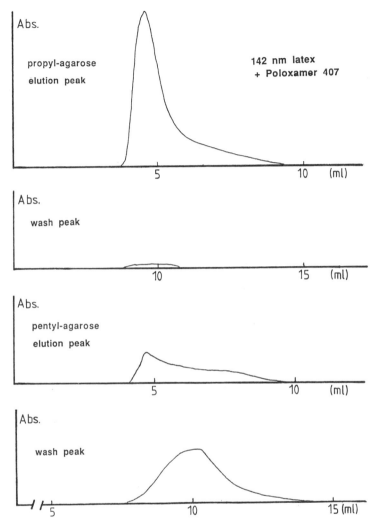

Fig. 9.1./7: Chromatograms obtained for Poloxamer 407 coated 142 nm latex particles on propyl- (upper two) and pentyl-gel (lower two). On the pentyl column the majority of the particles were retained and could only be washed off by using 0.1% Triton X-100 solution (large wash peak).

For both coatings, no particles could be eluted with buffer from hexyl-agarose column. Even using Triton X-100 solution, only the more hydrophilic Poloxamine 908 coated latex could be washed off (Fig. 9.1./5, wash peak on pentyl-gel).

Relation of the in vivo distribution to the surface characteristics

The HIC results from the pentyl- and hexyl-agarose columns prove that the Poloxamine and Poloxamer coatings are more hydrophobic on 142 nm than on 60 nm latex particles. In contrast to the 142 nm particles, only small amounts of the 60 nm coated latex remained on the pentyl-column (small wash peaks!, Fig. 9.1./1 and 2), and a large fraction of particles coated with both polymers could be eluted from the hexyl-column (Fig. 9.1./3 and 4).

The increased hydrophobicity of the coatings on the larger 142 nm particles can explain a reduced protection from RES clearance. The particle population is not homogenous in its surface hydrophobicity as indicated by the fact that a less hydrophobic portion of the particles can be eluted with buffer, whereas the more hydrophobic particles need to be washed off using surfactant solution. Particles from this more hydrophobic fraction are recognized and cleared by the liver and spleen. As a result, the liver/spleen activity increases from about 25% (coated 60 nm latex) to 30-35% within the first 15 minutes after injection of 142 nm latex.

As previously seen for the coating on 60 nm latex, the Poloxamer 407 coated 142 nm particles are more hydrophobic than the Poloxamine 908 coated ones. In vivo, the increased surface hydrophobicity of the Poloxamer 407 coated particles results in increased opsonization and
- bone marrow uptake for the coated 60 nm latex
- slightly increased liver clearance for the coated 142 nm latex
  (dissection data, c.f. 8.2.1).

The increased surface hydrophobicity corresponds with the reduction in the thickness of the coating layer. It is thought under these conditions, that parts of the more hydrophobic polypropylene oxide central region of the coating polymer molecule are exposed on the surface of the adsorbed layer. Therefore, the increased RES clearance is not due to a reduction in steric stabilization due to the thinner coating layer but to the increased surface hydrophobicity of the thinner coating layer.

9.1.3. Characterization of coated 383 nm latex particles

A larger number of the coated 383 nm particles are retained on the propyl-agarose columns compared to the 142 nm latex as indicated by the larger wash peaks obtained with Triton X-100 solution. On the pentyl-columns, only a few or no particles could be eluted with buffer, but some could be washed off with Triton X-100 (Fig. 9.1./8 and 9). The areas under the wash peaks in the chromatograms on the pentyl-columns are smaller than those found on columns which do not retain any particles (e.g. neutral agarose, ethyl-agarose). The reduced area under the curve (AUC) indicates that a portion of the particles binds irreversibly to the pentyl-agarose matrix because of its very hydrophobic surface.

284

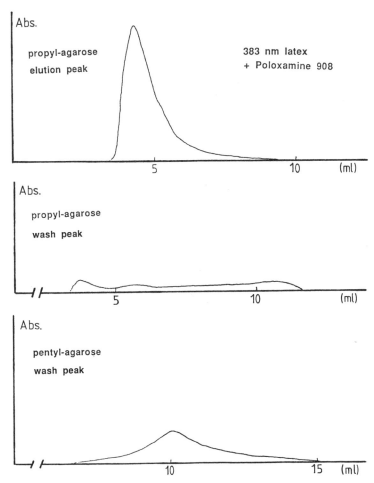

Fig. 9.1./8: Chromatograms of Poloxamine 908 coated 383 nm latex particles on propyl-gel (upper two, elution and wash peak) and on pentyl-gel (wash peak; lower chromatogram).

In contrast to the smaller coated latex particles, none of the coated 383 nm particles could be eluted with buffer or washed off with Triton X-100 from the hexyl-columns indicating the increased hydrophobicity of the coating layers of Poloxamine 908 and Poloxamer 407.
The rapid RES clearance of the coated 383 nm latex particles observed in the in vivo studies (c.f. 8.2.2.) is due to the increased hydrophobicity of the coating layers and subsequently their enhanced opsonization. The thinner adsorbed layer compared to coated 60 nm latex particles (c.f.

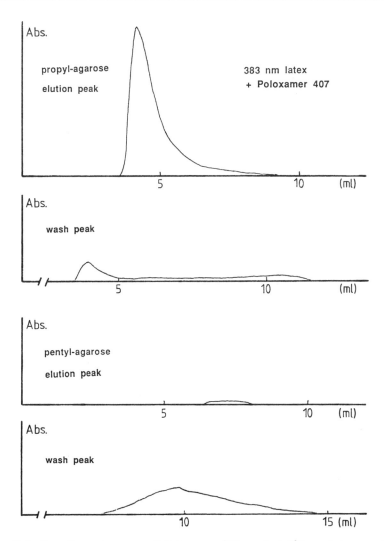

Fig. 9.1./9: Chromatograms of Poloxamer 407 coated 383 nm latex particles on propyl-gel (upper two) and on pentyl-gel (lower chromatograms, elution and wash peak respectively).

8.2.2.) implies a different conformation of the polymers on the particle surface, which may result in a change in the surface hydrophobicity.
In the HIC investigations, a difference in surface hydrophobicity between the Poloxamine 908 and Poloxamer 407 coating layer (as seen on smaller 60 and 142 nm particles) could not be detected on the 383 nm particles. The

chromatograms (shape, retention volume, AUC) are very similar indicating similar surface hydrophobicities. This corresponds well with the observed identical in vivo organ distribution for 383 nm particles coated with both polymers.

9.1.4. Characterization of coated 496 nm latex particles

A fraction of the Poloxamine 908 coated 496 nm latex particles passed through the propyl-column without interaction. The shape of the chromato-gram was similar to those obtained from the coated 60 nm latex particles but with a more distinct tailing towards an elution volume of 10 ml (Fig. 9.1./10). However, the portion retained on the column and washed off with buffered 0.1% Triton X-100 solution was relatively large. The AUC ratio of area under the elution peak (buffer) over area under the wash peak (buffered Triton X-100 solution) was 1.7 : 1.
No elution and no wash peak could be obtained with the Poloxamine 908 coated 496 nm latex on the pentyl-column. The particles were more hydrophobic than the 383 nm coated latex and bound too strongly to be washed off.

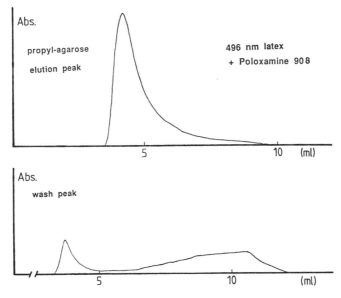

Fig. 9.1./10: Chromatograms of Poloxamine 908 coated 496 nm latex particles on propyl-agarose gel (upper - elution peak obtained by eluting with buffer, lower - wash peak with Triton X-100).

287

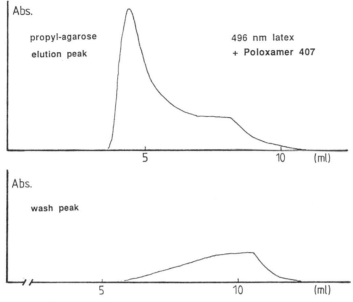

Fig. 9.1./11: Chromatograms of Poloxamer 407 coated 496 nm latex particles on propyl-agarose gel (upper - elution peak with distinct tailing obtained by eluting with buffer, lower - wash peak with Triton X-100).

The Poloxamer 407 coated latex particles showed a similar behaviour on the propyl-column (Fig. 9.1./11). However, the tailing was more distinct during the elution with buffer. The AUC ratio was 2.7 : 1 compared to 1.7 : 1 for the Poloxamine 908 coated latex. The larger portion of coated particles eluted with buffer indicates that the Poloxamer 407 coating is similar or even slightly more hydrophilic than the Poloxamine 908 coating. This is in contrast to the results obtained for coated 60 and 142 nm particles where the Poloxamer 407 coating proved to be more hydrophobic than the Poloxamine 908 one.

The chromatogram obtained for the Poloxamine 908 coated latex washed with Triton X-100 comprises a wash peak at approximately 4.5 ml similar to the void volume of the column and a second peak around 10 ml. This first peak is missing in the equivalent chromatogram for the Poloxamer coated latex. Possibly this fraction was eluted with the buffer, leading to the distinct tailing observed for Poloxamer 407 coated particles (elution peak with buffer).

No elution with buffer nor with buffered Triton X-100 solution could be obtained for the Poloxamer 407 coated 496 nm latex on the pentyl-column. This proves that both coatings on 496 nm latex particles are more

288

hydrophobic than on 383 nm latex particles. The measured increase in surface hydrophobicity in vitro corresponds well with the observed rapid clearance by liver and spleen in vivo. From the HIC in vitro characterization data, both coatings seem to be similar in surface hydrophobicity which is in agreement with the similar velocity of RES clearance and organ distribution observed in vivo.

9.1.5. Characterization of coated 910 nm latex particles

The surface hydrophobicity of the Poloxamine 908 and Poloxamer 407 coated 910 nm latex is similar to that of the 496 nm latex, as indicated by the shape of the chromatograms obtained on the propyl-column (Fig. 9.1./12 and 13). As observed with the 496 nm latex, the Poloxamer 407 coating showed a more distinct tailing of the elution peak with buffer. The particles retained on the column were more easily washed off (start off point of wash peak at 5 ml) than Poloxamine 908 coated particles which were retained on the column (start off point of the peak at 7.5 ml, Fig. 9.1./12). Therefore, as seen with the 496 nm latex, the Poloxamer 407 coating on the

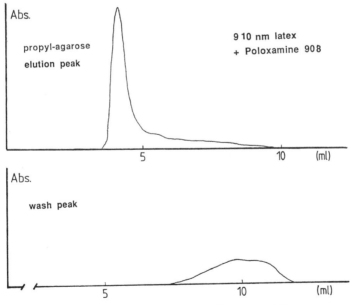

Fig. 9.1./12: Chromatograms of Poloxamine 908 coated 910 nm latex particles on propyl-agarose gel (upper - elution peak obtained by eluting with buffer, lower - wash peak with Triton X-100).

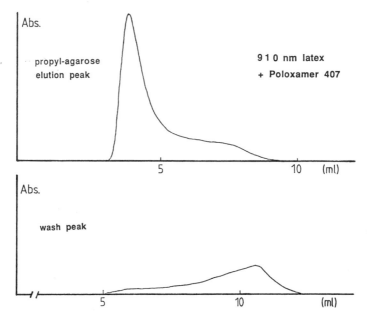

Fig. 9.1./13: Chromatograms of Poloxamer 407 coated 910 nm latex particles on propyl-agarose gel (upper - elution peak obtained with buffer, lower - wash peak with Triton X-100).

910 nm latex is similar or slightly more hydrophilic than the Poloxamine 908 adsorbed layer. No elution at all using buffer or Triton X-100 solution was possible on the pentyl-column.
The surface hydrophobicity of the coated 910 nm particles measured in vitro explains the RES clearance observed in vivo.

9.1.6. Characterization of coated 5600 nm latex particles

In cell culture studies, larger latex particles are used to investigate the effectiveness of coating materials in protecting against phagocytosis (Illum et al, 1987). The results obtained with coated 5 µm latex particles were regarded as also valid for smaller particles with a diameter of 60 nm. In the in vitro phagocytosis studies using peritoneal mouse macrophages, Poloxamine 908 and Poloxamer 407 coatings proved to be very protective for 5.25 µm latex. However, in vivo, large particles coated with these polymers were cleared rapidly by the RES (c.f. 8.2.3 and 8.2.4).
To investigate the reason for this rapid in vivo RES clearance, Poloxamine 908 and Poloxamer 407 coated 5600 nm latex particles were tried to pass

290

down on propyl- and pentyl-columns. The surface of the coated particles proved to be so hydrophobic that they bound irreversibly to both columns. Even extensive washing with 0.1% Triton X-100 could not elute any of the particles.

The relatively high surface hydrophobicity of these large coated particles leads to opsonization in vivo and subsequently to RES uptake. Serum is present in the culture medium used in the cell culture studies, but immunological recognition seems to be less dominant in the induced phagocytosis process. Only 10% serum was used in the culture medium and the serum does not contain all the components of the plasma (e.g. fibrinogen). As a result, less opsonins are present in the in vitro cell culture studies compared to in vivo conditions. Under these circumstances, the relatively hydrophobic surface of the Poloxamine 908 and Poloxamer 407 coating on 5600 nm latex led to a reduction in the phagocytic uptake due to reduced hydrophobic interaction with the macrophages. In vivo however, the particles are heavily opsonized and phagocytosis occurs by an immunological mediated process.

These results demonstrate the difficulties in predicting the in vivo behaviour of drug carriers solely from results obtained in in vitro cell culture studies. It also illustrates the need for additional physicochemical characterization of the particles.

9.1.7. Summary of the surface hydrophobicities of Poloxamine 908 and Poloxamer 407 coatings on particles different in size

To compare the hydrophobicities of the coatings on the latex particles, retention coefficients (void volume/elution volume) and the ratios of the area under the curves (AUC) of the elution peak (obtained with buffer) to the wash peak (obtained with buffered Triton X-100 solution) were calculated (Table 9.1./1). The elution volume is measured at the peaks' maximum intensity. To quantify the shape of the elution peaks obtained with buffer, a shape quotient was calculated:

$$\text{shape quotient} = \frac{\text{area of symmetrical peak}}{\text{area of symmetrical peak + tail}}$$

Looking only at the retention coefficients and the AUC ratios of elution and wash peak can be misleading when the elution peak shows a strong tailing. The particles eluted in the tail are much more hydrophobic than the ones at the elution peak maximum. Theoretically, a peak with no tailing

Table 9.1./1: Retention coefficients,AUC ratios and shape coefficients of
elution peaks of Poloxamine 908 (908) and Poloxamer 407 (407) coated
particles (EP/WP - elution/wash peak only).

latex size (nm)	coating polymer	alkyl-agarose	retention coefficient	AUC ratio elution/ wash peak	shape quotient of elution peak
60	908	propyl	0.93	EP -	0.54
		pentyl	0.99	9.0 : 1	0.61
		hexyl	0.91	1.0 : 1.3	0.80
	407	propyl	0.99	EP -	0.63
		pentyl	0.97	3.3 : 1	0.46
		hexyl	0.86	1 : 3	0.24
142	908	propyl	0.88	11.1 : 1	0.64
		pentyl	0.95	1.2 : 1	0.43
		hexyl	-	- WP	-
	407	propyl	0.89	16.2 : 1	0.64
		pentyl	0.95	1 : 1.8	0.29
		hexyl	-	- -	-
383	908	propyl	0.94	4.8 : 1	0.63
		pentyl	-	- WP	-
	407	propyl	0.97	5.6 : 1	0.50
		pentyl	0.58	1 : 12.5	broad
496	908	propyl	0.97	1.7 : 1	0.51
		pentyl	-	- -	-
	407	propyl	0.92	2.7 : 1	0.41
		pentyl	-	- -	-
910	908	propyl	0.97	1.8 : 1	0.63
		pentyl	-	- -	-
	407	propyl	0.97	2.9 : 1	0.45
		pentyl	-	- -	-
5600	908/407	no elution/wash peaks on propyl and pentyl			

and a peak with strong tailing can possess the same retention coefficients and AUC ratios. Calculation of the shape coefficient allows a differentiation between them to be made.

To quantify the shape of the wash peaks in a way covering all the different peak shapes obtained, appeared rather difficult and was not performed. The information about the proportion of particles retained on the column is determined in the AUC ratio.

On very hydrophobic columns (pentyl-or hexyl-agarose), not all of the particles retained can be washed off with 0.1% Triton X-100. A fraction might be irreversibly bound by strong hydrophobic interactions with the matrix. This portion of the retained particles does not appear in the wash peak and leads to an error when calculating the AUC ratio elution/wash peak. The particles appear falsely hydrophilic. To correct for this effect (if necessary) the fraction of particles eluted in the elution and wash peaks as a percentage of the applied sample was calculated.

The coated 60 nm latex proved to be the least hydrophobic of all the particles investigated. For both coating polymers, identical retention volumes of the elution peaks were obtained on all columns. However, the Poloxamer 407 coating was more hydrophobic than the Poloxamine 908 coating, as indicated by the lower AUC ratios on the pentyl-and hexyl-column. The elution peaks show a stronger tailing, resulting in lower shape coefficients; the Poloxamer-coated particles show a larger variation in surface hydrophobicity. This difference in surface hydrophobicity is most likely the cause of the differences in the in vivo organ distribution.

The coated 142 nm latex could not be eluted from the hexyl-column and only the Poloxamine coated latex could be washed off with Triton X-100. The retention volumes of the most hydrophilic fractions are similar to those obtained with coated 60 nm latex but the AUC ratios are lower indicating that the coating layers on the 142 nm latex are less hydrophilic. This leads to RES clearance of the more hydrophobic particle fraction in the population and an increased liver/spleen uptake. From the AUC ratios and the lower shape coefficient the Poloxamer 407 coated 142 nm latex are more hydrophobic than those coated with Poloxamine 908.

The larger 383 nm coated latex particles are even more hydrophobic. The hydrophobicities of the Poloxamer 407 and Poloxamine 908 coatings are similar (similar AUC ratio and shape coefficient).

A further increase in the surface hydrophobicity of the coatings was found on 496 nm and 910 nm latex particles. These coated particles could not be washed off the pentyl-column with Triton X-100. The Poloxamer 407 coating possesses the same hydrophobicity on both latices as indicated by similar retention coefficients, AUC ratios and shape coefficients. The same results were found for the Poloxamine 908 coatings. The Poloxamer 407 coating seemed to be slightly less hydrophobic with regard to the higher AUC ratios

Relation of the in vivo distribution to the surface characteristics

of 2.7/2.9 compared to 1.7/1.8 (on 496 nm/910nm particles respectively). However, the particles eluted with buffer show a stronger tailing reflected in the lower shape coefficients (Poloxamer 407: 0.41/0.45; Poloxamine 908 0.51/0.63). This means that a broader range in the degree of surface hydrophobicity and a larger portion of more hydrophobic particles is present in the eluted fraction. These two opposing effects most likely compensated each other resulting in the identical mean surface hydrophobicity and similar RES clearance observed in vivo.

The in vitro characterization of the surface hydrophobicities of the Poloxamine 908 and Poloxamer 407 coated latices of different sizes could explain their observed in vivo organ distribution.

9.2 Surface hydrophobicity of Antarox CO990 coated 67nm carriers

In the in vitro characterization studies of coated 60 nm latex particles, the Antarox CO990 coating was found to create surface properties similar to those produced by coating with Poloxamer 188. Both coating layers were around 75 Å thick and created the same charge reduction in 0.01 M buffer (c.f. chapters 2.1., 2.2. and 3.3.1.3.). In physiological salt concentrations, both coated particles will be uncharged.

On the basis of this data, the Antarox CO990 coated latex particles were selected for in vivo investigation of their organ distribution. It was expected that they would reduce the liver/spleen uptake in a similar way as Poloxamer 188 coated latex. The expected reduction in liver uptake was confirmed by the in vivo experiments (c.f. 8.3.). In addition, an increased affinity to the bone marrow similar to carriers coated with Poloxamer 407 was found. The uptake into the bone marrow seemed to be limited by the size of the sinusoidal fenestrations. Larger variations between the 3 NZW rabbits were observed because the coated carriers were about 85 nm (67 nm latex particles plus twice the thickness of the coating layer = appr. 85 nm). This is very close to the mean size of the fenestrations (about 100 nm) and restricted therefore the access for many of the carriers. Simultaneously, a competitive uptake by liver/spleen macrophages took place which reduced further the amount of particles accumulating in the bone marrow. As noted for Poloxamer 407 coated carriers, uptake into the bone marrow seems to be a much slower process than phagocytosis by Kupffer cells and spleen macrophages. If a competitive uptake occurs, the bone marrow uptake will be less distinct.

Determination of the surface hydrophobicity by HIC using a propyl-agarose column yielded a retarded elution peak (Fig. 9.2./1). The elution volume was 6.25 ml (close to the value found for Poloxamer 188 coated latex - 6.53 ml). The surface hydrophobicity is similar to that of Poloxamer 188-coated

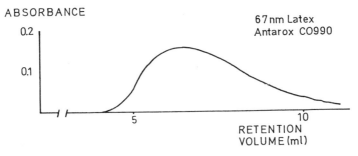

Fig. 9.2./1: Chromatogram of Antarox CO990 coated 67 nm latex particles on propyl-agarose (elution volume 6.25 ml).

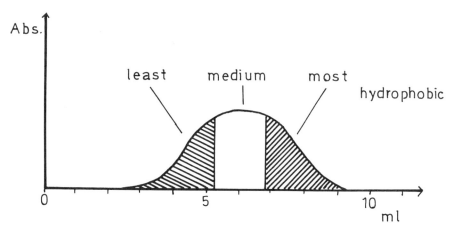

Fig. 9.2./2: Schematic representation of fractions with different surface hydrophobicity in the population of coated particles. The fractions possibly interact with different serum opsonins leading to variations in their organ distribution.

particles but higher than Poloxamer 407 coated particles, which passed the propyl-column without any retention.

It could be shown that the Poloxamer 407 coating on 60 nm latex particles is more hydrophobic than a Poloxamine 908 coating layer. It was therefore postulated that the more hydrophobic Poloxamer 407 layer is sufficiently hydrophobic to adsorb an opsonin which is recognized by phagocytosing cells in the bone marrow (BM opsonin). The Antarox CO990 coating is slightly more hydrophobic leading to the adsorption of the BM opsonin and further opsonization by components which make the particles recognizable by liver and spleen macrophages.

Further attention needs to be given to the fact that coated particles are not homogenous in their surface properties. A particle population contains different fractions with differing surface hydrophobicities. In the case of the Antarox CO990 coating, the least hydrophobic fraction (at around 5 ml elution volume) will not be opsonized at all and will circulate in the blood. The fraction with medium hydrophobicity might adsorb the BM opsonin resulting in bone marrow uptake. The most hydrophobic fraction adsorbs BM opsonin and further opsonins leading to a competitive uptake by bone marrow and the liver/spleen macrophages (Fig. 9.2./2). Due to the higher phagocytosis rate of the macrophages in liver and spleen most of these particles will localize in these organs.

9.3. Surface hydrophobicity of emulsion carriers

9.3.1. Surface hydrophobicity of egg lecithin emulsions

The RES clearance of i.v. administered fat emulsions is markedly below the clearance of non-coated particles (c.f. 8.4.). The egg lecithin used as emulsifier provides obviously surface properties which might be similar to the ones of chylomicrons leading to a reduction in macrophage uptake. Commercial products such as Lipofundin MCT and Intralipid show a reduced

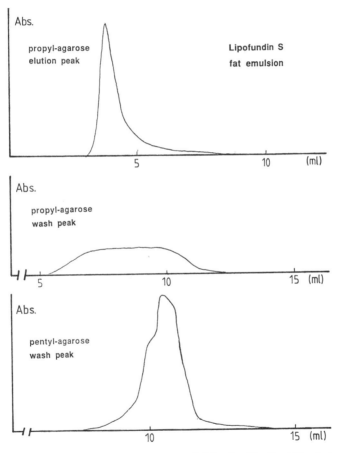

Fig. 9.3./1: Elution and wash peaks of Lipofundin S 10% fat emulsion obtained on propyl-agarose (upper two). On pentyl-agarose no emulsion could be eluted with buffer and only a wash peak with Triton X-100 was found (lower).

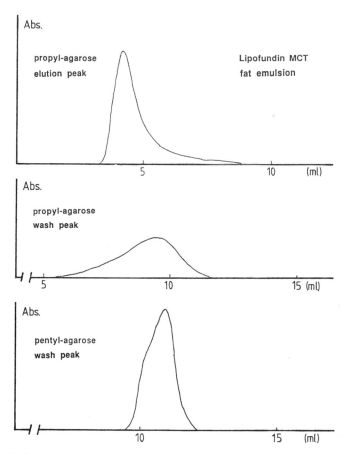

Fig. 9.3./2: Elution and wash peaks of Lipofundin MCT 10% fat emulsion obtained on propyl-agarose (upper two). On pentyl-agarose no emulsion could be eluted with buffer and only a wash peak with Triton X-100 was found (lower).

RES uptake and therefore causing no or little impairment of the RES function (Davis et al., 1990). It is much simpler to produce fat emulsions than polymeric carriers for drugs. Emulsion carriers are to be preferred if they provide the same properties (e.g. organ distribution) as coated polymeric particles. As shown with the Tagat R60 fat emulsion, the production of a fat emulsion led even to a reduction in the liver/spleen uptake compared to the Tagat R60 coated latex particles (c.f. 8.4.). To relate the reduction in RES clearance of emulsions to their surface properties, they were characterized by HIC.

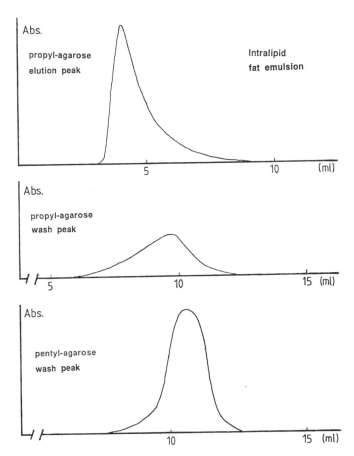

Fig. 9.3./3: Elution and wash peaks of Intralipid 10% fat emulsion obtained on propyl-agarose (upper two). On pentyl-agarose no emulsion could be eluted with buffer and only a wash peak with Triton X-100 was found (lower).

Three commercial fat emulsions based on egg lecithin were investigated:
Lipofundin S 10%, B. Braun Melsungen, FRG
Lipofundin MCT 10%, B. Braun Melsungen, FRG
Intralipid 10%, Kabi Vitrum, UK.
The majority of droplets of each fat emulsion passed the propyl-column without or with little interaction. A large fraction was retained on the column, but could be washed off using Triton X-100 solution (Fig. 9.3./1-3). The elution peaks from the propyl-column of all emulsions were of similar shape, but showed some broadening from Lipofundin S and MCT to

299

Relation of the in vivo distribution to the surface characteristics

Intralipid indicating a broader range in surface hydrophobicities of the emulsion droplets. The wash peaks were similar for Lipofundin MCT and Intralipid, Lipofundin S showed a broader wash peak. A droplet fraction was washed off at 5 to 7 ml which is missing in the chromatograms of the other emulsions. It has possibly already been eluted with buffer before (broadening of the elution peak for Lipofundin MCT and Intralipid).

None of the fat emulsions could be eluted with buffer from the pentyl-column. They could be washed off with Triton X-100 but a fraction seemed to be retained on the column as indicated by the AUC of the wash peak (Fig. 9.3./1-3).

Considering the elution behaviour on the columns, the egg lecithin based fat emulsions are more hydrophobic than coated Poloxamine 908 carriers. This fits well with the increased RES uptake of these fat emulsions compared to the coated polymeric particles.

9.3.2. Surface hydrophobicity of Poloxamine and Poloxamer emulsion carriers

Fat emulsions using Poloxamine 908 or Poloxamer 407 as surfactant proved to be physically stable, possess a suitable size (200 to 300 nm) for i.v. application and are therefore an alternative to polymeric carriers coated with these two polymers. However, due to a size larger than 100 nm,

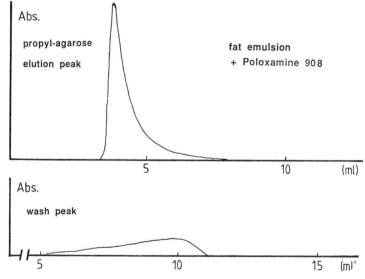

Fig. 9.3./4a: Chromatograms of Poloxamine 908 stabilized 10% soya oil emulsion on propyl-gel (elution and wash peak respectively).

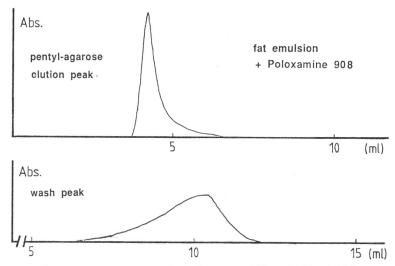

Fig. 9.3./4b: Chromatograms of Poloxamine 908 stabilized 10% soya oil emulsion on pentyl-gel (elution and wash peak respectively).

Poloxamer 407 emulsions do not have access to the bone marrow and are therefore not suitable for targeting to this tissue.

The surface hydrophobicity of fat emulsions prepared using Poloxamine 908 and Poloxamer surfactants (c.f. 6.) was investigated using HIC. The majority of the oil droplets of both emulsions passed the propyl- and pentyl-columns without interaction. Wash peaks were obtained for both emulsions on both columns, whereby the AUC of the wash peaks was larger on the pentyl-column (Fig. 9.3./4a, 4b and 5).

The wash peaks obtained for the emulsion with Poloxamer 407 were distinctly smaller than for the one with Poloxamine 908. It indicates a less hydrophobic surface of the Poloxamer 407 emulsion. This is similar to the findings for larger coated polystyrene latex particles (383 and 496 nm) where the Poloxamer coating seemed to be slightly less hydrophobic than the Poloxamine 908 coating. For smaller 60 nm latex particles coated with these polymers the opposite effect was found - the Poloxamine 908 coating is less hydrophobic than the Poloxamer 407 layer.

The differences in surface hydrophobicity could be resolved more distinct on the hexyl-column. No elution with buffer was possible for the Poloxamine 908 stabilized emulsion, only a large wash peak with Triton X-100 was obtained. A large elution peak with buffer was found with the Poloxamer 407 emulsion (Fig. 9.3./6). The relatively small wash peak indicated that only a small number of droplets was retained by the column and could not be eluted using the buffer.

301

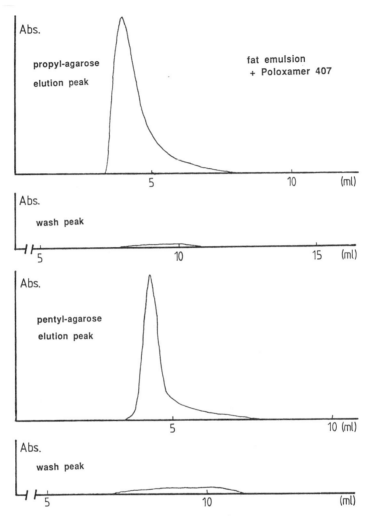

Fig. 9.3./5: Chromatograms of Poloxamer 407 stabilized 10% soya oil emulsion on propyl- (upper two) and pentyl-gel (lower two, elution and wash peak respectively).

9.3.3. Comparison of emulsion and coated polymeric carriers

The three commercial fat emulsions proved to be very similar in surface hydrophobicity (Table 9.3./1). The retention coefficients of the elution peaks on propyl-agarose were very close. The AUC ratios increased from

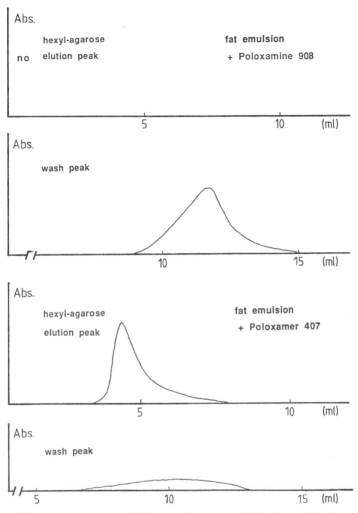

Fig. 9.3./6: Chromatograms of fat emulsions stabilized with Poloxamine 908 (upper two) and Poloxamer 407 (lower two) on hexyl-agarose.

Lipofundin S and MCT to Intralipid (1, 1.4 and 2.1 respectively) which indicates a decrease in surface hydrophobicity. However, the simultaneous decrease in the shape index (0.81, 0.69 and 0.53) shows a broader range of surface hydrophobicities in the droplet population and the presence of an increased fraction of more hydrophobic droplets in Lipofundin MCT and Intralipid compared to Lipofundin S. The mean droplet hydrophobicity is therefore most likely very similar and no major differences in the organ

303

Table 9.3./1: Retention coefficients,AUC ratios and shape coefficients of elution peaks of Poloxamine 908 and Poloxamer 407 coated particles (EP/WP - elution/wash peak only) and various fat emulsions carriers based on egg lecithin, Poloxamine 908 and Poloxamer 407 as surfactants (1.2%, 10% soya oil).

particles	alkyl-agarose	retention coefficient	AUC ratio elution/ wash peak	shape quotient of elution peak
60 nm latex	propyl	0.93	EP -	0.54
coated with Poloxamine 908	pentyl	0.99	9.0 : 1	0.61
	hexyl	0.91	1.0 : 1.3	0.80
	propyl	0.99	EP -	0.63
coated with Poloxamer 407	pentyl	0.97	3.3 : 1	0.46
	hexyl	0.86	1 : 3	0.24
142 nm latex	propyl	0.88	11.1 : 1	0.64
coated with Poloxamine 908	pentyl	0.95	1.2 : 1	0.43
	hexyl	-	- WP	-
	propyl	0.89	16.2 : 1	0.64
coated with Poloxamer 407	pentyl	0.95	1 : 1.8	0.29
	hexyl	-	- -	-
Lipofundin S	propyl	0.96	1 : 1	0.81
	pentyl	-	- WP	-
Lipofundin MCT	propyl	0.89	1.4 : 1	0.69
	pentyl	-	- WP	-
Intralipid	propyl	0.91	2.1 : 1	0.53
	pentyl	-	- WP	-
Poloxamine 908 emulsion	propyl	0.99	3.3 : 1	0.59
	pentyl	0.99	1 : 1.3	0.67
	hexyl	-	- WP	-
Poloxamer 407 emulsion	propyl	0.92	19.7 : 1	0.58
	pentyl	0.97	6.6 : 1	0.82
	hexyl	0.94	3.1 : 1	0.57

distribution of the fat emulsions are expected. In vivo studies of the impairment of RES function (NZW rabbits) by Lipofundin MCT and Intralipid as a result of emulsion phagocytosis, show a similar behaviour of both emulsions (Davis et al, 1990).

Comparing the HIC characterization parameters of the commercial egg lecithin-based emulsions and Poloxamine and Poloxamer polymeric particles shows that the emulsions are distinctly more hydrophobic than coated 142 nm latex particles (Table 9.3./1). The Poloxamine and Poloxamer fat emulsions are much less hydrophobic than the egg lecithin-based emulsions as shown by the elution properties on the pentyl- and hexyl-columns.

In comparison to Poloxamine 908 coated latex particles, the Poloxamine 908 emulsion is more hydrophobic than the coated 60 nm latex (lower AUC, similar shape coefficient) and similar hydrophobic to the 142 nm latex particles (lower AUC but higher shape coefficient on pentyl-column).

Compared to Poloxamer 407 coated latex particles, the surface of the Poloxamer 407 emulsion is of lower hydrophobicity than the coated 60 nm latex particles (and therefore of course much less hydrophobic than the coated 142 nm latex particles). On the propyl-column, the AUC ratios and shape quotients are similar for the emulsion and for the coated 60 nm latex particles. This indicates that this column is not suitable to dissolve the differences in surface hydrophobicity. On the pentyl- and hexyl-gels, the AUC ratios and the shape quotients of the Poloxamer 407 emulsion are much higher than for the Poloxamer 407 coated latex (6.6 and 3.1 compared to 3.3 and 0.3 respectively) (Table 9.3./1). A direct comparison of the chromatograms obtained on the hexyl-column shows the marked differences in the obtained elution and wash peaks (Fig. 9.3./7).

The Poloxamer 407 emulsion seems to be almost as little hydrophobic as the Poloxamine 908 coated 60 nm latex. The AUC ratios of the Poloxamer emulsion are slightly lower on the pentyl-column but this might be compensated by the higher shape quotient resulting in the same mean surface hydrophobicity of the particles. It is vice versa on the hexyl-column.

After i.v. administration it is expected that the Poloxamine 908 and Poloxamer 407 emulsions will circulate in the blood stream similar to Poloxamine 908 coated 60 nm latex particles. This was confirmed for Poloxamine 908 by in vivo studies (Davis et al., 1987b; Davis, 1989; Illum et al., 1989). A liver/spleen uptake of about 25% was observed after intravenous injection of a Poloxamine 908 stabilized fat emulsion. This is identical to the liver/spleen uptake of Poloxamine 908 coated 60 nm latex particles. The non-biodegradable coated latex particles remained in blood circulation whereas for the biodegradable emulsion a blood clearance was observed. However, the blood clearance of the Poloxamine emulsion was distinctly slower than the clearance of an egg lecithin emulsion. The incorporation of the drug amphotericin B led to a slightly enhanced blood

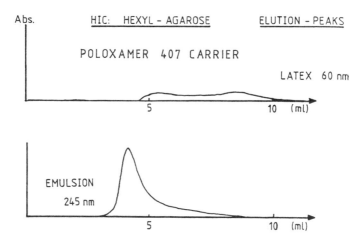

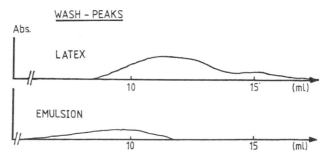

Fig. 9.3./7: Elution peaks (upper two) and wash peaks (lower two) obtained for Poloxamer 407 coated 60 nm latex particles and Poloxamer 407 stabilized soya oil emulsion. The emulsion is less hydrophobic than the coated particles as indicated by the large, not retarded elution peak and the small wash peak obtained with the emulsion.

clearance. The drug is intercalated at the interphase leading to a change of the surface properties and subsequently possibly different interactions with blood components (e.g. opsonins, apoproteins). This effect of enhanced clearance demonstrates the importance of the surface properties and contradicts a protection by steric stabilization.

9.4. Surface hydrophobicity of PHB carriers

9.4.1. HIC investigations of PHB carriers

The PHB carriers were characterized in their surface hydrophobicity to compare them with the Poloxamine and Poloxamer coated model carriers (60 nm latex particles). The characterization in terms of surface hydrophobicity, charge and interaction with charged blood components (c.f. 9.6) should enable to explain the observed in vivo distribution.

The surface hydrophobicity of uncoated, surfactant free PHB particles was not investigated by HIC. Characterization by contact angle measurements yielded a contact angle of about $67°$ for all the PHB polymers ranging in molecular weight from 3,000 to 70,000 (c.f. 2.5.). This is below the contact angle of polystyrene (around $90°$) but still very hydrophobic leading in vivo to the adsorption of opsonins onto uncoated PHB particles and subsequent RES clearance.

The production of PHB particles using sodium dodecyl sulphate (SDS) as surfactant led to the incorporation of SDS into the particle surface and possibly to a change in the surface properties of these PHB/SDS particles. Despite the SDS incorporation, the PHB/SDS particle surface proved to be

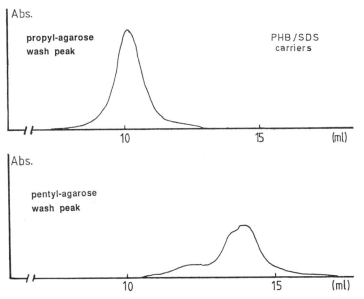

Fig. 9.4/1: Chromatograms of wash peaks obtained from uncoated PHB particles produced with SDS (PHB/SDS) on a propyl- (upper) and a pentyl-column (lower).

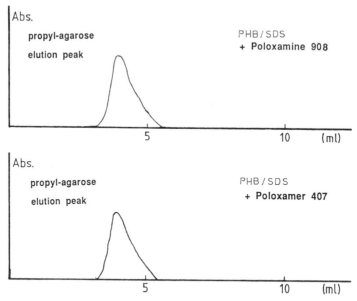

Fig. 9.4./2: Chromatograms of elution peaks from PHB/SDS particles coated
with Poloxamine 908 (upper) and Poloxamer 407 (lower) on propyl-agarose
gel. No wash peak was obtained with Triton X-100 solution indicating that
no particles were retained on the column.

relatively hydrophobic compared to coated model carriers. No particle
elution was possible from the propyl- and pentyl-agarose columns. However,
washing the columns with Triton X-100 solution could easily remove the
particles even from the pentyl-column (Fig. 9.4./1). This indicates the
less hydrophobic nature of the PHB compared to polystyrene particles and
correlates with the contact angles of the polymers. Polystyrene particles
could not be removed from a pentyl-gel. The charged and relatively
hydrophobic surface of the PHB/SDS particles led to a high uptake of
charged serum components indicated by the zeta potential of the particles
in serum. The measured -16.9 mV are similar to the values obtained for
polystyrene latex (c.f.9.6.). From the measured surface hydrophobicity it
was expected that the PHB/SDS particles would be cleared rapidly by the
liver and spleen which was confirmed in vivo by gamma-scintigraphy studies
(c.f. 8.5.2.).
PHB/PVA particles could not be coated with Poloxamine 908 or Poloxamer 407
or the coating layers obtained were very thin. However, for PHB/SDS
carriers a coating layer of 135 Å was obtained with Poloxamine 908.
Consideringg the theory of steric stabilization, the particles should be
protected against RES clearance. They were coated with the same polymer

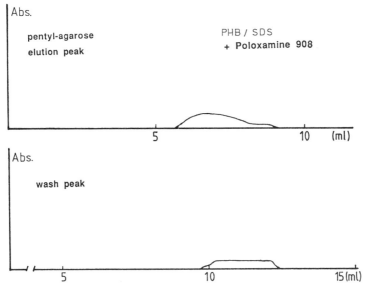

Fig. 9.4./3: Chromatograms of elution (upper) and wash peak (lower) obtained from PHB/SDS-908 particles on pentyl-agarose.

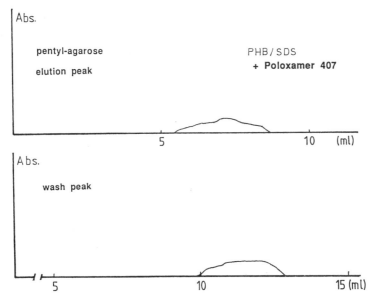

Fig. 9.4./4: Chromatograms of elution (upper) and wash peak (lower) obtained from PHB/SDS-407 particles on pentyl-agarose.

309

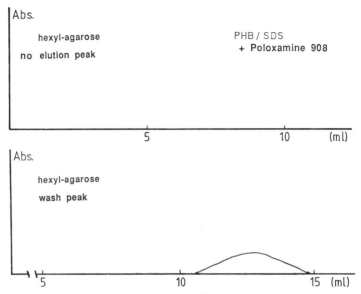

Fig. 9.4./5: Chromatogram of PHB/SDS-908 particles on hexyl-agarose. No particles could be eluted with buffer, only a wash peak was obtained with Triton X-100 solution.

(Poloxamine 908) and a coating layer similar in thickness to the coatings on 60 nm and 100 nm latex particles. Considering the simultaneously reduced uptake of charged serum components by these coated carriers (-7 mV for PHB/SDS-908), the particles were thought to be a promising candidate to avoid RES clearance and investigated in vivo. However, the particles were cleared by the liver and spleen. This led to a closer investigation of the properties of the coating layer using HIC.

PHB/SDS carriers coated with Poloxamine 908 and Poloxamer 407 passed the propyl-column without interaction and behaved similar to coated model latex (Fig. 9.4./2). No wash peak was detected. However, on the pentyl-column a retention of the elution peak and wash peaks were obtained for both coatings (Fig. 9.4./3 and 4). It was still possible to wash off all the particles from the column.

On the hexyl-gel, no particles coated with the polymers could be eluted. A wash peak was obtained for PHB/SDS-908 (Fig. 9.4./5), the Poloxamer 407 coated PHB/SDS could not be washed off the column at all. This shows that despite a similar coating layer thickness of 135 Å, the Poloxamine coating on the PHB/SDS is more hydrophobic than on the 60 nm latex particles. The increased surface hydrophobicity led to the removal by the RES despite of the provided steric stabilization. The more hydrophobic nature of the

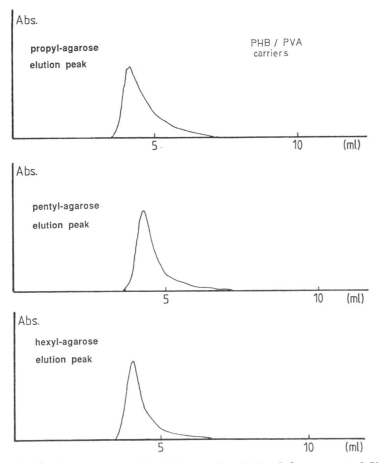

Fig. 9.4./6: Chromatograms of elution peaks obtained from uncoated PHB/PVA particles on propyl-, pentyl- and hexyl-agarose. No wash peaks were found.

Poloxamine coating film might be due to a different conformation of the adsorbed polymer on the surface resulting in an increased exposure of more hydrophobic propylene oxide groups. However, further investigations on the conformation of the adsorbed polymer films are necessary to confirm this.
The surface properties of PHB/PVA particles were determined to investigate the lack of coating by Poloxamine and Poloxamer polymers. Thin coating layers were found on PHB/PVA particles produced using a shorter sonication time. From this observation it was thought that the extent of coating by Poloxamine and Poloxamer depends on the amount of PVA incorporated in the carrier surface. Longer sonication times might increase the amount of PVA

311

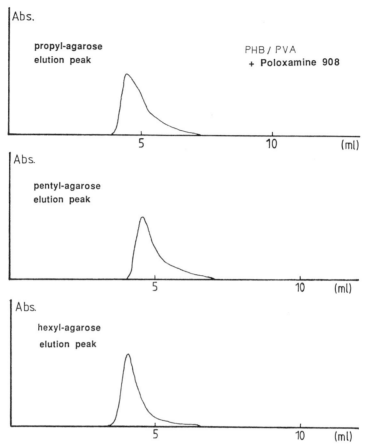

Fig. 9.4./7: Chromatograms of elution peaks obtained from Poloxamine 908 coated PHB/PVA particles (PHB/PVA-908) on propyl-, pentyl- and hexyl-agarose. No wash peaks were found. The chromatograms are identical to the ones of uncoated PHB/PVA particles (Fig. 9.4./6).

incorporated into the surface of the PHB/PVA particles leading to a reduction in surface hydrophobicity and consequently a poorer or non-existent coating layer.

To measure the extent of hydrophilisation of the particle surface caused by PVA incorporation, PHB/PVA particles produced with a long sonication time (10 min.) were investigated by HIC. Surprisingly, the PHB/PVA carriers passed all the columns (propyl- , pentyl- and hexyl-agarose) without interaction and any detectable wash peak (Fig. 9.4./6). As measured by HIC, the particles were at least as hydrophilic as 60nm latex coated with

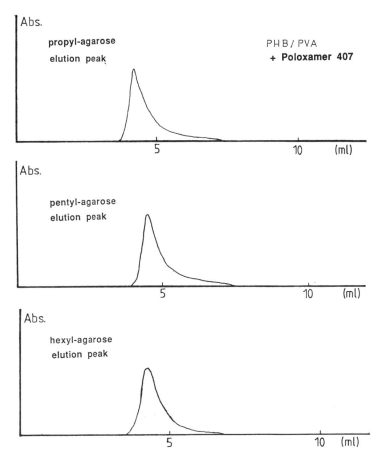

Fig. 9.4./8: Chromatograms of elution peaks obtained from Poloxamer 407 coated PHB/PVA particles (PHB/PVA-407) on propyl-, pentyl- and hexyl-agarose. No wash peaks were found. The chromatograms are identical to the ones obtained for uncoated PHB/PVA particles (Fig. 9.4./6).

Poloxamine 908 or Poloxamer 407. The change in surface properties compared to e.g. PHB/SDS particles is thought to be due to the incorporation of PVA polymer in the PHB surface. In addition, PHB/PVA particles were incubated with Poloxamine 908 and Poloxamer 407 and passed through the same columns to investigate if any coating took place which was not detected by PCS measurements. A decrease in the PCS-size due to deaggregation of carriers can compensate a simultaneous PCS-size increase due to polymer coating. However, the chromatograms obtained are identical to the ones from the PHB/PVA itself (Fig. 9.4./7 and 8).

Relation of the in vivo distribution to the surface characteristics

From these results, a coating does not seem to take place confirming the PCS measurements.

After these unexpected findings of low surface hydrophobicity, the PHB/PVA particles were characterized in terms of charge and uptake of charged serum components (c.f. 9.6.). In distilled water, the particles were practically uncharged indicating a thick polymer layer of PVA on the particle surface. In serum no charge could be measured due to little interaction with charged serum components similar to RES uptake reducing polymer coatings.

The particles seemed to fulfill all the requirements to reduce RES uptake, however, after i.v. administration the PHB/PVA carriers accumulated in the liver/spleen. It might be possible, that hydrophilicity in the chemical sense as determined with methods such as HIC, is not sufficient to avoid interaction with blood components. Chemical structures might be similarly low in hydrophobicity if hydrophobicity is quantified measuring the strength of hydrophobic interactions as performed by HIC. In HIC measurements, the hydrophobic interactions between the column matrices and the EO chains of Poloxamine 908 coated latex or the PVA molecules on the PHB particle surface seem to be similar. However, the PHB/PVA particle surface seems to be a complement activating surface leading to RES uptake.

A possible difference between the with regard to hydrophobic interactions similar chemical structures of PVA and EO chains are their extent of hydration and the structure of the water layer around the particles. EO chains attached to a particle create a surface which
- shows even less hydrophobic interactions than phospholipid based fat emulsions
- might be similar to chylomicrons in terms of hydrophobic interactions with blood components and the degree of hydration and water structure around the particle
- and seems not to activate the complement system.

At the present work is underway to investigate the role of hydration in the coating layer and the effect of the water structure around colloidal carriers on their in vivo fate.

As an alternative to the above PHB carriers, PHB particles were produced using Poloxamine 908 and Poloxamer 407 as surfactants. It was hoped that a similar polymer incorporation as observed with PVA would take place. Apart from the low yield of particles in the right size range, the PHB/908 and PHB/407 carriers could only pass the propyl-agarose column without interaction (Fig. 9.4./9 and 10). This is clearly a reduction in surface hydrophobicity compared to e.g. PHB/SDS carriers which could not pass the propyl-column (only wash peak with Triton X-100). As seen before with 60 nm polystyrene latex particles, the population of the Poloxamer 407 particles (PHB/407) seems to contain a fraction of more hydrophobic particles as indicated by the tailing of the elution peak.

314

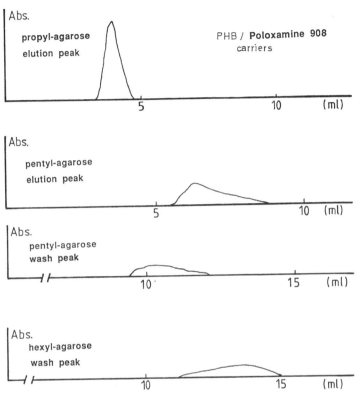

Fig. 9.4./9: Chromatograms of PHB particles produced with Poloxamine 908 as surfactant (PHB/908) on propyl- (elution peak), pentyl- (elution and wash peak) and hexyl-agarose (wash peak only).

In contrast to the propyl-agarose, on the pentyl-agarose column a retention of the elution peaks and wash peaks indicating particles retained on the column were obtained. In contrast to Poloxamine 908 and Poloxamer 407 coated 60nm latex, no fraction of the PHB/908 and PHB/407 particles could pass the hexyl-column (Fig. 9.4./9 and 10). Only a fraction of the particles retained on the column could be washed off with the surfactant solution. The surface hydrophobicity of the PHB/908 and PHB/407 particles is therefore higher than the one of 142 nm latex coated with Poloxamine 908 but lower than the the one of 383 nm coated latex. Considering the surface hydrophobicity, most of the particles will be cleared by the RES after intravenous administration. The amount of Poloxamine and Poloxamer physically entrapped in the PHB particle surface or adsorbed is not sufficient to provide a low surface hydrophobicity similar to the 60 nm coated latex.

315

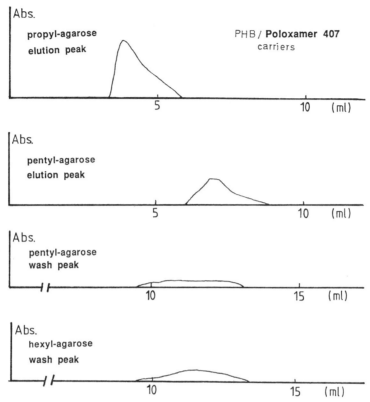

Fig. 9.4./10: Chromatograms of PHB particles produced with Poloxamer 407 as surfactant (PHB/407) on propyl- (elution peak), pentyl- (retarded elution and wash peak) and hexyl-agarose (wash peak only).

To obtain PHB particles which adsorb Poloxamine to a sufficient extent and in the right conformation, other surfactants have been used in the production process. Particles produced with Tween 85 (PHB/TW) did not pass the propyl-column, only a small fraction of the retained particles could be washed off with Triton X-100. However, the PHB/TW carriers could be coated with Poloxamine 908 (PHB/TW-908) and Poloxamer 407 (PHB/TW-407) which reduced their surface hydrophobicity. After coating, PHB/TW-908 and PHB/TW-407 passed the propyl-column, nothing was retained on the column (Fig. 9.4./11 and 12). However, both coated particles comprised a retention of the elution peak on the medium hydrophobic pentyl-column. A fraction of PHB/TW-407 was even retained on the column as indicated by the wash peak obtained. This proved a less efficient coating (in terms of created surface hydrophilicity) of Poloxamer 407 compared to Poloxamine 908.

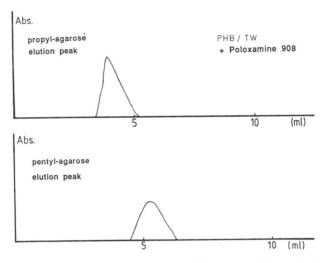

Fig. 9.4./11: Chromatograms of Poloxamine 908 coated PHB particles produced with Tween 85 as surfactant (PHB/TW-908) on propyl- and pentyl-agarose (elution peaks).

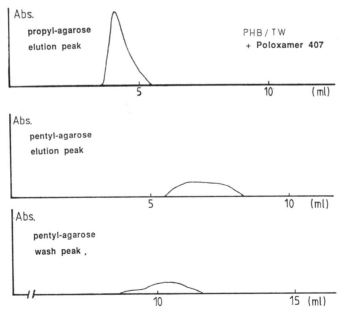

Fig. 9.4./12: Chromatograms of Poloxamer 407 coated PHB particles produced with Tween 85 as surfactant (PHB/TW-407) on propyl- and pentyl-agarose.

317

Relation of the in vivo distribution to the surface characteristics

A reduction in the uptake of charged serum components similar to Poloxamine 908 coated 60nm latex was found for PHB/TW-908, a slightly higher value for the particles produced with the less efficient coating polymer Poloxamer 407 (PHB/TW-407). From the obtained HIC characterization data, the PHB/TW coated carriers are not optimized enough to avoid RES clearance.

9.4.2 Comparison of surface hydrophobicity of PHB carriers and coated latex model carriers

The PHB/SDS particles coated with Poloxamine 908 and Poloxamer 407 are more hydrophobic than the corresponding coated 60 nm latex as indicated by the decrease in the retention coefficient and the lower AUC ratios on the pentyl-gel, and the lack of elution with buffer from the hexyl-gel (Table 9.4./1). They are more hydrophobic than the 142 nm coated latex particles as shown by the decrease in the retention coefficient on the pentyl-gel. Despite that their AUC ratio is slightly higher, they are more hydrophobic because the eluted peak is very broad. The elution peak was so broad that the calculation of a shape quotient was not possible. As seen in the in vivo studies, particles with a more hydrophobic surface than the coated 142 nm latex are cleared by the RES (c.f. 8.2.2. and 8.2.3.). The same fate was observed for the PHB/SDS-908 and PHB/SDS-407 carriers.

PHB/908 and PHB/407 particles produced using Poloxamine 908 and Poloxamer 407 as surfactant in the production process were very close in their surface properties to the coated PHB/SDS particles as indicated by identical retention coefficients, similar elution and wash peaks and shape quotients. They do not offer any advantage with regard to their surface hydrophobicity but they contain no residues of the toxic surfactant SDS.

PHB/PVA carriers produced using PVA as surfactant were found to be so hydrophilic in their surface properties that they passed the propyl-, pentyl- and hexyl-columns without interaction. The retention volumes and shape quotients were very similar to Poloxamine 908 coated 60 nm latex (Table 9.4./2). No wash peaks could be detected, the AUC of the elution peak was approximately in the expected size range equivalent for the elution of 100% of the sample put on the column. Therefore no or only a small fraction of particles were retained by the column indicating that the PHB/PVA are at least of similarly low surface hydrophobicity as the Poloxamine 908 coated 60 nm latex particles. In vivo however, they were cleared by liver and spleen. This suggests that another "hydrophilicity" parameter than the measured "low hydrophobic interactions" might be important, e.g. the extent of hydration of the coating layer and the water structure around the particle.

PHB/TW particles produced in the presence of Tween 85 as surfactant could

Table 9.4/1: Retention coefficients, AUC ratios and shape coefficients of elution peaks of Poloxamine 908 (908) and Poloxamer 407 (407) coated particles (EP/WP - elution/wash peak only) and various biodegradable PHB particles.

particles	alkyl-agarose	retention coefficient	AUC ratio elution/ wash peak	shape quotient of elution peak
60 nm latex	propyl	0.93	EP -	0.54
coated with Poloxamine 908	pentyl	0.99	9.0 : 1	0.61
	hexyl	0.91	1.0 : 1.3	0.80
coated with Poloxamer 407	propyl	0.99	EP -	0.63
	pentyl	0.97	3.3 : 1	0.46
	hexyl	0.86	1 : 3	0.24
142 nm latex	propyl	0.88	11.1 : 1	0.64
coated with Poloxamine 908	pentyl	0.95	1.2 : 1	0.43
	hexyl	-	- WP	-
coated with Poloxamer 407	propyl	0.89	16.2 : 1	0.64
	pentyl	0.95	1 : 1.8	0.29
	hexyl	-	- -	-
PHB/SDS	propyl	0.93	EP -	0.66
coated with Poloxamine 908	pentyl	0.66	2.3 : 1	broad
	hexyl	-	- WP	-
coated with Poloxamer 407	propyl	0.89	EP -	0.81
	pentyl	0.62	1 : 1.1	broad
	hexyl	-	- -	-
PHB/908	propyl	0.92	EP -	0.63
PHB produced with Poloxamine 908	pentyl	0.66	1.8 : 1	broad
	hexyl	-	- WP	-
PHB/407	propyl	0.96	EP -	0.47
PHB produced with Poloxamer 407	pentyl	0.61	2.0 : 1	broad
	hexyl	-	- WP	-

319

Table 9.4./2: Retention coefficients, AUC ratios and shape coefficients of elution peaks of Poloxamine 908 and Poloxamer 407 coated particles (EP/WP - elution/wash peak only) and various biodegradable PHB particles.

particles	alkyl-agarose	retention coefficient	AUC ratio elution/ wash peak	shape quotient of elution peak
60 nm latex	propyl	0.93	EP -	0.54
coated with Poloxamine 908	pentyl	0.99	9.0 : 1	0.61
	hexyl	0.91	1.0 : 1.3	0.80
coated with Poloxamer 407	propyl	0.99	EP -	0.63
	pentyl	0.97	3.3 : 1	0.46
	hexyl	0.86	1 : 3	0.24
PHB/PVA	propyl	0.88	EP _	0.52
PHB particles produced with PVA	pentyl	0.96	EP -	0.73
	hexyl	0.99	EP -	0.73
PHB/SDS	propyl	0.93	EP -	0.66
coated with Poloxamine 908	pentyl	0.66	2.3 : 1	broad
	hexyl	-	- WP	-
coated with Poloxamer 407	propyl	0.89	EP -	0.81
	pentyl	0.62	1 : 1.1	broad
	hexyl	-	- -	-
PHB/TW	propyl	0.93	EP -	0.49
coated with Poloxamine 908	pentyl	0.80	EP -	broad
	hexyl	-	- -	-
coated with Poloxamer 407	propyl	0.89	EP -	0.58
	pentyl	0.65	1.1 : 1	broad
	hexyl	-	- -	-

be coated similarly to the PHB/SDS carriers. The characterization by HIC did not reveal a large improvement in the surface properties compared to PHB/SDS-908 and PHB/SDS-407 (Table 9.4./2). The retention volumes were

320

similar, the AUC ratios slightly better for the PHB/TW particles. However taking into account the broadness of the elution peaks, the "mean" of the surface hydrophobicity might be very similar.

No biodegradable PHB carriers could be produced which adsorb or incorporate Poloxamine 809 or Poloxamer 407 to a sufficient extent and in the right conformation. The results obtained demonstrate, that by manipulation of the production process, a coating or an incorporation of the coating polymer in the carrier surface can be achieved. Optimization of the carrier production technique holds promise to create a system with required properties.

Most of the observed in vivo distributions could be explained by the surface hydrophobicity data. This shows the potential of the applied Hydrophobic Interaction Chromatography (HIC) to estimate the in vivo behaviour of drug carrier systems. Effects such as the RES clearance of PHB/PVA particles possessing a low surface hydrophobicity could not be explained by HIC alone and show the importance of additional characterization methods (e.g. charge measurements, measurements of interaction with blood components and determination of the degree of hydration of the coating layer). It demonstrates as well that the characterization methods allow only a "negative selection" of carriers with potential to avoid RES clearance. Carriers possessing a high surface hydrophobicity can be eliminated because they are likely to undergo RES clearance (negative selection). However, the measurement of a low surface hydrophobicity does not necessarily mean that the carrier will be able to avoid RES‧ uptake (e.g. PHB/PVA particles). Other requirements such as low charge and no functional groups which lead to immunological recognition (e.g. OH of PVA) need to be met as well.

9.5. Thickness of coating layers on latex particles different in size

The determination of the coating layer thickness by PCS measurements is less accurate with increasing particle size of the coated particles. In addition, most of the latex larger than 100 nm contained aggregates which were removed during the coating process. As a result the mean PCS diameter decreased due to the aggregate removal and interfered with the size increase of particles due to the adsorption of the coating layers. As seen with the 383 nm latex particles, the particle diameter after coating was still the same or even lower than before coating. However, the decrease in the polydispersity index indicated that a particle coating took place but no information about the coating layer thickness could be obtained.

Determination of the coating layer thickness on particles larger than 0.4 µm was not possible for the latex suspensions used due to the described interfering effects. Particles above 3 µm are outside the PCS measuring range. Information about the coating layer thickness can be obtained by small angle neutron scattering (SANS). This technique has high requirements with regard to equipment, data analysis and time and was not instantly available because of the necessary access to a reactor.

The coating layer thickness on latex particles larger than 3 µm is of great importance when such particles are used to study the influence of coating layers on the phagocytosis by macrophages. The assumption is not correct that the coating layer of a polymer on 60 nm and 5 µm latex is identical in thickness because the thickness is not influenced by the particle size (Illum et al., 1987). This assumption implies that because both particles are made from the same polymer they provide the same surface hydrophobicity. The surface hydrophobicity of the particles influences greatly the coating layer thickness and it could be shown that it is lower for particles larger than 60 nm (c.f. 3.4.1). Consequently the adsorption layers on particles of different size vary in thickness and surface properties (c.f. 9.1).

As an alternative to SANS studies, zeta potential measurements were performed. As discussed above, the polymer coating layer shifts the plane of shear to a greater distance from the particle surface resulting in a zeta potential reduction. The zeta potential reduction increases exponentially with increasing coating layer thickness due to the exponential decay of the potential in the diffuse layer.

A calibration was performed by plotting the measured zeta potential reduction versus the coating layer thickness of various Poloxamer polymers and Poloxamine 908 (Fig. 9.5./1). Coated latex particles of 60 nm and 145 nm were used for the calibration. Parallel to the zeta potential measurements, the coating layer thickness was determined by PCS. Both particle populations were relatively monodisperse and contained no aggregates which

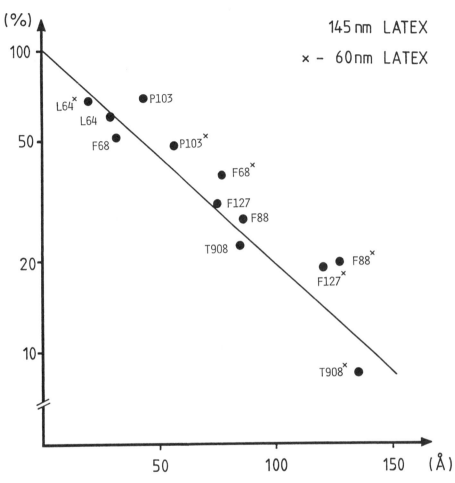

Fig. 9.5./1: <u>Zeta potential reduction (%) versus coating layer thickness</u>.
Semilogarithmic plot of the zeta potential of 60 nm (x) and 145 nm
particles after polymer coating versus the coating layer thickness of the
polymer. The zeta potential of the coated particles are calculated as
percentage of the zeta potential of the original uncoated latex particles.

could be removed by the coating process and interfere with the PCS
determination of the coating layer thickness. The reduced potential after
coating was calculated in percent of the original potential of the uncoated
latex particle and plotted versus the coating layer thickness in Ångström.
To obtain a straight line, a logarithmic y-axis was used for the zeta
potential percentage (100% = zeta potential of uncoated latex particle).

Relation of the in vivo distribution to the surface characteristics

To use this method, the thickness of the diffuse layer needs to be adjusted to about 100 Å. Polymer coating layers with a thickness in the range of around 120 to 150 Å will cover most of the diffuse layer and create a reduction of the zeta potential to about 10 to 20 percent of its original value. It needs to be considered that a zero potential cannot be obtained. The thickness of the diffuse layer is defined as the distance from the particle surface in which the potential drops to $1/e$ of its original value. That means there still remains a potential in a distance larger than 100 Å which drops exponentially towards zero. The measurements of the zeta potential reduction to calculate the coating layer thickness cannot be performed in distilled water. In distilled water the diffuse layer is larger than 1000 Å and the polymer coatings lead to zeta potential reductions which are too close together for all polymers. Zeta potentials between -40 and -30 mV were found for most of the Poloxamer coatings ranging in molecular weight from 2.000 to around 12.000 (c.f. Table 3.3.1./4). Larger differences were found by adjusting the diffuse layer using a buffered 0.001 M NaCl solution.

The addition of the salt compresses the diffuse layer to the desired thickness, the use of a 0.0001 M citrate-phosphate buffer in the sodium chloride solution stabilizes the pH at 5.0 and eliminates distortions by a

Table 9.5./1: Coating layer thickness on latex particles of different size determined by measurement of the zeta potential reduction after coating (*-the thicknesses on 60 and 145 nm particles are obtained by PCS, for the 383 nm latex the coating layer thickness determined by PCS is given in addition to the calculated value from the zeta potential reduction).

particle size	Coating layer thickness after coating with	
	Poloxamine 908	Poloxamer 407
60 nm	135 Å*	120 Å*
145 nm	80 Å*	75 Å*
383 nm	70 Å	50 Å
	75 Å *	50 Å*
496 nm	81 Å	71 Å
910 nm	62 Å	45 Å
5600 nm	70 Å	55 Å

possible pH-shift in the distilled water. Plotting the zeta potentials versus the coating layer thickness in a semilogarithmic manner yielded a straight line (Fig. 9.5./1). From theoretical considerations the zeta potential reduction observed should not depend on the particle size and the results obtained with both 60 and 145 nm latex particles could be plotted in one graph. The independence of the potential reduction on the particle size allows to apply the calibration diagram for calculating the coating layer thickness on larger particles using the measured zeta potential reduction after coating.

Latex particles of various sizes were coated with Poloxamine 908 and Poloxamer 407. The coating layer thicknesses were calculated from the measured reduction in zeta potential (Table 9.5./1). The 145 nm latex particles (Table 9.5./1) were used in the Rose Bengal studies where it has been shown that their surface was distinctly less hydrophobic compared to 60 nm particles. The reduced surface hydrophobicity influences the adsorption of the polymer leading to a thinner coating layer. Fortunately, the batch of 142 nm latex used in the in vivo distribution studies (c.f. 8.2.1.) comprised coating layers above 120 Å. A coating layer of such a thickness is sufficiently hydrophilic to avoid RES recognition and clearance.

The 383 nm latex particles possessed thinner coating layers (around 70 Å) than the 60 nm ones. The coating layers determined by PCS were similar to the values found by measuring the zeta potential reduction. In contrast to other batches of larger latex, the relatively low polidispersity of these large 383 nm particles allowed a PCS determination of the coating layers. However, some deaggregation in the latex dispersion might have taken place which could not be detected by a change in the polydispersity index (due to its high standard deviation). The coating layers determined by both methods, PCS and charge reduction measurements are in good agreement.

On the larger particles the coating layers for Poloxamine 908 were found to be in the range of 60 to 80 Å, for Poloxamer 407 between 45 and 70 Å. No obvious relationship between increase in particle size and coating layer thickness was found. The coating layers seemed to be very similar on the larger latex. This would correspond to the surface hydrophobicity of the latex particles measured by the Rose Bengal methods. The surface of the 60 nm latex was much more hydrophobic (hence resulting in a thick coating) compared to the latex > 100 nm. No large differences in surface hydrophobicity were found between e.g. 145 nm and 1000 nm particles which should theoretically result in a similar coating layer thickness of both particles. This could be confirmed by the above results.

The dependence of the coating layer thickness on the surface hydrophobicity could be demonstrated by coating of surface-modified polystyrene particles. The thickness of the Poloxamine 908 and Poloxamer 388 coating

Table 9.5./2: Coating layer thickness on polystyrene latex particles of different surface hydrophobicity (hydrophobicity characterized by the Rose Bengal binding constant) but similar size.

particle	coating layer thickness		binding constant (ml/µg)
	Poloxamine 908	Poloxamer 338	
PS-0.06	135 Å	140 Å	0.400
PS-0.145	85 Å	100 Å	0.289
PS-COOH (269nm)	67 Å	74 Å	0.060
PS-OH (238nm)	44 Å	63 Å	0.042

decreased with decreasing surface hydrophobicity (Table 9.5./2). The influence of the particle curvature on the polymer adsorption and properties of the coating layer needs to be discussed. The affinity of a coating polymer to the surface will be mainly determined by the surface hydrophobicity and less by the degree of curvature. Assuming the same number of adsorbed molecules per surface area, the thickness of the coating layer might be influenced by the particle curvature due to the "spatial dilution effect in the adsorbed layer" with increasing distance from the particle surface. This effect reduces the thickness of the coating layer on smaller sized particles. However. the reduced density of polymer chains per volume unit of the adsorbed layer might promote a more intense hydration of the chains leading to a more hydrophilic coating layer on small particles compared to layers of the same coating polymer on larger particles.

The particles used to describe the dependence of the coating layer thickness on surface hydrophobicity are of similar size (PS-0.142, PS-COOH and PS-OH) but larger than the 60 nm latex which could escape RES recognition after coating with Poloxamine 908. To investigate the effect of the change in surface hydrophobicity of 60 nm particles on the Poloxamine 908 coating, polystyrene particles produced with a charged co-monomer (styrene sulphonate) were used (c.f. 4.5.). The styrene sulphonate led to an increased number of charged groups on the particle surface which could be shown by an increase in the zeta potential. The charged groups on a particle surface are hydrated and reduce the surface hydrophobicity. Subsequently the coating layer decreased (Table 9.5./3).

It demonstrates that the properties of the surface (charged groups, hydrophobicity) have a major influence on the thickness of the resulting coating layers. Controlled manipulation of the surface properties can be

Table 9.5./3: Coating layers on 60nm latex particles with a different density of charged groups on the surface.

particle produced with	coating layer thickness		zeta potential (in water)
	Poloxamine 908	Poloxamer 407	
styrene monomer	135 Å	120 Å	- 59.8 mV
styrene and styrene sulphonate	109 Å	79 Å	- 75.2 mV

used as an opportunity to enhance the coating. Replacement of the surfactant PVA by SDS when producing PHB particles created a very thick coating layer but showed simultaneously, that thickness does not imply hydrophilicity.

The SDS modified PHB surface led most likely to a change in the conformation of the adsorbed Poloxamine 908 resulting in a more hydrophobic coating layer. Optimization of coated carriers needs to be performed by considering thickness and hydrophobicity of the coating layer.

9.6. Charge measurements of drug carriers

9.6.1. Charge measurements on coated polystyrene latex

Zeta potential measurements of coated latex in serum were performed to determine the interaction of coating films with charged serum components (c.f. 3.3.1.4.). Due the compression of the diffuse layer by the electro-,lytes present in serum, the zeta potentials measured will be in the range of approximately 0 to -20 mv. This is a small potential scale and similarly opsonized particles will differ little in the absolute value of the measured zeta potential. In addition, the serum coated particles were measured in distilled water. In distilled water the less compressed diffuse layer will lead to higher zeta potentials and enlarge the measured differences between the particles. Uncoated 60 and 383 nm latex exhibited potentials of -20.5 and -21.3 mV in serum, measurements in water enlarged the difference and the potentials obtained were -25.7 and -30.1 mV respectively (Table 9.6.1./1). This effect can however only be observed if no desorption of adsorbed serum components takes place after placing the serum coated particles in distilled water. Depending on the extent of desorption, the potential will be similar or even reduced.

The Poloxamine 908 and Poloxamer 407 coated 60 nm latex possessed a potential of around - 5 mV indicating a low adsorption of serum components. The potential was similar to results obtained in previous studies (c.f.

Table 9.6.1./1: Zeta potentials of uncoated and coated latex particles (60 and 383 nm) measured in serum and in water after serum incubation of the particles.

latex particles uncoated/coated	zeta potential (mV)	
	in serum	serum coated particles in dist. water
60 nm uncoated	- 20.5	- 25.7
+ Poloxamine 908	- 5.0	- 3.9
+ Poloxamer 407	- 4.9	- 5.6
383 nm uncoated	- 21.3	- 30.1
+ Poloxamine 908	- 15.1	- 20.2
+ Poloxamer 407	- 18.3	- 23.7

3.3.1.4.). The zeta potential in distilled water was not increased but the same as in serum. This can be explained by desorption of charged serum components from the hydrophilic coating after dilution in water (Table 9.6.1./1).

As seen in the HIC studies, the coating layers on 383 nm particles were more hydrophobic than on 60 nm latex. This leads to an increased adsorption of charged serum components resulting in distinctly higher zeta potentials in serum (-15 to -18 mV, Table 9.6.1./1). The potentials of the coated 383 nm latex are close to the -21.3 mV found for uncoated latex indicating the high degree of interaction with the serum. The strong adsorption of serum components onto these coating layers leads to RES recognition and is seen to be responsible for the RES uptake observed with these particles in vivo (c.f. 8.2.2.).

9.6.2. Charge measurements on fat emulsions

Fat emulsions produced with Poloxamine 908, Poloxamer 188 and 407 were used to investigate the interaction of emulsions with serum components. The composition of the fat emulsions was soya oil 10%, surfactant 1.0 % and glycerol 2.5 %. Considering the results obtained for the coating layers of these polymers onto latex particles an increased serum adsorption was expected for Poloxamer 188 compared to the other two polymers. The Poloxamer 188 emulsion adsorbed a relatively large amount of charged serum components resulting in a zeta potential of -16.2 mV (Table 9.6.2./1). This is slightly higher than the value obtained for coated 60 nm latex particles (-9.6 mV). The high degree of serum interaction corresponds with the small effect of Poloxamer 188 coatings on the reduction of the liver clearance in vivo (Illum et al., 1986). The zeta potential of the emulsion did not increase in water which indicates some desorption of serum components.

Table 9.6.2/1: Zeta potentials of soya emulsions with varying surfactants measured in serum and in water after serum incubation of the emulsions.

fat emulsions produced with surfactant	zeta potential (mV)	
	in serum	serum coated emulsion in dist. water
Poloxamer 188	- 16.2	- 14.9
Poloxamine 908	- 4.9	- 8.4
Poloxamer 407	- 3.4	- 5.2

Relation of the in vivo distribution to the surface characteristics

The Poloxamine 908 and Poloxamer 407 emulsions exhibited zeta potentials in
serum which are identical to the ones obtained for coated 60 nm latex
particles - despite the fact that the emulsion droplet sizes were 260 and
245 nm. As seen in the HIC investigations, the hydrophobicity of the
emulsion droplets was at least similar or even lower than the hydrophobicity of the coating layers of the polymers on 60 nm latex particles.
The results prove that it can be achieved to produce carriers of a larger
size but with the same surface properties (hydrophilicity and low serum
interaction) as known from coated 60 nm latex. It is only a question to
create a surface layer with the correct properties. The RES clearance of
latex particles larger in size (> 140 nm) is therefore not a size influence
but due to the lack of the correct surface properties (hydrophilicity and
correlated reduced opsonization). An important factor in getting the
surface properties of coating films right is the conformation of the
polymer. A thick coating layer is not sufficient when the polymer
conformation is different creating a more hydrophobic layer (as seen with
Poloxamine 908 coated PHB particles).

Fat emulsions prepared with polyoxypropylene - polyoxyethylene copolymers
possessing the correct surface properties show a reduction in RES clearance
(Jeppsson and Rössner, 1975). After the 1st edition of this book data have
been published about the organ distribution of Poloxamine 908 emulsions in
rabbits (Davis, 1989; Illum et al., 1989). The intravenously injected
emulsions circulate in the blood comparable to Poloxamine 908 coated 60 nm
latex particles.

In contrast to the Poloxamer 407 coated 60 nm latex, the Poloxamine 407
emulsion is as hydrophilic as the Poloxamine 908 coated 60 nm latex
particles. Therefore, for the Poloxamer 407 emulsion no affinity to the
bone marrow is expected due to the lack of interaction with the BM opsonin.
Furthermore, the emulsion droplets are above the required small size (< 100
nm) to get access to the bone marrow. Consequently the emulsions will
circulate in the blood stream similar to Poloxamer 407 coated 100-150 nm
latex particles and the Poloxamine 908 emulsion.

9.6.3. Charge measurements on PHB carriers

To determine the zeta potential of pure PHB, PHB powder was used as
received and dispersed in water. After 4 hours settling time of the PHB
suspension, the supernatant was taken for the determination of the zeta
potential. The PHB powder possessed a potential of about -30 mV in
distilled water.

The production of PHB particles using SDS as surfactant led to the
incorporation of SDS into the particle surface and to the adsorption of SDS

onto the particles. This resulted in an increase of the potential from -30 mV to about -50 mV (Table 9.6.3./1). Dialysis of the particles could remove adsorbed SDS indicated by the reduction in the zeta potential to -40 mV, but some remained on the surface (physically entrapped or possibly strongly adsorbed). The zeta potential measurements are in good agreement with the SSIMS investigations of the PHB/SDS particles (c.f. 3.5.2.). The SSIMS spectra showed a high SDS concentration on non-purified (non-dialyzed) PHB/SDS particles, a distinctly reduced SDS concentration after dialysis. Incubation of PHB/SDS particles with serum led to a high uptake of charged serum components resulting in a zeta potential of -16.9 mV. This uptake is similar to uncoated hydrophobic 60 nm polystyrene latex (-14.9 mV), indicating a strong opsonisation and RES recognition after injection. Measurements in serum will lead to low zeta potential values due to the

Table 9.6.3./1: Zeta potential of PHB carriers in distilled water, in serum and in distilled water after incubation with serum (PHB pure = PHB powder, mw 23,000).

particles	zeta potential (mV) in		
	dist. water	serum	dist. water after serum incubation
PHB pure	- 30.0	-	- 26.0
PHB/SDS	- 50.6	- 16.9	- 44.8
PHB/SDS dialysed	- 40.3	-	-
PHB/SDS-908	-	- 13.6	- 7.0
PHB/SDS-407	-	- 11.0	- 7.4
PHB/908	+ 0.5	- 10.8	+ 5.8
PHB/407	- 0.6	- 6.4	+ 3.3
PHB/TW	- 36.5	- 7.6	- 10.4
PHB/TW-908	-	- 4.3	-
PHB/TW-407	-	- 8.6	-
PHB/PVA	+ 0.1	- 6.4	+ 0.4

compression of the diffuse layer by the electrolytes present (appr. 0 to -16 mv). Different degrees of opsonisation will lead to zeta potential not very different in the absolute value. Performing zeta potential measurements of the serum incubated particles in water will enlarge the potential scale due to the larger extent of the diffuse layer. For the PHB/SDS particles, a zeta potential increase from -16.9 mV in serum to -44.8 mV of serum coated particles measured in water was found. The opsonization of the higher charged PHB/SDS particles seemed to be greater than for PHB powder as indicated by the zeta potentials in water (-44.8 mV and -26.0 mV respectively).

Due to the hydrophobic surface of uncoated PHB, the high charge and uptake of charged serum components by the PHB/SDS particles, they should be taken up by the RES after i.v. administration. A high liver/spleen uptake was observed in the in vivo study (c.f. 8.5.2.).

Coating of the PHB/SDS particles with Poloxamine 908 (PHB/SDS-908) and Poloxamer 407 (PHB/SDS-407) led to potentials of -11 mV and -13.5 mV in serum which is much higher than for coated 60 nm latex (around -5 mV). This shows a stronger adsorption of charged serum components due to the more hydrophobic character of the coating layers. This stronger interaction with serum components is regarded to be responsible for the in vivo clearance of the particles from the blood stream by liver and spleen macrophages - despite the sterically stabilizing coating layer of 135 Å. Zeta potential measurements of the serum coated particles in water did not lead to an increase in the negative potential (as observed with PHB/SDS) but to a decrease to around -7 mV. The decrease in the negative potential might be due to the desorption of the negatively charged serum components. The surface of the coating layer is much less hydrophobic than uncoated PHB surfaces therefore leading to the desorption during dilution. The more hydrophobic surface of PHB/SDS particles bound the serum components by much stronger hydrophobic interactions and no desorption occurred during the dilution with water.

PHB particles produced using Poloxamine 908 (PHB/908) and Poloxamer 407 (PHB/407) were uncharged in distilled water (Table 9.6.3./1). The surfactant incorporated was sufficient to create an uncharged particle. Most likely due to the relatively hydrophobic surface of the particles, the uptake of charged serum components was higher compared to 60 nm latex particles coated with these two polymers. Measuring the serum coated particles in water led to a decrease in the negative zeta potential and even a slightly positive potential was obtained. The reduction of the zeta potential is thought to be due to a desorption of serum components. The observed slightly positive potential cannot be explained but was observed before when Poloxamine 908 coated 60 nm latex particles were measured in Tris buffer at pH 7.4.

Charge measurements of drug carriers
_____

Alternatively to PHB/SDS, particles were produced using Tween 85 as
surfactant. The zeta potential of -7.5 mV indicates a reduction in the
uptake of serum components caused by the hydrophilisation of the particle
surface by incorporated Tween 85. The incorporation of uncharged Tween can
not increase the particle charge as seen with SDS. Therefore the PHB/TW
particles possess a similar potential as PHB powder (-36.4 and -30 mV,
respectively) in water. Measurement of the serum coated particles in water
yielded a slight increase in the potential. This indicates little or no
desorption of serum components as seen with the coated PHB particles.
Coating of the PHB/TW with Poloxamine 908 reduces the adsorption of serum
components, Poloxamer 407 coating seems to be poor and has little effect.
Considering the surface hydrophobicity of PHB/TW-908 and PHB/TW-407 particles, they are most likely to be taken up by liver and spleen after
injection (similar to PHB/SDS-908).
In the HIC investigations, a surprisingly low surface hydrophobicity was
found for the PHB/PVA particles. In distilled water, the particles were
practically uncharged similar to PHB/908 and PHB/407 indicating a polymer
layer of PVA on the surface. In serum a similar low charge compared to
Poloxamine 908 coated 60 nm latex was measured indicating little interaction with charged serum components. Measurement of the serum coated
particles in distilled water led to the desorption of serum components from
the PVA surface and the particles were uncharged identical to non-serum
incubated PHB/PVA.
From the in vitro characterisation data obtained, the PHB/PVA particles
fulfilled almost ideally the requirements to reduce the RES clearance:
- low particle size (100 - 200 nm)
- no charge in water
- low uptake of charged serum components
- hydrophilic surface (even more hydrophilic than Poloxamine 908 coated
  60 nm latex particles)
However after injection, the particles were taken up by liver and spleen. A
hydrophilic surface seems not sufficient , at least surface hydrophilicity
as it is measured by HIC. Based on these results, a certain chemical
structure seems to be required in the coating layer which avoids complement
activation. Ethylene oxide chains must provide a property to the particle
surface (degree of hydration ?) which eliminates RES recognition
(opsonization) and clearance.

9.7. Summary of surface characterization

The differences in the organ distribution of 60 nm latex, coated with the similar polymers Poloxamine 908 (blood circulation) and Poloxamer 407 (bone marrow accumulation) could be explained by the greater hydrophobicity of the Poloxamer 407 coating. It is suggested that this led to the adsorption of an opsonic factor (BM opsonin) which can only be recognized by phagocytosing cells in the bone marrow and not by liver and spleen macrophages. Larger Poloxamer 407 particles circulate in the blood, denied access to the bone marrow by the size restriction of the sinusoidal fenestrations.

The differences in the observed organ distribution of coated polystyrene latex particles varying in size could be explained by the different surface properties of the uncoated particles and the coating layers. The increase in liver and spleen uptake with increasing particle size (from 60 nm up to 1000 nm) is not related to the size but to the surface properties of the particles.

The surface hydrophobicity of latex particles larger than 100 nm is different to the surface hydrophobicity of 60 nm latex. This influences the adsorption of Poloxamine and Poloxamer 407 leading to thinner coating layers.

The thinner coating layers are more hydrophobic than the thicker layers. This leads to an increased adsorption of serum components and subsequently to liver/spleen uptake in vivo.

The coating layer thickness also depends on the surface hydrophobicity of the latex particle which is influenced by the number of charged, hydrated groups on the surface. Increasing the number of charged groups leads to formation of thinner coating layers (even on 60 nm latex).

Antarox CO990-coated latex particles are slightly more hydrophobic than Poloxamer 407 coated particles. They are however not homogenous in their surface hydrophobicity. The least hydrophobic fraction of coated particles circulates in the blood avoiding RES uptake, the medium fraction behaves similarly to Poloxamer 407 coated particles and shows affinity for the bone marrow, and the most hydrophobic fraction is taken up by liver and spleen.

The reduced RES uptake of egg lecithin-based fat emulsions is correlated to the low surface hydrophobicity of the oil droplets due to the emulsifier.

Poloxamine 908 and Poloxamer 407 fat emulsions (260 and 245 nm droplet size) are of similar or lower hydrophobicity than 60 nm latex particles coated with these two polymers. They also have a similar low adsorption of serum components and avoid/strongly reduce RES clearance in vivo. They indicate that it is possible to avoid/reduce RES clearance of larger particles when they possess the correct surface properties.

PHB particles produced with the surfactant SDS are highly charged and show strong adsorption of serum components, leading to RES clearance in vivo. Coating of these particles with a sterically stabilizing layer of Poloxamine did not protect the particles against liver/spleen uptake in vivo - despite the fact that the coating layer was of a similar thickness to that obtained on 60 nm latex particles (135 Å), which should have provided similar "steric stabilization" against phagocytosis. The observed liver uptake questions the validity of the theory of steric stabilization.

The in vivo RES clearance could be explained by the increased hydro-phobicity of the Poloxamine 908 coating layer on PHB particles compared to the layer on 60 nm latex. The increased hydrophobicity of the Poloxamine 908 coating layer led to increased adsorption of serum components and subsequently to RES recognition and clearance. It is not the thickness of the coating layer, but the conformation of the polymer in the coating layer and the resulting surface hydrophobicity of the layer which are the important factors determining the in vivo fate of carriers.

PHB particles produced with PVA as surfactant (PHB/PVA) were uncharged in water and were even less hydrophobic (as measured in terms of hydrophobic interactions by HIC) than 60 nm latex particles coated with Poloxamine 908. They also showed similar low interaction with charged serum components. They seemed to have ideal carrier properties for avoidance of RES clearance but were taken up by the liver and spleen in vivo.

The applied characterization methods were not able to detect the essential property provided by the ethylene oxide chains contained in coating layers responsible for the elimination of RES clearance. It seems that the presence of a certain chemical structure in the coating layer (e.g. EO chains) is required to avoid phagocytosis but the reason for this is unknown. A possible explanation might be the hydration layer provided by the EO chain and the resulting water structure around the particle.

For the rational design of carriers for the controlled release and
targeting of drugs, methods need to be available to
1. produce biodegradable carriers,
2. modify the carriers in a toxicologically acceptable way,
3. characterize the unmodified and modified carriers with regard to the
properties relevant to their in vivo fate.
In addition, information must be, available about the factors influencing
the in vivo distribution of carriers, in order to be able to design
intravenous controlled release or organ targeting formulations which can
escape the RES recognition.
The modification of carriers and the development of suitable characterization methods has been performed using a range of non-biodegradable
polystyrene model carriers with different surface properties.
In order to escape RES recognition, the carriers need to be uncharged and
to possess a hydrophilic surface. Carriers with such properties could be
produced by coating the model carriers with ethoxylated non-ionic polymers
by a simple adsorption process as previously described for Poloxamer
polymers by Illum and Davis (1984). In contrast to chemical modification by
attachment of polyethylene glycol (Abuchowski, 1977) the adsorption of
polymers is toxicologically more acceptable. Model carriers were coated
with polyoxyethylene-polyoxypropylene block co-polymers (Poloxamer,
Poloxamine), polyoxyethylated nonylphenols (Antarox, Gafac), polyoxylated
fatty acid alcohols (Tween) and phospholipids. The coating efficiency in
terms of the coating layer thickness was determined by Photon Correlation
Spectroscopy and related to the structure of the molecules.
The coating properties of comparable Poloxamer and Antarox surfactants were
similar. The synthesis of new coating surfactants based on the Antarox
structure could lead to the production of polymers with optimal coating
properties to replace Poloxamine 908 or Poloxamer 407. Optimization of the
hydrophobic anchor region and the hydrophilic ethylene oxide (EO) chain
length of the surfactant molecule increases the affinity for the carrier
surface and reduces the coating film hydrophobicity. Recently, calorimetric
studies demonstrated also the importance of the gain in water entropy
(Carstensen et al., 1990). The coating process might be endothermic but a
coating will take place if the gain in water entropy is sufficiently high.
Polymeric particles could be coated with phospholipids. This is of special
interest as emulsions based on phospholipids show a low RES uptake. It is
conceivable that particles coated with phospholipids may behave in a
similar way.
The model carriers used for the development of the characterization methods

337

were polystyrene standard latex particles of different sizes and surface properties which were varied by the introduction of different functional groups (e.g. OH and COOH). The latex model carriers were characterized before and after surface modification (coating with polymers) with regard to

- size
- charge
- charge reduction by polymer coating
- interaction with blood components
- surface hydrophobicity
- chemical composition of the surface
- stabilizing effect of coating layers.

Particle sizes were determined using Photon Correlation Spectroscopy (PCS), Laser Diffractometry and Transmission Electron Microscopy (TEM). Verification of the particle size proved to be necessary because most of the nominal sizes quoted by the manufacturers of the standard particles were found to be inaccurate.

Charge determinations were performed by electrophoresis experiments using Laser Doppler Anemometry (LDA) and Amplitude weighted Phase Structuration (AWPS). Comparitive studies were used to validate the new method of AWPS.

The dependence of the concentration and nature of electrolytes (NaCl, various buffer salts) on the charge reduction produced by coating with polymers was investigated. Even polymers which only formed thin coating layers (e.g. 30 Å) were found to produce uncharged carriers at physiological salt concentrations.

The interaction with charged blood components (opsonization) was determined by the measurement of particle charge in serum. Non-coated, hydrophobic model carriers heavily adsorbed serum components with a resultant particle zeta potential of -15 mV. Coating with polymers of increasing coating layer thickness and decreasing surface hydrophobicity of the coating layer led to a corresponding decrease in the zeta potential measured in serum, indicating reduced interaction with serum components. The polymers which produced lowest zeta potentials on coating (-5 mV, e.g. Poloxamer 338 and 407 and Poloxamine 908) led to a strong reduction or elimination of liver/spleen clearance of coated particles.

For the determination of the surface hydrophobicity, methods were applied which allowed measurements to be made in the original particle dispersion medium. Contact angle measurements were not regarded as suitable because the sample preparation caused too great a change in the sample.

The surface hydrophobicity of the non-modified polystyrene model carriers was determined by adsorption measurements and partitioning experiments using the hydrophobic dye, Rose Bengal. The surface hydrophobicity was expressed as a binding constant, calculated via a Scatchard analysis of the adsorption isotherms. From the partitioning experiments using Rose Bengal, a slope S was determined from the straight lines obtained by plotting the partitioning quotients of Rose Bengal versus the total surface area of the particles.

The Rose Bengal method was able to distinguish between the different surface hydrophobicities of the model carriers. An interesting finding was that polystyrene particles of different sizes were different in their surface hydrophobicity. This has consequences for the surface modification by polymer adsorption and the in vivo distribution of such carriers. The hydroxylated and carboxylated particles proved to be the least hydrophobic of those examined. For fluorescently-labelled particles between-batch differences in the surface hydrophobicity were observed. This is of relevance in investigations where the surface hydrophobicity is of importance, e.g. phagocytosis experiments in cell cultures. Some of the reproducibility problems encountered in such experiments might be due to changes in the surface properties of particles used. This demonstrates the need for intensive characterization of model particles.

The surface hydrophobicity of polymer coated particles could not be determined by Rose Bengal measurements, so the technique of Hydrophobic Interaction Chromatography (HIC) was employed. The latter was also used to investigate the polydispersity in the surface hydrophobicity of the uncoated polystyrene model carriers. The latex contained a broad distribution of surface properties; two populations differing in surface hydrophobicity were also found in chemically surface-modified latices.

The polymer coating layers on particles could be placed in order of decreasing hydrophobicity whereby Poloxamer 338 and 407 and Poloxamine 908 were found to be least hydrophobic. This corresponds well with their observed thick coating layer and their low interaction with charged serum components.

As an alternative to HIC, the partitioning of carriers between two aqueous phases (containing dextran and polyethylene glycol) of different hydrophobicities was used to characterize the surface hydrophobicity. This method could not differentiate between the hydrophobicity of uncoated polystyrene particles and particles coated with ethoxylated surfactants, possibly due to a specific interaction between the EO chains in the surfactants and the ethylene glycol-containing phase. Aqueous two-phase partitioning proved to be suitable for characterization of phospholipid-coated polymeric particles and phospholipid-based emulsion carriers.

The sterically stabilizing effect of the coating layers was assessed by the determination of the critical flocculation temperature (CFT) of coated particles.

Chemical analysis of the particle surfaces was performed by Static Secondary Ions Mass Spectrometry (SSIMS). The technique was able to detect detergent residues in drug carriers due to the production process and provided information about the chemical composition of the surface. SSIMS characterization of commercially obtained polystyrene model carriers revealed surfactant contamination even in supposedly 'surfactant-free' systems. Poor information about the production conditions and chemicals used did not allow identification of the source of contaminants. Therefore, surfactant-free polystyrene model carriers of different sizes were produced. Colloidal gold was incorporated into some of the particles to serve as possible radioactive label or marker for TEM investigation of particle localisation in tissues.

Non-biodegradable polystyrene particles were used as a model system for the basic investigation of the factors influencing the in vivo distribution of carriers, in order to optimize the surface modifications required to avoid RES uptake. For development of a practically applicable carrier system the non-biodegradable model carriers would need to be replaced by biodegradable particulates.

Biodegradable carriers of poly(hydroxybutyric acid) (PHB) and poly(lactic acid) (PLA) were produced by the solvent evaporation technique. The parameters influencing the production were studied and optimized. To obtain particles in a size range of 100 to 200 nm, a particle production technique using microfluidization was used. To follow the organ distribution of the carriers by gamma scintigraphy, a labelling method with radioactive In-111 was developed. The drug incorporation and release properties of the particles were studied using prednisolone and tetracaine as model drugs. The release was found to take place within about 3 days and proved to be slowest at a high drug to polymer ratio.

As a second biodegradable carrier, fat emulsions emulsified with polymers which had previously been shown to lead to a reduction in RES clearance of polystyrene carriers (Poloxamer 188, 338 and 407, Poloxamine 908) were produced. The influence of the surfactant concentration on the resulting droplet size of the emulsion carriers was determined. The stability of the carriers was investigated by stress testing (freeze-thaw cycling, electrolyte addition).

Cell cultures (peritoneal mouse macrophages) are discussed as possible in vitro test system for the selection of potential coating polymers for protecting drug carriers against RES clearance in vivo. Investigations in hepatocyte culture were performed to obtain information about the toxicity of coating polymers and to possibly elucidate the mechanism of their in vivo action. The polymers which reduced RES uptake showed no interaction with the hepatocyte cell membrane and did therefore not lead to membrane damage and enzyme loss from the cells.

60 nm polystyrene model carriers, coated with Poloxamine 908 escaped RES recognition and circulated in the blood (Illum et al., 1987a) whereas

particles coated with Poloxamer 407 chiefly localized to the bone marrow (>80%) (Illum and Davis, 1987b). However, 60 nm particles are not suitable for incorporation of a large payload of drug and are more difficult to prepare as controlled release systems for long-term release of drugs. Therefore the in vivo distributions of larger particles coated with Poloxamine 908 and Poloxamer 407 were investigated.

142 nm particles coated with these polymers showed a slightly increased liver uptake but the majority still stayed in blood circulation. In contrast to the 60 nm particles, none of the 150 nm particles coated with Poloxamer 407 accumulated in the bone marrow. This indicates a size exclusion effect, most likely by the sinusoidal fenestrations of the bone marrow. Therefore it can be concluded that Poloxamine 908 avoids recognition by macrophages in the liver, spleen and bone marrow whereas Poloxamer 407 avoids only recognition by the macrophages in the liver and spleen.

Larger coated 383 nm particles were cleared by the liver, but the rate of clearance was reduced compared to uncoated latex. The number of particles in the liver increased slowly but steadily during the first hour after i.v. injection. Although the coatings reduced the clearance velocity they did not eliminate the uptake. Coated 496 nm particles were rapidly cleared, indicating little protective effect due to coating. The same was observed for coated 910 nm particles.

The observed in vivo distributions could be explained by characterization of the particles using the methods developed.

The coating layers of Poloxamine 908 and Poloxamer 407 on 60 nm latex particles are of similar thicknesses (around 130 Å) and are identical in the charge-reducing effect. They both show little interaction with charged blood components. However, measurement of the surface hydrophobicity of the coating layers by HIC revealed a more hydrophobic surface for the Poloxamer 407 coating film. It is proposed that the more hydrophobic surface of the Poloxamer 407 films leads to its interaction with an opsonin in the blood (BM opsonin) which can only be recognized by the population of phagocytosing cells in the bone marrow. The recognition leads to adherence to or internalisation by these cells and therefore accumulation in the bone marrow.

The coating layers on the 142 nm particles were found to be slightly thinner and more hydrophobic than on the 60 nm latex. The hydrophobicity shows a polydispersity, leading to an RES uptake of the few most hydrophobic particles but with the majority of the less hydrophobic particles remaining in circulation.

The PCS determination of the coating layers on larger particles proved to be difficult because of a simultaneous size increase by the coating and a size decrease due to the removal of aggregates by the sterically stabilizing effect of the coating polymers. For determination of the coating layer thickness, a method was developed exploiting the charge reducing effect of polymer coating. These measurements revealed an even thinner coating layer on 383 nm and 496 nm particles. Simultaneously, these surfaces were more hydrophobic, leading to the observed RES recognition and clearance in vivo.

The thinner coating layer can be explained by the reduced surface hydrophobicity of the larger latex compared to the 60 nm latex particles. The reduced surface hydrophobicity influences the polymer adsorption and causes a lower density of adsorbed polymer per unit surface area (Rawlins and Kayes, 1983; Law and Kayes, 1983). In addition, at lower surface coverage the configuration of the polymers will be different (Kronberg, 1983); an increased adsorption of EO chains onto the surface will occur, leading to greater exposure of the hydrophobic propylene oxide parts of the molecule. This can explain the increased hydrophobicity of the thinner coating layers on larger latex.

67 nm and 142 nm latex particles were coated with an ethoxylated nonylphenol, Antarox CO990, which contains 100 EO units per molecule. The larger particles were cleared by the liver, whereas the smaller particles showed a reduced liver uptake similar to that observed with Poloxamer 188. These particles had affinity for the bone marrow but this seemed to be restricted by the size of the sinusoidal fenestrations. The diameter of the 67 nm particles was increased to about 85 nm after coating, a size close to that of the sinusoidal fenestrations (about 100 nm). A reduction in the carrier size should increase the accumulation in the bone marrow.

The Antarox coating was found to be more hydrophobic than the Poloxamer 407 coating. Considering the within-batch polydispersity in surface hydrophobicity, the Antarox coated particle population will contain very hydrophilic particles which remain in circulation, particles of medium hydrophobicity which are only recognized by the bone marrow and not the liver and spleen, and more hydrophobic particles which are recognized and cleared by liver and spleen. The organ distribution observed with the Antarox coating indicates the potential for the synthesis of new coating polymers with similar properties to Poloxamer 407 and Poloxamine 908 but increased affinity for the surface of hydrophobic drug carriers. The Poloxamer and Poloxamine 908 coatings do not possess a sufficient affinity for the surface of the relatively hydrophilic biodegradable drug carriers to be able to produce a satisfactory coat.

Model carriers (76 nm) were coated with an ethoxylated nonylphenol with similar coating properties to Poloxamer 188 but carrying a charged phosphoric acid group at the end of the EO chain (Gafac RE960). The in vivo distribution of this carrier should give evidence as to the validity of the theory of steric stabilization (Illum et al., 1987a; Davis and Illum,

1988). If steric stabilization can protect against macrophage clearance, the Gafac RE960 coated latex should show a similar reduction in liver uptake as that described for Poloxamer 188 (Illum et al., 1986). Both polymers create a coating layer of similar thickness, which would therefore be similarly sterically stabilizing. However, as the clearance of the Gafac RE960 particles did not differ from uncoated latex, it can be assumed that steric stabilization alone does not protect against RES uptake. It is thought that the Gafac RE960 coating layer is a complement activating surface (Kazatchkine and Carreno, 1988) due to the presence of charged groups.

Coating of 60 nm latex particles with ethoxylated glycerides (Tagat I) and ethoxylated castor oil (Tagat R60) did not lead to a reduction in liver uptake. The Tagat I coating was too thin and too hydrophobic to avoid recognition, whereas the Tagat R60 coating layer was possibly contaminated by lipophilic compounds which would lead to opsonization. In the production of a fat emulsion carrier the lipophilic contaminants were hidden because they partitioned into the oily core of the droplets. Only the ethoxylated compounds were present in the emulsifier film forming a more hydrophilic surface than the Tagat R60 coated latex and leading to a reduction in liver uptake.

The in vivo distribution of radioactively labelled biodegradable Polyhydroxybutyrate (PHB) particles was determined by gamma scintigraphy. Non-modified particles were cleared by the RES and accumulated in liver and spleen. Coating of the PHB particles with Poloxamine 908 led to a coating layer thickness of 135 Å, identical to the coating layers on 60 nm latex particles escaping RES recognition. If the theory of steric stabilization is valid, the Poloxamine 908 coated PHB particles should not be taken up by the RES. However, after injection. the particles were rapidly cleared by the RES.

Surface characterization revealed that the Poloxamine 908 coating layer on the PHB particles was more hydrophobic than on 60 nm latex. This probably led to opsonization and active receptor mediated uptake of the carriers. A sterically stabilizing polymer layer therefore does not protect against internalisation by macrophages in the case of an active, receptor-mediated process following immunological recognition of the particles. The protective mechanism of the Poloxamine 908 coating layer is seen only as a charge masking and a dysopsonic effect and not as a steric stabilization correlated to the coating layer thickness. The dysopsonic effect is related to the coating layer thickness because the thickness is related to the adsorbed polymer configuration and therefore the surface hydrophobicity. In a thick layer, the hydrophobic moiety of the molecule is orientated to the particle surface, with the hydrophilic moieties protruding into the dispersion medium (Cosgrove et al., 1983) to create a less hydrophobic (more dysopsonic) coating film. However, in a thin coating layer, as seen at low surface coverage, parts of the EO chain of the molecule are adsorbed onto the particle surface (Kronberg, 1983) and the more hydrophobic propylene oxide parts of the molecule are exposed at the outer boundary of the coating layer, leading to a more hydrophobic (and less dysopsonic) coating film. For Poloxamer 181 and 182 which create a very thin coating layer, flat adsorption of the molecule on the surface is described (Kayes and Rawlins 1979).

A hydrophilic surface leads to reduced opsonization. PHB particles produced with polyvinyl alcohol proved to be at least as hydrophilic as Poloxamine 908 coated 60 nm latex particles which were shown to eliminate RES clearance. Considering surface hydrophilicity alone as the main factor necessary for avoiding RES uptake, the polyvinyl PHB particles should avoid phagocytosis by the RES. However, after intravenous injection they were cleared by the RES - despite their hydrophilic surface. This is seen as an indication that hydrophilicity alone is not sufficient and that certain chemical structures are required which create a 'non-activating' surface. The hydroxyl groups of the polyvinyl alcohol on the particle surface possibly led to the activation of the complement system as described for the hydroxyl groups on Cuprophane membranes (Wegmuller et al., 1986).

A 'non-activating' surface possesses a 100 fold higher affinity for complement factor H than for factor B (Kazatchkine and Carreno, 1988). Polyvinyl alcohol and ethyleneoxide (EO) chains are both strongly hydrated, but the water molecules are highly orientated around the EO chains. This hydration feature of EO chains might create a 'non-activating' surface with reduced affinity for factor B and explain the dysopsonic effect of Poloxamine 908 layers.

The RES clearance of particles is reported to be size-dependent, with larger particles being cleared more rapidly (Davis, 1981). A faster clearance was observed for larger polymeric particles coated with Poloxamine 908 and Poloxamer 407 but this effect could be related to an increased hydrophobicity and opsonization of the coating layers. Characterization of larger sized Poloxamine 908 and Poloxamer 407 fat emulsion carriers revealed a surface hydrophobicity similar to coated 60 nm latex particles (c.f. chapter 9.3.3.). This corresponds to the reduced liver clearance of Poloxamer emulsions (Jeppsson and Rössner, 1975) and the avoidance of liver clearance by Poloxamine 908 emulsions (Davis et al, 1987b). It suggests that larger particles are not automatically cleared faster than smaller ones if the surface is not recognized as foreign and therefore not opsonized. The particle size becomes more important when opsonization takes place. The requirements for carriers to avoid RES clearance and therefore to be available for use as intravenous controlled release formulations or as carriers targetable to tissues can be summarized:

1. The carriers need to be non-charged.
2. The surface needs to be hydrophilic, e.g. by coating with polymers.
3. Surface hydrophilicity alone is not sufficient, the surface needs to provide simultaneously a certain chemical structure creating a non-activating surface.
4. The required structure seems to be provided by ethylene oxide chains, possibly related to their high degree of hydration.
,5. The adsorption of charged serum components to the carrier surface needs to be low.
6. The coating layer needs to be of above minimum thickness. The thickness is correlated with the polymer configuration but the thickness effect is not due to steric stabilization.
7. RES uptake reducing polymers do not seem to interact with and damage cell membranes (from cell culture studies), this is possibly related to their general lack of interaction with proteins (blood components).
8. In order to reduce RES clearance the drug carrier size does not need to be small. If the carrier surface is 'non-activating' even larger carriers will not be cleared by the RES.
9. All the requirements need to be fulfilled simultaneously. If one requirement is not met, the carriers will be cleared by the RES.

The importance of the adsorbed blood components on the fate of i.v. injected particles led to the new concept of "differential adsorption" (Müller, R.H., 1989; Müller, R.H. and Heinemann, 1989). The surface of drug carriers can be modified to allow preferential adsorption of blood components which mediate the adhesion to the desired target cell (e.g. opsonins, apoproteins). It has to be distinguished between "differential opsonization" and "differential protein adsorption" depending whether opsonins or proteins such as apoproteins are the adhesion mediating blood components (Müller, R.H. and Heinemann, 1989).

During the last few years, the view of theoretical considerations about the factors relevant for the in vivo distribution of particulates has been reviewed. Insight into the interaction of carriers with blood components might soon lead to further modification in the proposed theories.

11. REFERENCES

Abuchowski, A., van Es, T., Palczuk, N.C. and Davis, F.F., Alteration of immunological properties of bovine serum albumin by covalent attachment of polyethylene glycol, J. Biol. Chem. 252, 3578-3581 (1977)

Agostini, S., Synthesis and characterization of PHB, Ph.D. thesis, Case Western University, USA (1971)

Albertsson, P.-A., Particle fractionation in liquid two-phase systems: The composition of some phase systems and the behaviour of some model particles in them. Application to the isolation of cell walls from microorganisms, Biochim. Biophys. Acta 27, 378 (1958)

Albertsson, P.-A., Partition of Cell Particles and Macromolecules, John Wiley and Sons New York (1971)

Albertsson, P.-A., Partition between polymer phases, J. Chromatogr. 159, 111 (1978)

Artursson, P., Laakso, T. and Edman, P., Acrylic microspheres in vivo: Blood elimination kinetics and organ distribution of microparticles with different surface characteristics, J. Pharm Sci. 72, 1415-1420 (1983)

Artursson, P. and Sjöholm, I., Effect of opsonins on the macrophage uptake of polyacrylstarch microparticles, Int. J. Pharm. 32, 165-170 (1986)

Artursson, P., Martensson, I.-L. and Sjöholm, I., Biodegradable microspheres III: Some immunological properties of polyacryl starch microparticles, J. Pharm. Sci. 75, 697-701 (1986)

Artursson, P., Amo, E., Edman, P., Ericsson, J.L.E. and Sjöholm, I., Biodegradable microspheres V: Stimulation of macrophages with microparticles made of various polysaccharides, J. Pharm. Sci. 76, 127-133 (1987)

Bachman, L., Schmitt-Fumian, W.W., Hammel, R. and Lederer, K., Size and shape of fibrinogen. I. Electron Microscopy of the hydrated molecule, Makromol. Chem. 176, 2603-2618 (1975)

Baptist, J.N., U.S. Patent 3,044,942 (1962)

Barber, L.C., Enzymatic disruption of poly-beta hydroxybutyrate isolated from sporulating cells of bacillus cereus, Ph.D. thesis Washington State University (1973)

Bar-Shavit, Z., Ofek, I., Goldman, R., Mannose residues on phagocytes as receptors for the attachment of Escherichia coli and Salmonella typhi, Biochem. Biophys. Res. Comm. 78, 455-460 (1977)

Beck, L.R., Pope, V.Z., Cowsar, D.R., Lewis, D.H. and Tice, T.R., Evaluation of a new three-month injectable contraceptive microsphere system in primates (baboons), Contracept. Deliv. Syst. 1, 79-86 (1980)

Beck, L.R., Flowers, C.E., Pope, V.Z., Tice, T.R. and Wilborn, W.H.,

References

Clinical evaluation of an improved injectable microcapsule contraceptive system, Amer. J. Obstet. Gynecol. 147 (7), 815-821 (1983)

Beck, L.R., Pope, V.Z., Flowers, C.E., Cowsar, D.R., Tice, T.R., Lewis, D.H., Dunn, R.L., Moore, A.B. and Gilley, R.M., Poly(d,l-lactide-co-glycolide)/norethisterone microcapsules: An injectable biodegradable contraceptive, Biol. Reprod. 28, 186-195 (1983a)

Benita, S., Friedman, D. and Weinstock, M., Physostigmine emulsion: a new injectable controlled release delivery system, Int. J. Pharm. 30, 47-55 (1986)

Berken, A. and Benacerraf, B., Properties of antibodies cytophilic for macrophages, J. Exp. Med. 123, 119-144 (1966)

Bernhard, G.C., Cheng, W. and Talmage, D.W., The reaction of rheumatoid factor and complement with y-globulin coated latex, J. Immunol. 88, 750-762 (1962)

Bindschaedler, C., Leong, K., Mathiowitz, E. and Langer, R., Polyanhydride microsphere formulation by solvent extraction, J. Pharm. Sci. 77, 696-698 (1988)

Bissery, M.C., Valeriote, F. and Thies, C., In vitro and in vivo evaluation of CCNU-loaded microspheres prepared from poly(+/-)-lactide and poly(β-hydroxybutyrate), in Microspheres and Drug Therapy (Davis, S.S., Illum, L., McVie, J.G. and Tomlinson, R., eds.), Elsevier Amsterdam, 217 (1984)

Bodmeier, R. and McGinity, J.W., The preparation and evaluation of drug-containing poly(dl-lactide) microspheres formed by the solvent evaporation method, Pharmaceutical Research 4, 465-471 (1987)

Bodmeier, R. and McGinity, J.W., Solvent selection in the preparation of poly(DL-lactide) microspheres prepared by the solvent evaporation method, Int. J. Pharm. 43, 179-186 (1988)

Braud, C. and Vert, M., Poly(β-malic acid) as a source of polyvalent drug carriers: possible effects of hydrophobic substituents in aqueous media, in Polymers as Biomaterials (Shalaby, S.W., Hoffman, A.S., Ratner, B.D. and Horbett, T.A., eds.), Plenum Publishing Corp. New York, 1-15 (1984)

Braud, C., Bunel, C. and Vert, M., Poly(β-malic acid): a new polymeric drug-carrier, evidence for degradation in vitro, Polym. Bull. 13, 293-299 (1985)

Bräuer, A., Aschmann, C. and Müller, R.H., Ethoxylated surfactants for the coating of colloidal drug carriers - Interaction with hepatocytes in culture, Arch. Pharm. 322, 754 (1989)

Bräuer, A., PhD thesis, Department of Pharmaceutics, University of Kiel (FRG), in preparation (1990)

Brasseur, F., Couvreur, P., Kante, B., Deckers-Passau, L., Roland, M., Deckers, C. and Speiser, P., Actinomycin D adsorbed on polymethylcyanoacrylate nanoparticles: increased efficiency against an experimental tumor, Eur. J. Canc. 16, 1441-1445 (1980)

Briggs, D., Applications of XPS in polymer technology, in 'Practical

347

Colloidal Carriers for Controlled Drug Delivery and Targeting

Surface Analysis by Auger and X-ray Photoelectron Spectroscopy' (Briggs, D. and Seah, M.P., eds.), John Wiley & Sons Chichester (1983)

Briggs, D., Analysis and chemical imaging of polymer surfaces by SIMS, in 'Polymer Surfaces and Interfaces' (Feast, W.J. and Munro, H.S., eds.) John Wiley & Sons New York (1987)

Brophy, M.R. and Deasy, P.B., In vitro and in vivo studies on biodegradable polyester microparticles containing sulphamethi˜ zole, Int. J. Pharm. 29, 223 (1986)

Brown, F.J., Complement, in Fundamental Immunology (Paul, W.E., ed.) Raven Press New York, 645-667 (1985)

Brynda, E., Cepalova, N.A. and Stol, M., Equilibrium adsorption of human serum albumin and human fibrinogen on hydrophobic and hydrophilic surfaces, J. Biomed. Mater. Res. 18, 685-693 (1984)

Bundgaard, H., Hansen, A.B. and Kofod, H. (eds.), Optimization of drug delivery, Munksgaard Copenhagen (1982)

Burger, J.J., Tomlinson, E.T., Mulder, E.M.A. and McVie, J.G., Albumin microspheres for intra-arterial tumour targeting.I. Pharmaceutical aspects, Int. J. Pharm. 23, 333-344 (1985)

Burkhanov, S.A., Kosykh, V.A., Repin, V.S., Saatov, T.S. and Torchilin, V.P., Interaction of liposomes of different phospholipid and ganglioside composition with rat hepatocytes, Int. J. Pharm. 46, 31-34 (1988)

Burnham, W.R., Hansrani, P.K., Knott, C.E., Cook, J.A. and Davis, S.S., Stability of a fat emulsions based intravenous feeding mixture, Int. J. Pharm. 13, 9-22 (1983)

Burstein, S., Cancer therapy using drug-antibody conjugates, Acta Pharm. Suec. 13 (Suppl.), 19 (1976)

Buscall, R. and Ottewill, R.H., The stability of polymer latices, in Polymer Colloids (Buscall, R. Corner, T. and Stageman, J.F., eds.), Elsevier Applied Science Publishers London, 141-217 (1986)

Capo, C., Garrouste, F., Benoliel, A.M., Bongrand, P. and Depieds, R., Nonspecific binding by macrophages - evaluation of the influence of medium-range electrostatic repulsion and short-range hydrophonic interaction, Immunol. Comm. 10, 35-43 (1981)

Carstensen, H., Müller, B.W. and Müller, R.H., Microcalorimetric studies of the adsorption of ethoxylated surfactants on polystyrene particles, Arch. Pharm., in press (1990)

Chainey, M., Wilkinson, M.C. and Hearn, J., Preparation of overcoated polymer latices by a 'shot-growth' technique, Ind. Eng. Chem. Prod. Dev. 21, 171-176 (1982)

Clark, D.T. and Kilcast, D., Study of cone and valency energy levels of PTFE, Nature (Phys. Sci.) 233, 77-79 (1971)

Cook, E.J. and Lagace, A.P., U.S. Patent 4,533,254 (1985)

Cosgrove, T., Crowley, T.L. and Vincent, B., The configuration of adsorbed

References

polymers at the solid-solution interface, Faraday Symp. Chem. Soc. 16, 101-108 (1981)

Cosgrove, T., Crowley, T.L. and Vincent, B., An experimental study of polymer conformations at the solid/solution interface, Adsorpt. Solution Symposium, 287-297 (1983)

Couvreur, P., Tulkens, P., Roland, M., Trouet, A. and Speiser, P., Nanocapsules: a new type of lysomotropic carrier, FEBS Letters 84 (2), 323-326 (1977)

Couvreur, P., Kante, B., Roland, M., Guiot, P., Bauduin, P. and Speiser, P., Polycyanoacrylate nanocapsules as potential lysosomotropic carriers: preparation, morphological and sorptive properties, J. Pharm. Pharmacol. 31, 331-332 (1979)

Couvreur, P., Kante, B. and Roland, M., Les vecteurs lysosomotropes, J. Pharm. Belg. 35 (1), 51-60 (1980)

Couvreur, P., Roland, M. and Speiser, P., U.S. Patent 4,329,332 (1982)

Couvreur, P., Kante, B., Grislain, L., Roland, M. and Speiser, P., Toxicity of polyalkylcyanoacrylate nanoparticles II: Doxorubicin-loaded nano-particles, J. Pharm. Sci. 71, 790-792 (1982)

Couvreur, P., Polyalkylcyanoacrylates as colloidal drug carriers, CRC Critical Reviews in Therapeutic Drug Carrier Systems, Vol. 5, CRC Press Inc. Boca Raton (FL, USA), 1-20 (1988)

Couvreur, P., personal communication (1988a)

Cowell, C., Li-Lin-On, F.K.R. and Vincent, B., Flocculation of sterically stabilised dispersions, J. Chem.Soc., Faraday Trans. 74 (1), 337 (1978)

Crommelin, D., Peptides and proteins: A challenge for drug delivery, Acta Pharm. Technol. 33, 1-2 (1987)

Cummins, H.S. and Pike, E.R. (eds.), Photon Correlation Spectroscopy and Velocimetry, Plenum New York (1977)

Dahlgren, C. and Sunquist, T., Phagocytosis and hydrophobicity: A method of calculating contact angles based on the diameter of sessile drops, J. Immunol. Meth. 40, 171-179 (1981)

Davies, M.C., Pharmacy Department at Nottingham University, personal communication

Davies, M.C. and Brown, A., The surface chemical analysis of polymeric drug delivery systems by static secondary ion mass spectrometry (SSIMS) and SIMS imaging, in Recent Advances in Controlled Release Technology (Lee, P.I. and Good, W.R., eds.) ACS Symposium Series (1987)

Davies, M.C., Wright, J., Koosha, F., Müller, R.H. and Davis, S.S., Surface chemical analysis and site-specific delivery, Proceed. Int. Symp. Control. Rel. Bioact. Mater. 13, Toronto, 111-112 (1987)

Davies, M.C., Short, R.D., Khan, M.A., Watts, J.F., Brown, A., Eccles, A.J., Humphery, P. and Vickerman, J.C., A XPS, static SIMS and Time-of-

349

Flight SIMS analysis of biodegradable biomedical polyesters, Surf. Interf. Anal., in press (1988a)

Davies, M.C. and Brown, A., SSIMS and SIMS imaging analysis of a drug delivery system, Surf. Interf. Anal. 12, in press (1988b)

Davies, M.C., Koosha, F., Müller, R.H., Characterisation of PVA coated PHB carriers, in preparation (1988c).

Davies, W., Thomas, M., Linkson, P. and Penny, R., Phagocytosis and the gamma globulin monolayer: Analysis by particle electrophoresis, Journal of the Reticuloendothelial Society 18, 136-148 (1975)

Davis, J.M., Narachi, M.A., Alton, N.K. and Arakawa, T., Structure of human tumor necrosis factor α derived from recombinant DNA, Biochemistry 26, 1322-1326 (1987)

Davis, M.A. and Taube, R.A., Pulmonary perfusion imaging: acute toxicity and safety factors as a function of particle size, J. Nucl. Med. 19, 1209-1213 (1978)

Davis, S.S., Pharmaceutical aspects of intravenous fat emulsions, J. Hosp. Pharm., 165-171 (1974)

Davis, S.S., The emulsion - obsolete dosage form or novel drug delivery system an therapeutic agent, Journal of Clinical Pharmacy 1, 11-27 (1976)

Davis, S.S. and Hansrani, P., The influence of emulsifying agents on the phagocytosis of fat emulsions, J. Pharm. Pharmacol. 32 Suppl., 61 (1980)

Davis, S.S., Colloids as drug-delivery systems, Pharmaceutical Technology 5, 71-88 (1981)

Davis, S.S., Emulsion systems for the delivery of drugs by the parenteral route, in Optimization of Drug Delivery (Bundgaard, H., Hansen, A.B. and Kofod, H., eds.), Munksgaard Copenhagen, 333-347 (1982)

Davis, S.S., The use of scintigraphic methods for the evaluation of drug dosage forms in the gastrointestinal tract, in Topics in Pharmaceutical Sciences (Breimer, D.D. and Speiser, P.) 205-215, Elsevier Amsterdam (1983)

Davis, S.S., Intravenous emulsions for parenteral nutrition and drug delivery, paper presented at the 5th Int. Colloquium on Lecithin, 10-12 April Cannes - France, Proc. to be published (1989)

Davis, S.S. and Hansrani, P., The influence of emulsifying agents on the phagocytosis of lipid emulsions by macrophages, Int. J. Pharm. 23, 69-77 (1985)

Davis, S.S., Douglas, S., Illum, L., Jones, P.D.E., Mak, E. and Müller, R.H., Targeting of colloidal carriers and the role of surface properties, in Targeting of Drugs with Synthetic Systems (Gregoriadis, G., Senior, J. and Poste, G., eds.), Plenum Press New York, 123-146 (1986)

Davis, S.S., The design and evaluation of controlled release dosage forms for oral delivery, S.T.P. PHARMA 3 (5), 412-417 (1987)

Davis, S.S., Illum, L., West, P. Galloway, M., Studies on the fate of fat

References

emulsions following intravenous administration to rabbits and the effect of added electrolyte, Clinical Nutrition 6, 13-19 (1987)

Davis, S.S., Mills, S.N. and Tomlinson, E., Chemically cross-linked albumin microspheres for the controlled release of incorporated Rose Bengal after intramuscular injection into rabbits, J. Controlled Release 4, 293-302 (1987a)

Davis, S.S., Washington, C., West, P., Illum, L., Liversidge, G., Sternson, L. and Kirsh, R., Lipid emulsions as drug delivery systems, Annals N.Y. Acad. Sci. 507, 76-88 (1987b)

Davis, S.S. and Illum, L., Polymeric microspheres as drug carriers, Biomaterials 9, 111-115 (1988)

Davis, S.S., Illum, L., Müller, R.H., Landry, F., Wright, J. and Harper, G., Studies on the uptake of fat emulsions following intravenous administration to rabbits, Clin. Nutr. , in press (1990)

Dobbie, J.W., Evans, R., Gibson, D.V., Smitham, J.B. and Napper, D.H., Enhanced steric stabilization, J. Colloid Interf. Sci. 45, 557-565 (1973)

Domb, A.J., Ron, E., Kothari, R., Giannos, S., Flores, C., Kim, R., Doh, L. and Langer, R., New polyanhydrides: aliphatic-aromatic homopolymers and unsaturated polymers, Proceed. Intern. Symp. Control. Rel. Bioact. Mater. 14, 138-139 (1987)

Douglas, S., The preparation and characterisation of Poly(butyl 2-cyano-acrylate)nanoparticles, Ph.D. thesis Nottingham University (1985)

Duncan, R., Soluble polymers: use for controlled drug delivery, Proceed. Intern. Symp. Control. Rel. Bioact. Mater. 14, 127-128 (1987)

Edebo, L and Richardson, N., Enhancement of hydrophobic interaction, negative charge and phagocytosis by dinitrophenyl ligand coupling to Salmonella typhimurium 395 MS, Int. Archs. Allergy appl. Immun. 78, 345-352 (1985)

Edman, P., Ekman, B. and Sjöholm, I., Immobilization of proteins in microspheres of biodegradable polyacryldextran, J. Pharm. Sci. 69, 838-842 (1980)

Edman, P., Sjöholm, I. and Brunk, U., Ultrastructural alterations in macrophages after phagocytosis of acrylic microspheres, J. Pharm. Sci. 73, 153-156 (1984)

Entenmann, G., Freund, B.W.J., Zierenberg, B., Controlled release systems with short release times, Proceed. Intern. Symp. Control. Rel. Bioact. Mater. 14, 117-118 (1987)

Eriksson, E., Albertsson, P.-A. and Johansson, G., Hydrophobic surface properties of erythrocytes studied by affinity partition in aqueous two-phase systems, Mol. and Cell. Biochem. 10, 123 (1976)

Eriksson, E. and Albertsson, P.-A., The effect of the lipid composition on the partition of liposomes in aqueous two-phase systems, Biochim. Biophys. Acta 507, 425 (1978)

Fitzgerald, P., Hadgraft, J., Kreuter, J. and Wilson, C.G., A y-scintigraphic evaluation of microparticulate ophthalmic delivery systems: liposomes and nanoparticles, Int. J. Pharm. 40, 81-84 (1987)

Franzky, H.-J., Mikroemulsionen, Mizellen oder Lösungen?, Ph.D. thesis, Pharmacy Department, University of Kiel (1986)

Gabius, H.-J., Vertebrate lectins and their possible role in fertilization, development and tumor biology (Review), in vivo 1, 75-84 (1987)

Gabius, H.-J., Bokemeyer, C., Hellmann, T. and Schmoll, H.-J., Targeting of neoglycoprotein-drug conjugates to cultured human embryonal carcinoma cells, J. Cancer Res. Clin. Oncol. 113, 126-130 (1987)

Gabius, H.-J., Engelhardt, R., Hellmann, T., Midoux, P., Monsigny, M., Nagel, G.A. and Vehmeyer, K., Characterization of membrane lectins in human colon carcinoma cells by flow cytofluorometry, drug targeting and affinity chromatography, Anticancer Research 7, 109-112 (1987a)

Gabius, H.-J., Gabius, S., Vehmeyer, K., Schauer, A., Nagel, G.A., Endogene Tumorlektine: Neue Tumormarker und Zielpunkte für Krebstherapie?, Onkologie 10, 184-185 (1987b)

Gabius, H.-J., Vehmeyer, K., Gabius, S. and Nagel, G.A., Clinical application of various plant and endogenous lectins to leukemia, Blut 56, 1-6 (1988)

GAF Technical Bulletin 7583-039, GAF (Great Britain) Co. Ltd., Tilson Road Roundthorn, Manchester M23 9PH (1969)

GAF Corporation, Antarox CO Technical Bulletin 2550-023, 140 West 51 Street, New York NY 10020

GAF Corporation, Mulgofen ON870 Technical Bulletin 9676-010,140 West 51 Street, New York NY 10020

Galazka, V., A study of the surface modification of polymers when treated by oxygen plasma and irradiation, sandwich training report, Pharmacy Department at Nottingham University (1987)

Galazka, V. Khan, A.M., Davies, M.C. and Müller, R.H., Effect of gamma-irradiation and plasma etching on the surface of polymers, Archiv der Pharmazie 320, 980 (1987)

Gallo, J.M., Hung, C.T. and Perrier, D.G., Analysis of albumin microsphere preparation, Int. J. Pharm. 22, 63-74 (1984)

Gardella, J.A. and Hercules, D.M., Static SIMS of polymer systems, Anal. Chem. 52, 226-232 (1980)

Gardner, C., Drug targeting: potentials and limitations, in Topics in Pharmaceutical Sciences (Breimer, D.D. and Speiser, P., eds.), Elsevier Science Publishers, 291-303 (1983)

Ghosh, P., Das, P.K. and Bachawat, B.K., Targeting of liposomes towards different cell types of rat liver through the involvement of liposomal surface glycosides, Archiv. Biochem. Biophys. 213, 266-270 (1982)

Gipps, E.M., Groscurth, P., Kreuter, J. and Speiser, P., Distribution of

References

polyhexylcyanoacrylate nanoparticles in nude mice over extended times and after repeated injection, J. Pharm. Sci. 77, 208-209 (1988)

Gilding, D.K., Biodegradable polymers, Biocompat. Clin. Implant. Mater. 2, 209 (1981)

Gilley, R.M., Tice, T.R., Staas, J.K. and Beck, L.R., Development of controlled-release progesterone microcapsules for the regulation of fertility during lactation, Proceed. Intern. Symp. Control. Rel. Bioact. Mater. 11, Ft. Lauderale, FL July 23-25 (1984)

Goodwin, J.W., Hearn, J., Ho, C.C. and Ottewill, R.H., The preparation and characterisation of polymer latices formed in the absence of surface active agents, Br. Polym. J. 5, 347-362 (1973)

Goodwin, J.W., Hearn, J., Ho, C.C. and Ottewill, R.H., Studies on the preparation and characterisation of monodisperse polystyrene latices. iii. Preparation without added surface-active agents, Colloid & Polym. Sci. 252, 464-471 (1974)

Gould, P.L., Holland, S.J. and Tighe, B.J., Polymers for biodegradable medical devices, IV. Hydroxybutyrate-valerate copolymers as non-desintegrating matrices for controlled-release oral dosage forms, Int. J. Pharm. 38, 231 (1987)

Green, C.J. (ed.), Animal anaesthesia, Laboratory Animals Ltd., 138 (1979)

Gregoriadis, G., Neerunjun, D.E. and Hunt, R., Fate of liposome-associated agent injected into normal and tumour-bearing rodents. Attemps to improve localization in tumour tissues, Life Sci. 21, 357-370 (1977)

Gregoriadis, G., Kirby, C. and Senior, J., Targeting of drugs with liposomes: studies on optimization, in Optimization of Drug Delivery (Bundgaard, H., Hansen, A.B. and Kofod, H., eds.) Munksgaard Copenhagen, 365-383 (1982)

Gregoriadis, G., Senior, J. and Trouet, A. (eds.), Targeting of Drugs, Plenum Press New York and London (1982a)

Grislain, L., Couvreur, P., Lenaerts, V., Roland, M., Deprez-Decampeneere, D. and Speiser, P., Pharmocokinetics and distribution of a biodegradable drug-carrier, Int. J. Pharm. 15, 335-345 (1983)

Gurny, R., Simmons, S.P., Banker, G.S. and Myers, R.D., A new biocompatible drug delivery system for chronic implantation in animal brain, Pharm. Acta Helv. 54 (12), 349-352 (1979)

Gurny, R., Peppas, N.A., Harrington, D.D. and Banker, G.S., Development of biodegradable and injectable latices for controlled release of potent drugs, Drug Dev. Ind. Pharm. 7 (1), 1-25 (1981)

Gurny, R., Boye, T. and Ibrahim, H., Ocular therapy with nanoparticulate systems for controlled drug delivery, J. Controlled Release 2, 353-361 (1985)

Hara, T., Ishihara, H., Aramaki, Y. and Tsuchiya, S., Specific uptake of asialofetuin-labeled liposomes by isolated hepatocytes, Int. J. Pharm. 42, 69-75 (1988)

Colloidal Carriers for Controlled Drug Delivery and Targeting

Harmia, T., Speiser, P. and Kreuter, J., A solid colloidal drug delivery system for the eye: encapsulation of pilocarpin in nanoparticles, J. Microencapsulation 3 (1), 3-12 (1986)

Haynes, L.C. and Cho, M.J., Mechanism of nile red transfer from o/w emulsions as carriers for passive drug targeting to peritoneal macrophages in vitro, Int. J. Pharm. 45, 169-177 (1988)

Heller, J., Biodegradable polymers in controlled drug delivery, in CRC Critical Reviews in Therapeutic Drug Carrier Systems, Vol. 1, CRC Press, Inc., Boca Raton (FL, USA), 39-90 (1985)

Heller, J. and Himmelstein, K.J., Poly(ortho ester) biodegradable polymer systems, in Drug and Enzyme Targeting, Part A, Methods in Enzymology, Vol. 112, (Widder, K.J. and Green, R., eds.) Academic Press New York, 422-435 (1985)

Higuchi, W.I., Fox, J.L., Ho, N.F.H., Kusai, A., Hsu, C.C., Yu, C.D. and Gordon, N.A., The prodrug approach to the target-site delivery of Ara-A (vidarabine) in the vaginal membrane of the mouse and in hairless mouse skin, in Optimization of Drug Delivery, (Bundgaard, H., Hansen, A.B. and Kofod, H., eds.), Munksgaard Copenhagen, 211-224 (1982)

Hilditch, T.E., Kwok, C.S. and Amanat, L.A., Lacrimal scintigraphy. I. Compartmental analysis of data, Br. J. of Ophth. 67, 713-719 (1983)

Hoes, C.J.T., Potman, W., van Heeswijk, W.A.R., Mud, J., de Grooth, B.G., Greve, J. and Feijen, J., Optimization of macromolecular prodrugs of the antitumor antibiotic adriamycin, J. Controlled Release 2, 205-213 (1985)

Holland, S.J., Tighe, B.J. and Gould, P.L., Polymers for biodegradable medical devices. 1. The potential of polyesters as controlled macromolecular release systems, J. Controlled Release 4, 155-180 (1986)

Holland, S.J., Jolly, A.M., Yasin. M. and Tighe, B.J., Polymers for biodegradable medical devices, II. Hydroxybutyrate-hydroxyvaleriate copolymers; hydrolytic degradation studies, Biomaterials 8, 289 (1987)

Holmes, P.A., Wright, L.F. and Collins, S.H., European Patent 0,052,459 (1981)

Holmes, P.A., Collins, S.H. and Wright L.F., U.S. Patent 4,477,654 (1984)

Huh, Y., Donaldson, G.W. and Johnson, F.T., A radiation-induced bonding of iodine at the surface of uniform polystyrene particles, Radiat. Res. 60, 42-53 (1974)

Hunter, R.J., Zeta Potential in Colloid Science: principles and applications, Academic Press London (1981)

Hurwitz, E., Attempts at site-directed experimental chemotherapy with antibody drug-conjugates, in Optimization of Drug Delivery (Bundgaard, H., Hansen, A.B. and Kofod, H., eds.), Munksgaard Copenhagen, 253-269 (1982)

Ikada, Y. and Tabata, Y., Phagocytosis of bioactive microspheres, Journal of Bioactive and Compatible Polymers 1, 32-46 (1986)

Ikada, Y. Hyon, S.-H., Jamshidi, K., Release of antibiotic from composites

References

of hydroxyapatite and poly(lactic acid), J. Controlled Release 2, 179-186 (1985)

Illum, L. and Davis, S.S., The targeting of drugs parenterally by use of microspheres, J. Parenter. Sci. Technol. 36, 242-251 (1982)

Illum, L., Davis, S.S., Wilson, C.G., Thomas, N.W., Frier, M. and Hardy, J.G., Blood clearance and deposition of intravenously administered colloidal particles. The effects of particle size, nature and shape, Int. J. Pharm. 12, 135-146 (1982)

Illum, L. and Davis, S.S., Effect of the non-ionic surfactant Poloxamer 338 on the fate and deposition of polystyrene microspheres following intra- venous administration, J. Pharm. Sci. 72, 1086-1089 (1983)

Illum, L., Jones, P.D.E., Kreuter, J., Baldwin, R.W., and Davis, S.S., Adsorption of monoclonal antibodies to polyhexylcyanoacrylate nanoparticles and subsequent immunospecific binding to tumour cells in vitro, Int. J. Pharm. 16, 105-113 (1983)

Illum, L. and Davis, S.S., The organ uptake of intravenously administered colloidal particles can be altered using a non-ionic surfactant (Poloxamer 338), FEBS Lett. 167, 79 (1984)

Illum, L., Jones, P.D.E., Baldwin, R.W. and Davis, S.S., Tissue distri- bution of poly(hexyl-2-cyanoacrylate) nanoparticles coated with monoclonal antibodies in mice bearing human tumour xenografts, J. Pharmacol. Exper. Therapeut. 230, 733-736 (1984)

Illum, L., Hunneyball, I.M. and Davis, S.S., The effect of hydrophilic coatings on the uptake of colloidal particles by the liver and by peritoneal macrophages, Int. J. Pharm. 29, 53-65 (1986)

Illum, L., Jacobsen, L.O., Müller, R.H., Mak, E. and Davis, S.S., Surface characteristics and the interaction of colloidal particles with mouse peritoneal macrophages, Biomaterials 8, 113-117 (1987)

Illum, L, Davis, S.S., Müller, R.H., Mak, E. and West, P., The organ distribution and circulation time of intravenously injected colloidal carriers sterically stabilized with a blockcopolymer - Poloxamine 908, Life Sci. 40, 367-374 (1987a)

Illum, L. and Davis, S.S., Targeting of colloidal particles to the bone marrow, Life Sci. 40, 1553-1560 (1987b)

Illum, L. and Davis, S.S. (eds.), Polymers in Controlled Drug Delivery, Wright Bristol (1987c)

Illum, L., West, P., Washington, C. and Davis, S.S., The effect of stabilising agents on the organ distribution of lipid emulsions, Int. J. Pharm. 54, 41-49 (1989)

Ishizaka, T., Endo, K. and Koishi, M., Preparation of egg albumin microcapsules and microspheres, J. Pharm. Sci. 70 (4), 358-363 (1981)

James, A.M., Electrophoresis of particles in suspensions, in Surface and Colloid Science, Vol.11 (Good, R.J. and Stromberg, R.R.) Plenum Press New York, 121 (1979)

Colloidal Carriers for Controlled Drug Delivery and Targeting

Jamshaid, M., Farr, S.J., Kearney, P. and Kellaway, I.W., Poloxamer sorption on liposomes: comparison with polystyrene latex and influence on solute efflux, Int. J.Pharm. 48, 125-131 (1988)

Jeppsson, R. and Rössner, S., The influence of emulsifying agents and of lipid soluble drugs on the fractional removal rate of lipid emulsions from the blood stream of the rabbit, Acta pharmacol. et toxicol. 37, 134-144 (1975)

Johnson, S.A., B. Med. Sci. thesis, Medical School, The University of Nottingham (1986)

Juliano, R.L. and Stamp, D., Pharmacokinetics of liposome-encapsulated anti-tumor drugs, studies with vinblastine, actinimycin D, cytosine arabinoside, and daunomycin, Biochem. Pharmac. 27, 21-27 (1978)

Juliano, R.L., Stamp, D., McCullough, N., Pharmacokinetics of liposome-encapsulated antitumor drugs and implications for therapy, Ann. N.Y. Acad. Sci. 308, 411-425 (1978)

Juliano, R.L., Hsu, M.J. and Regen, S.L., Interactions of polymerized phospholipid vesicles with cells. Uptake, processing and toxicity in macrophages, Biochim. Biophys. Acta 812, 42-48 (1985)

Juni, K., Nakano, M. and Kubato, M., Controlled release of aclarubicin, an anticancer antibiotic, from poly-β-hydroxybutyric acid microspheres, J. Controlled Release 4, 25 (1986)

Kandzia, J., Scholz, W., Anderson, M.J.D. and Müller-Ruchholtz, W., Magnetic albumin/protein A immunomicrospheres. I. Preparation, antibody binding capacity and chemical stability, J. Immunol. Meth. 75, 31.41 (1984)

Kanke, M., Simmons, G.H., Weiss, D.L., Bivins, B.A. and DeLuca, P.P., Clearance of ^{141}Ce labeled microspheres from blood and distribution in specific organs following intravenous and intraarterial administration in Beagle dogs, J. Pharm. Sci. 69, 755-762 (1980)

Kanke, M., Sniecinski, I and Deluca, P.P., Interaction of microspheres with blood constituents: Uptake of polystyrene spheres by monocytes and granulocytes and effect on immune responsiveness of lymphocytes, J. Parent. Sci. Techn. 37 (6), 210-217 (1983)

Kante, B., Couvreur, P., Dubois-Krack, G., De Meester, C., Guiot, P., Roland, M., Mercier, M. and Speiser, P., Toxicity of polyalkylcyanoacrylate nanoparticles I: Free nanoparticles, J. Pharm. Sci. 71, 786-790 (1982)

Karino, A., Hayashi, H., Yamada, K. and Ozawa, Y., Effect of particle size and emulsifiers on the blood clearance and deposition of injected emulsions, J. Pharm. Sci. 76, 273 (1987)

Kayes, J.B. and Rawlins, D.A., Adsorption characteristics of certain polyoxyethylene-polyoxypropylene block copolymers on polystyrene latex, Colloid & Polymer Sci. 257, 622-629 (1979)

Kazatchkine, M.D. and Carreno, M.P., Activation of the complement system at the interface between blood and artifical surfaces, Biomaterials 9, 30-35 (1988)

Kazatchkine, M.D. and Nydegger, U.E., The human alternative complement pathway: biology and immunopathology of activation and regulation, Prog. Allergy 30, 193-234 (1982)

Kazatchkine, M.D. and Nydegger, U.E., Complement-mediated injury, in the Reticuloendothelial System. A Comprehensive Treatise: Hypersensivity (Phillips, S.M. and Escobar, M.R., eds.) Plenum Press New York, 173-196 (1986)

Kazatchkine, M.D., Fearon, D.T. and Austen, K.F., Human alternative complement pathway: membrane associated sialic acid regulates the competition between B and beta-1H for cell bound C3b, J. Immunol. 122, 75-81 (1979)

Kitchel, J.P. and Wise, D.L., Poly(lactic/glycolic acid) biodegradable drug-polymer matrix systems, in Methods in Enzymology, Vol. 112 (Widder, K.J. and Green, R., eds.), 436 (1985)

Kolb, H., Kolb-Bachofen, V. and Schlepper-Schäfer, J., Cell contacts mediated by D-galactose-specific lectins on liver cells, Biol. Cell 36, 301-308 (1979)

Kolb, H., Vogt, D., Herbertz, L., Corfield, A., Schauer, R. and Schlepper-Schäfer, J., The galactose-specific lectins on rat hepatocytes and Kupffer cells have identical binding characteristics, Hoppe-Seyler's Z. Physiol. Chem. 361, 1747-1750 (1980)

Kolb-Bachofen, V., Hepatic receptor for asialoglycoproteins. Ultra-structural demonstration of ligand-induced microaggregation of receptors, Biochem. Biophys. Acta 645, 293-299 (1981)

Kolb-Bachofen, V., Schlepper-Schäfer, J., Vogell, W. and Kolb, H., Receptor-mediated particle uptake by liver macrophages: the galactose-particle receptor mediates uptake via coated and also non-coated structures, Exptl. Cell Res. 148, 173-182 (1983)

Kolb-Bachofen, V., Schlepper-Schäfer, J., Roos, P., Hülsmann, D. and Kolb, H., GalnAc/Gal-specific rat liver lectins: their role in cellular recognition, Biol. Cell. 51, 219-226 (1984)

Koopal, L.K., Hlady, V. and Lyklema, J., Electrophoretic study of polymer adsorption: dextran, polyethylene oxide and polyvinyl alcohol on silver iodide, J. Colloid Interf. Sci. 121, 49-62 (1988)

Koosha, F. and Müller, R.H., Production of Polyhydroxybutyrate (PHB) micro- and nanoparticles, Archiv der Pharmazie 320, 913 (1987)

Koosha, F., Müller, R.H. and Washington, C., Production of Polyhydroxy-butyrate (PHB) nanoparticles for drug targeting, J. Pharm. Pharmacol. Suppl. 39, 136P (1987)

Koosha, F. and Müller, R.H., Nanoparticle production by microfluidization, Archiv der Pharmazie Suppl. 321, 680 (1988)

Koosha, F. and Müller, R.H., Radioactive labelling of biodegradable PHB and PLA drug carriers, Acta Pharm. Technol. 34, 24S (1988a)

Koosha, F. and Müller, R.H., Production of polymeric drug carriers for drug targeting, Acta Pharm. Technol. 34, 24S (1988b)

Colloidal Carriers for Controlled Drug Delivery and Targeting

Koosha, F., Müller, R.H. and Davis, S.S., Organ distribution of intra-venously injected PHB carriers, unpublished data (1988)

Koosha, F., Müller, R.H. and Davis, S.S., A continuous flow system for in vitro evaluation of drug-loaded biodegradable colloidal carriers, J. Pharm. Pharmacol. Suppl. 40, 131P (1988a)

Koosha, F., Preparation and characterisation of biodegradable polymeric drug carriers, Ph.D. thesis, Pharmacy Department, Nottingham University (1989)

Koosha, F. and Müller, R.H., Production parameters influencing the particle properties in a solvent evaporation process, in preparation (1989)

Koosha, F. and Müller, R.H., Drug release from PHB and PLA nanoparticles, in preparation (1989a)

Koosha, F., Müller, R.H. and Davis, S.S., Poly-β-hydroxybutyrate as a drug carrier, CRC Critical Reviews Vol. 6, 117-130 (1989)

Kopecek, J., Targetable drug carriers: structure - properties relationship, Proceed. Intern. Symp. Control. Rel. Bioact. Mater. 14, 125-126 (1987)

Korsatko, V.W., Wabnegg, B., Tillian, H.M., Braunegg, G. and Lafferty, R.M. , Poly-D(-)-3-hydroxybutyric acid - a biodegradable carrier for long term medication dosage / 2. Comm.: The biodegradation in animal organism and in vitro - in vivo correlation of the liberation of pharmaceuticals from parenteral matrix retard tablets, Pharm. Ind. 45, 1004-1007 (1983)

Korsatko, V.W., Wabnegg, B, Braunegg, G., Lafferty, R.M. and Strempfli, F., Poly-D-3-hydroxybutyric acid (PHBA) - a biodegradable carrier for long term medication dosage / 1. Comm.: Development of parenteral matrix tablets for long term application of pharmaceuticals, Pharm. Ind. 45, 525-527 (1983a)

Korsatko, V.W., Wabnegg, B., Tillian, H.M., Egger, G., Pfragner, R. and Walser, V., Poly-D(-)-3-hydroxybutyric acid (poly-HBA) - a biodegradable former for long term medication dosage /3. Comm.: Studies on the compatibility of poly-HBA-implantation tablets in tissue culture and animals, Pharm. Ind. 46, 952-954 (1983b)

Kramer, P.A. and Burnstein, T., Phagocytosis of microspheres containing an anticancer agent by tumor cells in vitro, Life Sci. 19, 515-520 (1976)

Krause, H.-J. and Rohdewald, P., Preparation of gelatin nanocapsules and their pharmaceutical characterization, Pharmaceutical Research (5), 239-243 (1985)

Kreuter, J., Nanoparticles and nanocapsules - new dosage forms in the nanometer size range, Pharm. Acta Helv. 53 (2), 33-39 (1978)

Kreuter, J., Täuber, U., and Illi, V., Distribution and elimination of poly(methyl-2-^{14}C-methacrylate) nanoparticle radioactivity after injection in rats and mice, J. Pharm. Sci. 68, 1443-1447 (1979)

Kreuter; J., Evaluation of nanoparticles as drug delivery systems III; Materials, stability, toxicity, possibilities of targeting and use, Pharm. Acta Helv. 58, 9-10 (1983)

Kreuter, J., Evaluation of nanoparticles as drug-delivery systems, I:

358

References

Preparation methods, Pharm. Acta Helv. 58, 196-209 (1983a)

Kreuter, J., Evaluation of nanoparticles as drug-delivery systems, II. Comparison of the body distribution of nanoparticles with the body distribution of microspheres (diameter > 1μm), liposomes and emulsions, Pharm. Acta Helv. 58, 217-226 (1983b)

Kronberg, B., Käll, L. and Stenius, P., Adsorption of nonionic surfactants on latexes, J. Dispersion Sci. Technol. 2, 215-232 (1981)

Kronberg, B., Thermodynamics of adsorption of non-ionic surfactants on latexes, J. Colloid Interf. Sci., 96, 55-68 (1983)

Kronberg, B. and Stenius, P., The effect of surface polarity on the adsorption of nonionic surfactants I. Thermodynamic considerations, J. Colloid Interf. Sci. 102, 410-417 (1984)

Kronberg, B., Stenius, P. and Igeborn, G., The effect of surface polarity on the adsorption of nonionic surfactants, J. Colloid Interf. Sci. 102, 418-423 (1984)

Kronenthal, R.L., Biodegradable polymers in medicine and surgery, in Polymers in Medicine and Surgery (Kronenthal, R.L., User, Z. and Martin, E., eds.), Plenum Press New York, 126 (1974)

Laakso, T., Artursson, P. and Sjöholm, I., Biodegradable microspheres IV: Factors affecting the distribution and degradation of polyacryl starch microparticles, J. Pharm. Sci. 75, 962-967 (1986)

Lagaly, G., Energetische Wechselwirkungen in Dispersionen und Emulsionen, in Technologie von Salben, Suspensionen und Emulsionen (Asche, H., Essig, D. and Schmidt, P.C., eds.), APV Paperback vol. 10, Wissenschaftliche Verlagsgesellschaft Stuttgart, 32-61 (1984)

Lambe, R., Tadros, Th.F. and Vincent, B., The effect of temperature, particle volume fraction and polymer concentration on the stability of aqueous polystyrene latex dispersions in the presence of poly(vinyl alcohol), J. Colloid Interf. Sci. 66, 77 (1978)

Laurencin, C.T., Domb, A.J., Morris, C.D., Brown, V.I., Chasin., M., McConnel, R.F. and Langer, R., High dosage administration of polyanhydrides in vivo: studies of biocompatibility and toxicology, Proceed. Intern. Symp. Control. Rel. Bioact. Mater. 14, 140-141 (1987)

Law, S.L. and Kayes, J.B., Adsorption of non-ionic water-soluble cellulose polymers at the solid-water interface and their effect on suspension stability, Int. J. Pharm. 15, 251-260 (1983)

Law, S.K. and Levine, R.P., Interaction between the third complement protein and cell surface macromolecules, Proc. Natl. Acad. Sci. USA 74, 2701-2705 (1977)

Lazar, G., The reticuloendothelial-blocking effect of rare earth metals in rats, J. Retic. Soc. 13, 231-237 (1973)

Lee, R.G., Adamson, C. and Kim, S.W., Competitive adsorption of plasma proteins onto polymer surfaces, Thrombosis Research 4, 485-490 (1974)

Lee, T.K., Sokoloski, T.D. and Royer, G.P., Serum albumin beads: An injectable, biodegradable system for the sustained release of drugs, Science 213, 233-235 (1981)

Lee, K.C., Koh, I.B., Kim, W.B. and Lee, Y.J., Size and morphological analysis of albumin microspheres in the lungs and liver of mice, Int. J. Pharm. 44, 49-55 (1988)

Lemoigne, M., The origin of β-hydroxybutyric acid obtained by bacterial process, Compt. rend. 180, 1539 (1925)

Lemoigne, M., β-hydroxybutyric acid and bacterial cells, Bull. Coc. Chem. Biol. 8, 770 (1926)

Lemoigne, M., Etudes sur l'autolys microbienne, origine de l'acid β-oxybutyrique formed par autolyse, Ann. Inst. Pastur. 41, 148 (1927)

Lensen, H.G.W., Bargeman, D., Bergveld, P., Smolders, C.A. and Feijen, J., High-performance liquid chromatography as a technique to measure the competitive adsorption of plasma proteins onto latices, J. Colloid Interf. Sci. 99, 1-8 (1984)

Lherm, C., Müller, R.H., Blunk, T., Perie, M., Depraetere, P. and Couvreur, P., Physico-chemical characterisation of cyanoacrylate particles, Archiv der Pharmazie 321, 682 (1988)

Li, V.H.K., Wood, R.W., Kreuter, J., Harmia, T. and Robinson, J.R., Ocular drug delivery of progesterone using nanoparticles, J. Microencapsulation 3 (3), 213-218 (1986)

Littenberg, R.L., Anaphylactoid reaction to human albumin microspheres, J. Nucl. Med. 16 (3), 236-237 (1974)

Lucks, J.-S., Müller, B.W. and Müller, R.H., Effect of electrolytes on the stability of parenteral fat emulsions, Archiv der Pharmazie 321, 683 (1988)

Lundgern, D.G., Alper, R., Schna, C. and Marchessault, R.H., Characterization of poly-β-hydroxybutyrate extracted from different bacteria, J. Bacteriol. 89, 245 (1965)

Lynn, R., Müller, R.H., Davies, M.C., unpublished data, Pharmacy Department at Nottingham University (1988)

Magnusson, K.-E. and Johansson, G., Probing the surface of Salmonella typhimurium SR and R bacteria by aqueous biphasic partitioning in systems containing hydrophobic and charged polymers, FEMS Microbiology Letters 2, 225-228 (1977)

Magnusson, K.-E., Stendahl, O., Tagesson, C., Edebo, L. and Johansson, G., The tendency of smooth and rough Salmonella typhimurium bacteria and lipopolysaccharide to hydrophobic and ionic interaction, as studied in aqueous polymer two-phase systems, Acta Path. Microbiol. Scand., Sect. B 85, 212 (1977)

Maillet, F., Carreno, M.P., Labarre, D., Jozefowicz, M. and Kazatchkine, M.D., Carboxymethylation suppresses the ability of Sephadex to activate the human alternative pathway by facilitating inactivation of bound C3b with H and I, Complement 4, 188 (1987)

Majid, M.I.A., Pouton, C.W. and Notarianni, L.J., Catalytic degradation of

References

poly-D-(-)3-hydroxybutyrate (PHB) in non-aqueous solution, J. Pharm. Pharmacol. Suppl. 39, 34P (1987)

Mak, E., Davis, S.S., Illum, L. and Müller, R.H., Determination of surface properties of 'standard' latex particles, Abstr. British Pharmaceutical Conference, 22-24 September Jersey, 100P (1986)

Mak, E., Müller, R.H., Davis, S.S. and Illum, L., Hydrophobic Interaction Chromatography and Laser Doppler Anemometry for the characterisation of coated drug carriers, Acta Pharm. Technol. 34, 23S (1988)

Mak, E., Müller, R.H., Davis, S.S. and Illum, L., Characterisation of colloidal carriers for drug targeting, Acta Pharm. Technol. 34, 20S (1988a)

Malik, J.K., Schwarz, L.R. and Wiebel, F.J., Assessment of membrane damage in continuous cultures of mammalian cells, Chem.-Biol. Interactions 45, 29-42 (1983)

Malton, C.A., Hallworth, G.W., Padfield, J.M., Perkins, A. and Davis, S.S., Deposition and clearance of inhalation aerosols in dogs and rabbits using a gamma camera, J. Pharm. Pharmacol. 34 Suppl., 64 (1982)

Mantovani, B., Rabinovitch, M. and Nuissenzweig, V., Phagocytosis of immune complexes by macrophages. Different roles of the macrophage receptor sites for complement (C3) and for immunoglobulin (IgG), J. Exp. Med. 135, 780-792 (1972)

Marty, J.J. and Oppenheim, R.C., Colloidal systems for drug delivery, Austr. J. of Pharm. Sci. 6 (3), 65-76 (1977)

Marty, J.J., Oppenheim, R.C. and Speiser, P., Nanoparticles - a new colloidal drug delivery system, Pharm. Acta Helv. 53 (1), 17-23 (1978)

Mathiowitz, E. and Langer, R., Polyanhydride microspheres as drug carriers, I. Hot-melt microencapsulation, J. Controlled Release 5, 13-22 (1987)

Mauk, M.R., Gamble, R.C. and Baldeschwieler, J.D., Targeting of lipid vesicles: Specifity of carbohydrate receptor analogues for leukocytes in mice, Proc. Natl. Acad. Sci. USA 77, 4430-4434 (1980)

McClure, R.J. and Graven, B.M., X-ray data for four crystalline forms of serum albumin, J. Mol. Biol. 83, 551-555 (1974)

Merrick, J.M. and Doudroff, M., Depolymerization of poly(β-hydroxybutyric acid) by an intracellular enzyme system, J. Bacteriol. 88, 60 (1964)

Merz, J., Simultane Messung von Diffusionskonstante und elektrophoretischer Beweglichkeit hochdisperser Systeme mit Hilfe der amplituden-gewichteten Phasenstrukturfunktion, Ph.D. thesis Kiel University, West Germany (1985)

Miller, N.D. and Williams. D.F., On the biodegradation of poly-β-hydroxybutyrate (PHB) homopolymer and poly-β-hydroxybutyrate-hydroxyvaleriate copolymers, Biomaterials 8, 129 (1987)

Mills, S.N., Maher, S.E., Davis, S.S., Hardy, J.G. and Wilson, C.G., The use of gamma scintigraphy for the in vivo assessment of colloidal dosage forms intended for parenteral use, J. Pharm. Pharmacol. Suppl. 32, 85 (1980)

Miörner, H., Myhre, E., Bjorck, L. and Kronvall, G., Effect of specific binding of human albumin, fibrinogen and immunoglobulin G on surface characteristics of bacterial strains as revealed by partition experiments in polymer phase systems, Infect. Immun. 29, 879 (1980)

Miörner, H., Albertsson, P.-A. and Kronvall, G., Isoelectric points and surface hydrophobicity of gram-positive cocci as determined by cross-partition and hydrophobic affinity partition in aqueous two-phase systems, Infect. Immun. 36, 227 (1982)

Mirro, J., Schwartz, J.F. and Civin, C.I., Simultaneous analysis of cell surface antigens and cell morphology using monoclonal antibodies conjugated to fluorescent microspheres, J. Immunol. Meth. 47, 39-48 (1981)

Mizushima, Y., Yanagawa, A. and Hoshi, K., Prostaglandin E_1 is more effective, when incorporated in lipid microspheres, for treatment of peripheral vascular diseases in man, J. Pharm. Pharmacol. 35, 666-667 (1983)

Molday, R.S., Dreyer, W.J., Rembaum, A. and Yen, S.P.S., New immunolatex spheres: Visual markers of antigens on lymphocytes for scanning electron microscopy, J. Cell Biol. 64, 75-88 (1975)

Müller, B.W. (ed.), Controlled Drug Delivery, Wissenschaftliche Verlags-gesellschaft Stuttgart (1987)

Müller, B.W., Merz, J. and Müller, R.H., Simultane Bestimmung von elektro-phoretischer Beweglichkeit und Teilchengröße bei überlagerter Konvektion an Suspensionen und Emulsionen, Colloid & Polymer Sci. 263, 342-347 (1985)

Müller, B.W. and Fischer, W., Method and apparatus for the manufacture of a product of a drug embedded in a carrier, German patent P 37 44 ' 329.1, US patent 07/287.918 (1989)

Müller, R.H., Polydispersität und elektrophoretische Beweglichkeit hoch-disperser Systeme, PhD thesis University of Kiel, West Germany (1983)

Müller, R.H. and Mak, E., Analysis of particle charge and surface hydrophobicity of colloidal drug carriers, Abstr. NATO Advanced Studies Institute meeting "Targeting of Drugs with Synthetic Systems", 24. June - 5. July Cape Sounion Greece (1985)

Müller, R.H. and Merz, J., Moderne Meßmethoden zur Bestimmung der Teilchen-ladung, Pharmazeutische Verfahrenstechnik 1, 141-144 (1985)

Müller, R.H., unpublished data, 1986-1988

Müller, R.H., Müller, B.W. and Davis, S.S., Amplitude Weighted Phase Structuration - a new method for simultaneous charge and size determination of colloidal drug carriers, Proc. 4th Int. Conf. on Pharmaceutical Technology, 3.-5. June Paris, 1, 205 (1986)

Müller, R.H., Davis, S.S., Illum, L. and Mak, E., Colloidal carriers for drug targeting - charge reduction by coating with polymers, Abstr. 32. Annual Meeting of the Intern. Pharm. Assoc. (APV), 16-19 April Leiden, The Netherlands (1986a)

Müller, R.H., Davis, S.S., Illum, L. and Mak, E., Surface characterisation

References

of colloidal drug carriers coated with polymers, Macromolecular Preprints, 161 (1986b)

Müller, R.H., Davis, S.S., Illum, L. and Mak, E., Particle charge and surface hydrophobicity of colloidal drug carriers, in Targeting of Drugs with Synthetic Systems (Gregoriadis, G., Senior, J. and Poste, G., eds.) Plenum New York, 239-263 (1986c)

Müller, R.H., West, P.E., Koosha, F. and Davis, S.S., Coulter Counter und Laser Diffraktometer - Vergleich der beiden Meßmethoden, Scientia Pharmaceutica 3, 225 (1986d)

Müller, R.H. and Heinemann, S., Stabilitätsuntersuchungen an TPN-Regimen, Archiv der Pharmazie 320, 981 (1987)

Müller, R.H., Davies, M.C. and Koosha, F., Characterisation of PHB drug carriers by SSIMS, Abstr. 2nd Int. Conf. Biointeractions '87, 6-8 July Cambridge (1987a)

Müller, R.H., Koosha, F. and Davies, M.C., Determination of toxic residues in drug carriers by SSIMS, Archiv der Pharmazie 320, 980 (1987b)

Müller, R.H., Heinemann, S. and Niemann, W., Stability determination of parenteral emulsions - a comparison of conventional and laser light scattering techniques, J. Pharm. Pharmacol. Suppl. 39, 135P (1987c)

Müller, R.H. and Koosha, F., In vitro characterisation of i.v. drug carriers - a new theory of the relevant factors determining their in vivo behaviour, Archiv der Pharmazie 321, 622 (1988)

Müller, R.H. and Lucks, J.-S., Relevance of stress tests for the estimation of the long-term stability of parenteral fat emulsions, Archiv der Pharmazie 321, 685 (1988)

Müller, R.H. and Wallis, K., unpublished data (1988)

Müller, R.H., Koosha, F., Davis, S.S. and Illum, L., In vitro and in vivo release of In-111 from PHB and PLA nanoparticles, Proceed. Intern. Symp. Control. Rel. Bioact. Mater. 15, 15-19 August Basel, 378-379 (1988)

Müller, R.H., Lucks, J.-S., Davis, S.S. and Wallis, K., Long term stability of parenteral fat emulsions, Archiv der Pharmazie 321, 676 (1988a)

Müller, R.H., Lherm, C., Jaffray, P. and Couvreur, P., Toxicity of cyanoacrylate particles in L929 fibroblast cell cultures - relation between toxicity and in vitro characterisation parameters, Archiv der Pharmazie 321, 681 (1988b)

Müller, R.H., Nohne, J., Davis, S.S. and Heinemann, S., Characterisation of fat emulsions for parenteral nutrition, Acta Pharm. Technol. 34, 23S (1988c)

Müller, R.H., Davis, S.S. and Niemann, W., Stability assessment of feeding mixtures for total parenteral nutrition, Acta Pharm. Technol. 34, 17S (1988d)

Müller, R.H., Blunk. T. and Koosha, F., Determination of the thickness of adsorbed polymer layers on colloidal drug carriers by charge measurements, Archiv der Pharmazie Suppl. 321, 678 (1988e)

363

Müller, R.H., Differential adsorption for the targeting of drug carriers, Acta Pharm. Technol. 36, 34S (1989)

Müller, R.H. and Heinemann, S., Surface modelling of microparticles as parenteral systems with high tissue affinity, in Bioadhesion - Possibilities and Future Trends (Gurny, R. and Junginger, H.E., eds.), Wissenschaftliche Verlagsgesellschaft Stuttgart, 202-214 (1989)

Müller, R.H., Davis, S.S. and Mak, E., Surface characterization of colloidal drug carriers for drug targeting by aqueous two-phase partitioning in Separations Using Aqueous Phase Systems (Fisher, D. and Sutherland, I.A., eds.), Plenum Press New York, 149-155 (1989)

Napper, D.H, Steric stabilization and the Hofmeister series, J. Colloid Interf. Sci. 33, 384-392 (1970)

Napper, D.H, Steric stabilization, J. Colloid Interface Sci. 58, 390-407 (1977)

Napper, D.H., Polymeric Stabilization of Colloidal Dispersions, Academic Press London (1983)

Ney, P., Zetapotentiale und Flotierbarkeit, Springer Wien-New York (1973)

Nguyen, T.H., Shih, C., Himmelstein, K.J., Higuchi, T., Hydrolysis of some poly(ortho-ester)s in homogenous solutions, J. Pharm. Sci. 73, 1563-1568 (1984)

Nguyen, T.H., Himmelstein, K.J. and Higuchi, T., Some equilibrium and kinetic aspects of water sorption in poly(ortho-ester)s, Int. J. Pharm. 25, 1-12 (1985)

Nguyen, T.H., Higuchi, T. and Himmelstein, K.J., Erosion characteristics of catalyzed poly(ortho-ester) matrices, J. Controlled Rel. 5, 1-12 (1987)

Norde, W. and Lyklema, J., Thermodynamics of protein adsorption, J. Colloid Interf. Sci. 71, 350-366 (1979)

Norde, W., MacRitchie, F., Nowicka, G. and Lyklema, J., Protein adsorption at solid-liquid interfaces: Reversibility and conformation aspects, J. Colloid Interf. Sci. 112, 447-456 (1986)

Ogmundsdottir, H. and Weir, D.M., Mechanism of macrophage activation, Clin. Exp. Imm. 40, 223-234 (1980)

O'Mullane, J.E., Davison, C.J., Petrak, K. and Tomlinson, E., Adsorption of fibrinogen onto polystyrene latex coated with the non-ionic surfactant, poloxamer 338, Biomaterials 9, 203-204 (1988)

Ondracek, J., Boller, F.H., Zulliger, H.W. and Niederer, R.R., Vergleich zwischen fünf Methoden zur Prüfung der physikalischen Stabilität von O/W-Emulsionen, Acta Pharm. Technol. 31, 42-48 (1985)

Oppenheim, R.C., Solid colloidal drug delivery systems: nanoparticles, Int. J. Pharm. 8, 217-234 (1981)

Oreskes, I. and Singer, J.M., The mechanism of particulate carrier reactions.I. Adsorption of human y-globulin to polystyrene latex particles, J. Immunol. 86, 338-344 (1961)

References

Ovadia, H., Carbone, A.M., Paterson, P.Y., Albumin magnetic microspheres: a novel carrier for myelin basic protein, J. Immunol. Meth. 53, 109-122 (1982)

Ozil, P. and Rochat, M.H., Experimental design, an efficient tool for studying the stability of parenteral nutrition, Int. J. Pharm. 42, 11-14 (1988)

Paborji, M., Riley, C.M. and Stella, V.J., A novel use of Intralipid for the parenteral delivery of perilla ketone (NSC-348407), an investigational cytotoxic drug with a high affinity for plastic, Int. J. Pharm. 42, 243-249 (1988)

Pahlmann,S, Rosengren, J. and Hjerten, S., Hydrophobic Interaction Chromatography on uncharged Sepharose derivatives. Effects of neutral salts on the adsorption of proteins. J. Chromatogr. 131, 99-108 (1977)

Papisov, M.I. and Torchilin, V.P., Magnetic drug targeting II: Targeted drug transport by magnetic microparticles: factors influencing therapeutic effect, Int. J. Pharm 40, 207-214 (1987)

Papisov, M.I., Savelyev, V.Y., Sergienko, V.B. and Torchilin, V.P., Magnetic drug targeting. I. In vivo kinetics of radiolabelled magnetic drug carriers, Int. J. Pharm. 40, 201-206 (1987)

Patel, H.M., Boodle, K.M. and Vaughan-Jones, R., Assessment of the potential use of liposomes for lymphoscintigraphy and lymphatic drug delivery, Biochim. Biophys. Acta 801, 76-86 (1984)

Pierre, T.St., and Chiellini, E., Biodegradability of synthetic polymers for medical and pharmaceutical applications: part 3 - pendent group hydrolysis and general conclusions, Journal of Bioactive and Compatible Polymers 2, 238-257 (1987)

Pimm, M.V., Embleton, M.J., Perkins, A.C., Price, M.R., Robins, R.A., Robinson, G.R. and Baldwin, R.W., In vivo localization of anti-osteogenic sarcoma 791T monoclonal antibody in osteogenic sarcoma xenografts, Int. J. Cancer 30, 75-85 (1982)

Polysciences data sheet no. 238, Polysciences, Inc., Warrington, P.A. 18976, USA (1984)

Ponpipom, M.M:, Bugianesi, R.L., Robbins, J.C., Doebber, T.W. and Shen, T.Y., Cell-specific ligands for selective drug delivery to tissues and organs, J. Med. Chem. 24, 1388-1395 (1981)

Poste, G., Drug targeting in cancer chemotherapy, in Receptor-mediated Targeting of Drugs (Gregoriadis, G., Poste, G., Senior, J. and Trouet, A., eds.), Plenum Press New York, 427-474 (1984)

Pouton, C.W., Majid, M.I.A. and Notarianni, L.J., Degradation of poly(β-hydroxybutyrate) and related copolymers, Proceed. Intern. Symp. Control. Rel. Bioact. Mater. 15, 15-19 August Basel, 181-182 (1988)

Rabinovitch, M. and De Stefano, M.J., Particle recognition by cultivated macrophages, J. Immunol. 110, 695-701 (1973)

Rawlins, D.A. and Kayes, J.B., Pharmaceutical suspension studies I. A comparison of adsorption of polyvinylalcohol at the diloxanide furoate B.P. and polystyrene latex-water interface, Int. J. Pharm. 13, 145-158 (1983)

Reitherman, R., Flanagan, S.D. and Barondes, S.H., Electromotive phenomena in partition of erythrocytes in aqueous polymer two-phase systems, Biochim. Biophys. Acta 297, 193 (1973)

Riddick, T.M., Zeta-Meter Manual, Zeta-Meter Inc. New York (1968)

Roberts, M.J.J., Pharmacy Department, University of Nottingham, personal communication (1988)

Roberts, M.J.J., Khan, A.M., Williams, P. Davis, S.S. and Davies, M.C., Detection of surface contaminants of polystyrene latices using SSIMS and XPS, in preparation (1988)

Royer, G.P., Lee, T.K. and Sokoloski, T.D., Entrapment of bioactive compounds within native albumin beads, Journal of Parenteral Science and Technology 37 (2), 34-37 (1983)

Rupprecht, H., Gesichtspunkte zur Optimierung arzneilicher Suspensionen, Pharmazeutische Zeitung 120, 1265-1274 (1975)

Saettone, M.F., Giannaccini, B., Delmonte, G, Campigli, V., Tota, G. and Marca, F.L., Solubilization of tropicamide by poloxamers: physicochemical data and activity data in rabbits and humans, Int. J. Pharm. 43, 67-76 (1988)

Samaha, M. and Naggar, V.F., Micellar properties of non-ionic surfactants in relation to their solubility parameters, Int. J. Pharm. 42, 1-9 (1988)

Sanders, L.M., Kell, B.A., McRae, G.I. and Whitehead, G.W., Poly(lactic-co-glycolic) acid: Properties and performance in controlled release delivery systems of LHRH analogues, Proceed. Intern. Symp. Control. Rel. Bioact. Mater. 12, 177-178 (1985)

Sanders, L.M., McRae, G.I., Vitale, K.M. and Kell, B.A., Controlled delivery of an LH-RH analogue from biodegradable injectable microspheres, J. Controlled Rel. 2, 187-195 (1985a)

Sato, Y., Kiwada, H. and Kato, Y., Effects of dose and vesicle size on the pharmacokinetics of liposomes, Chem. Pharm. Bull. 34, 4244-4252 (1986)

Saunders, J.E., Drug targeting using albumin microspheres, PhD thesis Nottingham University (1988)

Schätzel, K. and Merz, J., Measurement of small electrophoretic mobilities by light scattering and analysis of the amplitude weighted phase structure function, J. Chem. Phys. 81(5), 2482 (1984)

Scheffel, U., Rhodes, B.A., Natarajan, T.K. and Wagner, H.N., Albumin microspheres for study of the reticuloendothelial system, J. Nucl. Med. 13 (7), 498-503 (1972)

Schmeling, F.D. and Zettervall, O., Quantitative phagocytosis by human polymorphonuclear leucocytes, Immunology 32, 491-497 (1977)

Schreier, H., Abra, R.M., Kaplan, J.E. and Hunt, C.A., Murine plasma fibronectin depletion after intravenous injection of liposomes, Int. J. Pharm. 37, 233-238 (1987)

Schroeder, H.G., Bivins, B.A., Sherman, G.P. and DeLuca, P.P., Physiological effects of subvisible microspheres administered intravenously to beagle dogs, J. Pharm. Sci. 67, 508-513 (1978)

Schroit, A.J., Hart, I.R., Madson, J. and Fidler, I.J., Selective delivery of drugs encapsulated in liposomes: natural targeting to macrophages involved in various disease states, Journal of Biological Response Modifiers 2, 97-100 (1983)

Schwendener, R.A., Lagocki, P.A. and Rahman, Y.E., The effect of charge and size on the interaction of unilamellar liposomes with macrophages, Biochim. Biophys. Acta 772, 93-101 (1984)

Schwope, A.D., Wise, D.L. and Howes, J.F., Lactic/glycolic acid polymers as narcotic antagonist delivery systems, Life Sci. 17, 1877-1886 (1975)

Scieszka, J.F., Vidmar, T.J., Haynes, L.C. and Cho, M.J., Biochemical stability in serum of a lipid-soluble probe molecule entrapped in an o/w emulsion as carrier for passive drug targeting, Int. J. Pharm. 45, 165-168 (1988)

Seglen, P.O., Preparation of isolated rat liver cells, Methods Cell Biol. 13, 29-83 (1976)

Senior, J, Crawley, J.C.W. and Gregoriadis, G., Tissue distribution of liposomes exhibiting long half-lives in the circulation after intravenous injection, Biochim. Biophys. Acta 839, 1-8 (1985)

Sezaki, H, Hashida, M and Muranishi, S., Gelatin microspheres as carriers for antineoplastic agents, in Optimization of Drug Delivery (Bundgaard, H., Hansen, A.B. and Kofod, H., eds.), Munksgaard Copenhagen, 316-332 (1982)

Shanbag, V.P. and Axelsson, C.-G., Hydrophobic interaction determined by partition in aqueous two-phase systems. Partition of proteins in systems containing fatty acid esters of poly(ethylene glycol), Eur. J. Biochem. 60, 17 (1975)

Sharpe, P.T. and Warren, G.S., The incorporation of glycolipids with defined carbohydrate sequence into liposomes and the effects on partition in aqueous two-phase systems, Biochim. Biophys. Acta 772, 176 (1984)

Shen, B.W., Lipid-Protein interaction at solid-water interface, adsorption of human apo-high density lipoprotein to amphiphilic interfaces, J. Biol. Chem. 260 (2), 1032-1039 (1985)

Shepherd, V.L., Lee, Y.C., Schlesinger, P.H. and Stahl, P.D., L-Fucose-terminated glycoconjugates are recognized by pinocytosis receptors on macrophages, Proc. Natl. Acad. Sci. USA 78, 1019-1022 (1981)

Shirahama, H. and Suzawa, T., Adsorption of bovine serum albumin onto styrene/acrylic acid copolymer latex, Colloid & Polymer Sci. 263, 141-146 (1985)

Singer, J.M., Lavie, S., Adlersberg, L., Ende, E., Hoenig, E.M. and Tchorsh, Y., The use of radionated latex particles for in vivo studies of phagocytosis, in The Reticuloendothelial System and Atherosclerosis

Colloidal Carriers for Controlled Drug Delivery and Targeting

(DiLuzio, N.R. and Padelti, R., eds,) Plenum Press New York, 18-24 (1967)

Sinkula, A.A. and Yalkowski, S.H., Rational for design of biologically reversible drug derivatives: Prodrugs, J. Pharm. Sci. 64, 181-210 (1975)

Slack, J.D., Kanke, M., Simmons, G.H. and DeLuca, P.P., Acute hemodynamic effects and blood pool kinetics of polystyrene microspheres following intravenous administration, J. Pharm. Sci. 70, 660-664 (1981)

Smith, A. and Hunneyball, I.M., Evaluation of poly(lactic acid) as a biodegradable drug delivery system for parenteral administration, Int. J. Pharm. 30, 215-220 (1986)

Soderquist, M.E. and Walton, A.G., Structural changes in proteins adsorbed on polymer surfaces, J. Colloid Interf. Sci. 75, 386-397 (1980)

Souhami, R.L., Patel, H.M. and Ryman, B.E., The effect of reticuloendothelial blockade on the blood clearance and tissue distribution of liposomes, Biochim. Biophys. Acta 674, 354-371 (1981)

Speiser, P., Ultrafine solid compartments as carriers for drug delivery, in Optimization of Drug Delivery (Bundgaard, H., Hansen, A.B. and Kofod, H., eds.), Munksgaard Copenhagen, 305-315 (1982)

Spenlehauer, G., Vert, M., Benoit, J.-P., Chabot, F. and Veillard, M., Biodegradable cisplatin microspheres prepared by the solvent evaporation method: Morphology and release characteristics, J. Controlled Rel. 7, 217-229 (1988)

Spilizewski, K.L., Marchant, R.E., Hamlin, C.R., Anderson, J.M, Tice, T.R., Dappert, T.O. and Meyers, W.E., The effect of hydrocortisone acetate loaded poly(DL-lactide)films on the inflammatory response, J. Controlled Rel. 2, 197-203 (1985)

Sugibayashi, K., Morimoto, Y, Nadai, T. and Kato, Y., Drug-carrier property of albumin microspheres in chemotherapy. I. Tissue distribution of microsphere-entrapped 5-fluorouracil in mice, Chem. Pharm. Bull. 25 (12), 3433-3434 (1977)

Tack, B.F., The alpha-Cys-β thiolester bond in human C3, C4 and alpha 2 macroglobulin, Semin. Immunopathol. 6, 359-364 (1983).

Tadros, Th.F. and Vincent, B., Influence of temperature and electrolytes on the adsorption behaviour of poly(ethylene oxide)-poly(propylene oxide) block copolymer on polystyrene latex and on the stability of the polymer coated particles, J. Phys. Chem. 84, 1575 (1980)

Thomas, S.M.B., Stability of Intralipid in a parenteral nutrition solution, J. Hosp. Pharm. 17, 115-117 (1987)

Tice, T.R. and Lewis, D.H., Microencapsulation process, U.S. Patent 4,389,330, June 21 (1983)

Tice, T.R. and Gilley, R.M., Preparation of injectable controlled-release microcapsules by a solvent-evaporation process, J. Contolled Rel. 2, 343-352 (1985)

Tonaki, H., Saba, T.M., Mayron, L.W. and Kaplan, E., Phagocytosis of gelatinized "R. E. Test Lipid Emulsion" by Kupffer cells: electronmicro-

References

scopic observations, Exp. Molec. Path. 25, 189-201 (1976)

Tröster, S.D. and Kreuter, J., Contact angle of surfactants with a potential to alter the body distribution of colloidal drug carriers on poly(methyl methacrylate) surfaces, Int. J. Pharm. 45, 91-100 (1988)

Van Oss, C.J., Gillman, C.F., and Neumann, A.W., Phagocytic engulfment and cell adhesiveness as cellular surface phenomena, Marcel Dekker New York (1975)

Van Oss, C.J., Absolom, D.R. and Neumann, H.W., Interaction of phagocytes with other blood cells and with pathogenic and nonpathogenic microbes, Ann. N.Y. Acad. Sci. 416, 332-350 (1984)

Verdun, C., Couvreur, P., Vranckx, H., Lenaerts, V. and Roland, M., Development of a nanoparticle controlled-release formulation for human use, J. Controlled Rel. 3, 205-210 (1986)

von Hippel, P.H. and Schleich, T., The effects of neutral salts on the structure and conformational stability of macromolecules in solution. In Structure and Stability of Biological Macromolecules" (Timasheff, S.N., Fasman, G.D., eds.) Marcel Dekker, New York, 417-574 (1969)

Vroman, L. amd Leonard, E.F., The behaviour of blood and its components at interfaces, Ann. N.Y. Acad. Sci. 283 (1977)

Wallis, K.H. and Müller, R.H., Stabilität von Poloxamer and Poloxamine Coatingfilmen auf Polystyrol Nanopartikeln, Acta Pharm. Technol., in press (1990)

Washington, C. and Davis, S.S., The production of parenteral feeding emulsions by Microfluidizer, Int. J. Pharm. 44, 169-176 (1988)

Washington, C., Taylor, S.J. and Davis, S.S., The structure of colloidal formulations of amphotericin B, Int. J. Pharm. 46, 25-30 (1988)

Wakiyama, N., Juni, K. and Nakano, M., Preparation and evaluation in vitro of polylactic acid microspheres containing local anaesthetics, Chem. Pharm. Bull. 29 (11), 3363-3368 (1981)

Walter, H., Garza, R. and Coyle, R.P., Partition of DEAE-dextran in aqueous dextran-polyethylene glycol phases and its effect on the partition of cells in such systems, Biochim. Biophys. Acta 156, 409 (1968)

Walter, H. and Krob, J., Hydrophobic affinity partition in aqueous two-phase systems containing poly(ethylene glycol)-palmitate of right-side-out and inside-out vesicles from human erythrocyte membranes, FEBS Lett. 61, 290 (1976)

Walter, H. and Selby, F.W., Effects of DEAE-dextran on the partition of red blood cells in aqueous dextran-polyethylene glycol two-phase sytems, Biochim. Biophys. Acta 148, 517 (1967)

Wegmuller, E., Mondandon, A., Nydegger, U.E. and Descoeudres, C., Biocompatibility of different hemodialysis membranes: activation of complement and leukopenia, Int. J. Artif. Organs 9, 85-92 (1986)

Widder, K.J., Senyei, A.E., Scarpelli, D.G., Magnetic microspheres: A model system for site specific drug delivery in vivo, Proc. Soc. Exp. Biol. Med.

58, 141-146 (1978)

Widder, K.J., Flouret, G. and Senyei, A., Magnetic microspheres: Synthesis of a novel parenteral drug carrier, J. Pharm. Sci. 68, 79-82 (1979)

Widder, K.J., Senyei, A.E., Ranney, D.F., In vitro release of biologically active adriamycin by magnetically responsive albumin microspheres, Cancer Research 40, 3512-3517 (1980)

Widder; K.J. and Green, R. (eds.), Drug and Enzyme Targeting, Part A, Methods in Enzymology, Vol. 112, Academic Press New York (1985)

Wikström, M.B., Elwing, H. and Möller, A.J.R., Proteins adsorbed to a hydrophobic surface used for determination of proteolytic activity, Enzyme Microb. Technol. 4, 265-268 (1982)

Wilkins, D.J. and Myers, P.A., Studies on the relationship between the electrophoretic properties of colloids and their blood clearance and organ distribution in the rat, Brit. J. Exp. Path. 47, 568-576 (1966)

Williams, D.F. and Miller, N.D., The degradation of polyhydroxybutyrate (PHB), Biomater. Clin. Appli. 7, 471 (1987)

Willmott, N. and Harrison, P.J., Characterisation of freeze-dried albumin microspheres containing the anti-cancer drug adriamycin, Int. J. Pharm. 43, 161-166 (1988)

Wilson, C.G., Hardy, J.G., Frier, M. and Davis, S.S. (eds.), Radionuclide Imaging in Drug Research, Croom Helm London (1982)

Wilson, C.G., Olejneik, O. and Hardy, J.G., Precorneal drainage of polyvinyl alcohol solutions in the rabbit assessed by gamma scintigraphy, J. Pharm. Pharmacol. 35, 451-454 (1983)

Wise, D.L., McCormick, G.J., Willet, G.P. and Anderson, L.C., Sustained release of an antimalarial drug using a copolymer of glycolic/lactic acid, Life Sci. 19, 867-874 (1976)

Wise, D.L., McCormick, G.J., Willet, G.P., Anderson, L.C. and Howes, J.F., Sustained release of sulphadiazine, Life Sci. 30, 686-689 (1978)

Wise, D.L., Fellmann, Th.D., Sanderson, J.E. and Wentworth, R.L., Lactic/glycolic acid polymers, in Drug Carriers in Medicine (Gregoriadis, G., ed.), Academic Press London, 237-270 (1979)

Wise, D.L., Rosenkrantz, H., Gregory, J.B. and Esber, H.J., Long-term controlled delivery of levonorgestrel in rats by means of small biodegradable cylinders, J. Pharm. Pharmacol. 32, 399-403 (1980)

Wright, J.J., Targeting of colloidal drug carriers, Ph.D. thesis Nottingham University (1988)

Yoshioka, T., Hashida, M., Muranishi, S. and Sezoki, H., Specific delivery of mitomycin C to the liver, spleen and lung; nano and microspherical carriers of gelatin, Int. J. Pharm. 81, 131 (1981)

Zilversmit, D.B., Boyd, G.A. and Brucer, M., The effect of particle size on blood clearance and tissue distribution of radioactive gold colloids, J. Lab. Clin. Med. 40, 255-260 (1952)

12. APPENDICES

12.1 Chemicals

Aquacide™ 11, sodium carboxymethylcellulose , mw 500,000
(Calbiochem, distributed by Behring)

Chloroauric acid, trihydrate (HAuCl$_4$) (Sigma)

Dextran 20, 100, 500 (Sigma)

Dipalmitoylphosphatidylcholine, DPPC (Nattermann)

Egg-PC-H (Nattermann)

Egg-PG (Nattermann)

Endolipide 10%, 20% (Braun, Bruneau)

Hydrophobic Interaction Chromatography (HIC) matrices:

        Sepharose CL-4B (neutral agarose, cross linked, Pharmacia)

        Agethane (ethyl-agarose, Pharmacia)

        propyl-agarose (propylamine-agarose, Sigma)

        butyl-agarose (butylamine-agarose, Sigma)

        pentyl-agarose (pentylamine-agarose, Sigma)

        hexyl-agarose (hexylamine-agarose, Sigma)

        octyl-agarose (octylamiine-agarose, Sigma)

Infusol™ (Nattermann)

Intralipid 20% (KabiVitrum)

Lipoid E80 (Lipoid KG)

Lipofundin MCT 10%, 20% (Braun)

Lipofundin S 10%, 20% (Braun)

NC 95 (Nattermann)

Polhydroxybutyrate (Chemie Linz and Marlborough)

Poly(lactic acid) (Boehringer Ingelheim)

Polystyrene latex particles (Polysciences)

Potassium persulphate (BDH)

Sodium citrate (BDH)

Sodium styrene sulphonate (Polysciences)

Soya-PE-H (Nattermann)

Spectra/Por™ molecular porous membrane (m.w. cutoff: 6,000 -
8,000 (Spectrum Medical Industries, Inc.)

Styrene (Aldrich)

Tagat surfactants (Goldschmidt)

TechneScan™ (Mallinckrodt)

Venolipid 20% (Morishita)

12.2 Manufacturers

Aldrich Chemicals Co. LTD., Gillingham, Dorset, UK

Calbiochem (Behring Diagnotics - Hoechst, LaJolla, CA92037)

Chemie Linz AG, St. Peter-Str. 25, A-4021 Linz (Austria)

BDH Chemicals Ltd., Poole, Dorset, UK

Boehringer Ingelheim, Ingelheim (FRG)

B. Braun Melsungen AG, D-3508 Melsungen (FRG)

GAF Europe, Esher, Surrey, UK

Goldschmidt AG, Essen (FRG)

Lipoid KG, D-6700 Ludwigshafen (FRG)

Mallinckrodt Diagnostica (Holland) B.V., Petten, Holland

Malvern Instruments, Malvern (UK)

Marlbrough, (subsidiary of ICI) UK

Morishita Pharmaceutical Co. Ltd., Japan

Nattermann GmbH, Köln, West Germany

Pharmacia, S-751 82 Uppsala, Sweden

Polysciences Inc., Warrington, UK

Sigma Chemical Co. Ltd., Fancy Road, Poole, Dorset, BH17 7NH, UK

Spectrum Medical Industries, Inc., 60916 Terminal Annex, Los Angeles 90054

Sympatec GmbH, Burgstätterstr. 6, D-3392 Clausthal-Zellerfeld, FRG

```
┌─────────────────────────────────────────────────────────────────────┐
│                                                                       │
│  13. ACKNOWLEDGEMENTS                                                 │
│                                                                       │
│                                                                       │
└─────────────────────────────────────────────────────────────────────┘
```

I would like to express my sincere thanks to **Prof. B.W. Müller**, Department of Pharmaceutics and Biopharmaceutics at the University of Kiel, West Germany, for the encouragement during the preparation of this habilitation thesis and for the support during the course of my work in Nottingham and in Paris.

Many thanks to **Prof. S.S. Davis**, Pharmacy Department at Nottingham University, for the stimulating discussions and the cooperation. I am grateful to Nottingham University for the opportunity to undertake research in the Pharmacy Department.

For their cooperation, many thanks to **Dr. C.G. Wilson**, Department of Physiology and Pharmacology, and to **Dr. M. Frier**, Department of Medical Physics, Queen's Medical Centre, Nottingham. Despite the fact that both of them were extremely busy they had always time to offer a helping hand. Thank you.

My sincere thanks to **Prof. P. Couvreur** and **Prof. F. Puisieux**, Université de Paris-Sud, Laboratoire de Pharmacie Galénique et Biopharmacie, for their cooperation and the research facilities provided.

My research has been supported by the:
- **Deutsche Forschungsgemeinschaft** (DFG, Bonn, West Germany)
- **Ministry of Research and Technology** (Bonn, West Germany) within
  the frame work of the research program Gene Technology
- **European Commission in Bruxelles** (Belgium) within the program
  Biotechnology.
I would like to express my sincere thanks to these organisations which gave me the financial suppport to work as a freelance scientist in the pharmaceutical departments at Nottingham University and at the University of Paris.

For their support of my research and/or their cooperation I would like to thank the pharmaceutical companies **Ciba Geigy Pharmaceuticals** (Horsham, UK), **B. Braun Melsungen** AG (Melsungen, FRG), **Chemie Linz** (Linz, AU), **Th. Goldschmidt** (Essen, FRG) and **Boehringer Ingelheim** (FRG).

A lot of thanks to my Ph.D. student **Silke Heinemann** for her excellent contribution to the presented work, especially in the area of parenteral fat emulsions. Special thanks for her help to complete the research work against all odds.

My sincere thanks also to the Ph.D. students who I co-supervised in Nottingham, to Eric Mak who died in a tragic way in 1987 and to Fariba Koosha. My thanks to Mr. T. Blunk for his excellent scientific contribution and his commitment to the research work, to Frédérique Landry for intensive data analysis and to Irena Wowk and Anish Gupta for their assistance in research. Special thanks to Vanda Galazka.

Many thanks to my friends in the Pharmacy Department at Nottingham University who have been very helpful during my time in England:
Sincere thanks to Brian Plummer, Gordon Martin and Tony Waite who made life much easier for me in the department.

Acknowledgements

A lot of thanks to Judith Housden and Bridget Camps, to the secretaries, Kathy Moss, Julie Mitchell and Carol Overy for the extensive use of their offices for phone calls to Germany and other lovely places (outside their tea breaks of course).

Thanks to my colleagues, Martyn C. Davies and Colin Melia , two members of CAMRA, who gave me a deeper understanding of English real ale and English peculiarity (we don't mind and we are not unhappy).

Many thanks to Derek O'Hagan for the training in Liverpool accent and the introduction to the Irish, to Steve Douglas (esp. for our marathon through Athens to get to our hotel), to Julia Wright, Phil D.E. Jones and especially to Nidal Farraj.

My thanks as well to Margret and Pauline from level 4. A lot of thanks to Vony and Joan, the two hearts of the Sydenham Court in the Queen's Medical Centre in Nottingham. My appreciation to Jasper J.R. Carrot for the entertainment. Many thanks to Margrit, Susan and Ken for hospitality and friendship.

Sincere thanks to Eric Shed for the reading and critical review of the manuscript of this book.

I would like to thank Andrea Bräuer, Pharmacy Department, University of Kiel, for her cell culture work.

I am most grateful for the help of my colleagues Stefan Lucks, Rüdiger Smal and Wolfgang Waßmus, Pharmacy Department, University of Kiel, for their help to catch the deadline for the submission of the 1st edition of this book.

G. s. t. Q.

14. SUBJECT INDEX